THE Gift

RON REYNOLDS

THE Gift

published by momentum media

Published by Momentum Media, a division of VideoPlus, L.P.

200 Swisher Road
Lake Dallas, Texas 75065
U.S.A.
Toll-free: 800.752.2030
Tel: 940.497.9700
www.VideoPlus.com
www.TapesAndTools.com

To learn more about Ron Reynolds, please visit his Web site at www.RonaldLReynolds.com.

VideoPlus is a registered trademark of VideoPlus, L.P.

Printed in the United States of America.

Cover and text design by Erica Jennings.

Cover photograph: Douglas Johns/StockFood Creative/Getty Images

ISBN: 978-0-9790341-0-7

Dedication

This book is dedicated to all those who believe themselves to be seekers of truth, students of reason, and participants in the grand and worthy battle against mediocrity.

This story is not fictitious. The struggle contained in these pages is a story being lived in the real world by countless numbers of people who walk the fragile boundary between those who are confused and those who are hopelessly lost.

Only the conspiracy on which this book is based is fictional, and if we are fortunate at all, even that will soon prove to be more fact than fiction.

My gratitude to Noah, who began as a figment of imagination, but whose principles made him as real as the writer to whom he spoke.

Contents

Preface 2007

America has become a house divided against itself. While the government fashioned by the Founding Fathers has endured for more than two and one-quarter centuries, it has been captured and is now held hostage by two political parties who have made party politics paramount over the progress that only a spirit of cooperation can make possible. That must—if we are to endure and remain free—be changed.

It is that spirit of change, of cooperation, of following a clear vision, and of helping people to help themselves that will be found within this book; but the theme of this book goes much deeper than that, for its story is about you, your family and the people you know who could do better in life if they would work harder on themselves than on anything else. For if the quality of our life is to get better, we must get better. We do not attract what we want; we attract what we are.

In 1983, the year I wrote this book, America was turning toward a new and better direction. We had put skyrocketing interest rates behind us, and the long lines at the gas pumps, along with the shockingly high gas prices Americans were paying, had disappeared. The hostages from the United States Embassy who were held by Iran for 444 days had been released, the United States Olympic Hockey Team defeated the invincible Soviet team, and we discovered a new national spirit of high expectation. It was in this setting that I wrote the book you now hold in your hands.

In the years following the original publication of *The Gift*, the story of Noah and his intervention has been unfolding before us. It is left to the imagination of those who read the first edition of *The Gift* to determine for themselves the ultimate conclusion of Noah's plan for protecting us against ourselves.

It has now been nearly a quarter century since this book was first published, and that printing—in 1983—sold out within months. It was my personal decision not to reprint this story, but to let those who managed to secure a copy of that first printing to internalize the concepts contained in its pages and to become part of the story by sharing its message with others.

Because of someone who attended one of my seminars and had been searching for her own copy, you now hold this book in your hands. Her words to me were like a key being inserted into a lock, and just as Noah's words were "spoken to me" over an eleven-month period in 1983, the words of this woman reversed my resolve to leave this book unpublished; she simply reminded me of the subtitle of the first edition: "A Gift to Be Used and Shared."

Within a few days I had lunch with Stuart Johnson, an entrepreneurial publisher and the founder and owner of VideoPlus, who proposed a new release of a number of my books, including *The Gift*. Without reservation or hesitation, and because of the words of a woman and the proposal by Stuart, I felt passionately that a new, defining moment had come. It was time for Noah's message to find its way into the hands of the 300,000,000 Americans who are eager and ready to have their lives impacted by its message.

As you read this book, you will find a number of phrases that are incompatible with our current times. You will encounter references to videotapes rather than CDs or DVDs; you will find references to the Dow Jones Industrial average of the stock market being at 800, rather than its current level of nearly 12,000.

As antiquated as some of the specific references may be, I would ask that you remember why we have chosen to let those references remain rather than to revise and update them. As you read, you are going to be moved by the many predictions and projections spoken by Noah that have come to pass in our current generation. As you come to understand the purpose of Noah, his message and his plan, you will understand that to alter specific references would be to alter the prophetic value of the dialogues that take place between the characters in the story. A few of the terms and concepts may be antiquated, but the principles and the philosophies in the story are timeless; by reading those, and not allowing yourself to become unduly distracted by a few minor and outdated terms, your life can dramatically change for the better. By assimilating the concepts of Noah, and allowing them to become part of who you are, you can start a process of changing how you are. By altering how you are, you can revise and improve where you are, how you feel, what you do, and what you have. That is, perhaps, the greatest value of this book, and it is the major reason why thousands of people have appealed to me to allow *The Gift* to be released once again.

And now, as you begin to read *The Gift,* I would remind you that this story, written more than two decades ago, continues today, and you are part of that saga and the challenge it presents to all those who read it. In this very moment, as your eyes follow these words, a process of change is at work. How the story really concludes, and the legacy we leave to the next generation, is—at least in part— in your hands.

As you read, and as you believe, you shall become, and by becoming more, we begin a remarkable new journey toward having more. That was the wish of Noah; may you be found among those who fulfill that wish.

Ron Reynolds
Dallas, Texas
January 12, 2007

Preface to the
First Edition

History reveals to us the basic human tendency to permit things of value to *lose* their value with the passage of but a little time. To be somewhat more accurate, valuable things do not diminish in value; rather it is our *perception* of their value that diminishes, and as a consequence, we lose that which we once cherished and admired.

At this moment in time, dreams are becoming obscured by reality, hope is giving way to doubt, freedoms are lost to emerging and cumbersome law, and the unique spirit of achievement within the American system of capitalism is being swallowed by a monster whose chief assets are pessimism, gossip, greed, and defeatism.

So all encompassing is our negative attitude toward our collective future and our individual chances for success that few among us can refrain from participating in the chorus of self-condemnation, ridicule, and anger directed toward no one in particular, but everyone in general. As a result of this national obsession for condemning ourselves, America has lost faith in itself and in its leaders. Within our ranks, the seeds of discontent have been planted and are watered by the words of pessimism and criticism emanating from a media that thrives on stories of despair, and adds to its own power by questioning and condemning any and all efforts by our elected leaders designed to reach a sensible solution.

But within our midst also lies the sleeping solution to our individual and collective dilemma. We have within ourselves the power to change circumstance, to renew hope, to rekindle our dreams of past years, and to design plans that lead to unparalleled achievement. While our past and current attitudes have led us to where we *are*, our future attitudes— attitudes created by a new excitement and enthusiasm, can lead us to where we would *prefer* to be. Our *aspirations* are triggered by inspiration. Once we allow ourselves to become *inspired*, and when we again learn to dream—to higher accomplishments—then will we once again regain both our momentum and our stature as a respected leader among the nations of the world.

And such is the purpose of Noah, the bearer of a simple gift that he seeks to share among a disillusioned people. Noah represents a quiet voice of inspiration—a voice that speaks in a strange way and to a small but select group of uncommon individuals who learn to dream again . . . to care again . . . and to hope again.

If God cares for us at all, this story is being carried out at this very moment, while the masses linger in doubt and complain about their circumstances.

Perhaps there is as much *truth* in this fictional story as there is *fiction* in our own true circumstances. In either case, the story *could* have happened . . . and perhaps *did*.

Prologue

"Has he returned?"

"Not yet, sir."

"The moment he gets here, I want to see him."

"Yes, sir."

The old man began to drum his fingers unconsciously in time with the fading footsteps of his assistant. Where was Noah? He was long overdue. Perhaps something had gone wrong with the plan. The plan! He had only reluctantly agreed to give Noah full charge this time. The old man still had difficulty accepting the number of years that had passed since he had first taken Noah on as a member of the inner circle. It was a much younger, less confident Noah he had had to lead every step of the way back then. Still, he had to give the young man his due: He had carried out every phase of the detailed plan to the letter. And now, a much older and wiser Noah had formulated and was now implementing the second stage of a plan of his own devising. It was the second stage of a plan necessitated by the failure of the first. For several thousand years, mankind fought against reason, against justice, and against harmonious co-existence. Nation had risen against nation, and brother against brother until the intricate bond that had held humanity together had become so fragmented as to make life on earth a never-ending process of war and calamity. Humans seemed committed to their own self-annihilation over issues unworthy of little more than a debate.

It was a mere two centuries ago that Noah had been selected to implement and mastermind *The First Intervention*. A new country was forming. It was a land of great hope and promise. It was a land that could indeed be the homeland of a great work and a marvelous wonder. It was a bold act that Noah should be sent to intervene directly in the affairs of mankind, yet it seemed to be the last great hope for the restoration and promulgation of reason amid a troubled world.

I did not permit Noah to exercise full authority that time, the old man thought. *Perhaps it was unwise to give the responsibility for implementing a plan to one so new . . . to one who must implement an intricate plan not of his own design. After all, the men to whom Noah gave his instructions were capable men. They were loyal and tenacious. But the generations that followed had misinterpreted the written law and words of admonition so flagrantly. Was the plan that ill conceived? Surely Noah had performed brilliantly . . .*

The old man closed his eyes for a moment, and his thoughts continued.

I gave them freedom and they slowly twisted it into an ugly form of personal and economic slavery, he thought to himself.

The old man sat at the end of a long conference table staring upward through the glass ceiling toward the turquoise sky and beyond to the silvery planet that circled above in the midday sky. The twinkling planet reflected in his eyes, and his mind pondered the events that he would need to solve in the coming moments.

How could such a plan for perfection become so hopelessly distorted? he wondered. *How many plans must be devised to prevent them from becoming hopelessly lost or, worse yet, destroying themselves?*

His mind pondered the past, reflected on the present, and studied the horrid future that his creations had all but made hopelessly inevitable.

They rob and plunder. Their lies have become commonplace, and truth has become whatever seems expedient for the moment. They take what freedom is rightfully theirs—the freedom to speak, the freedom to prosper and grow, the freedom to create, build and magnify their calling—and through their greed and selfishness give new meaning to the concept of freedom. To them, freedom is their right to promote plans and schemes that make attractive those things that can lead only to their eventual self-destruction. They become increasingly immoral. They resort to unnatural chemicals to enhance their awareness and uplift their senses, knowing not that such things provide only temporary escape from situations that still remain long after the means of escape has worn away.

That which was once sacred is now the subject of jokes and ridicule, and those who promote a return to basic truths are considered illogical and antiquated—conservative and old-fashioned, they call it.

Though his head shook slowly from side to side, there was still a faint look of hope signaled by his eyes. He wanted so much for his project to succeed, but the evidence was becoming overwhelmingly negative. He held out one last hope for success.

Perhaps the failure is my own, he thought. *Perhaps I have given them more opportunity and more liberty than they are prepared to accept with their limited view of eternal existence.*

I failed in Egypt—then Greece and finally Rome, the old man remembered regretfully. *Maybe it is good that I let Noah handle this one on his own—the perspective of youth, the advantage of fresh ideas.* "Maybe," the old man mused aloud, "I'm just getting too old for this sort of thing." Then, laughing at his own remark, he reached over to take another look at the only existing copy of the plan. It was simply titled *America: The Final Intervention.*

One thing was certain: Noah had been right in choosing the West over another attempt in the East. The first intervention attested to this fact. But he was still troubled by this, the final intervention. The timing was so critical . . . and finding the right people would be a challenge. The timing and the participants—those were the keys upon which the success or failure of the entire plan would hinge, and this would have to be the final attempt at intervention.

Heavy footsteps approached, and in an instant the familiar face was before him.

The old man embraced him fondly. "You look pleased, Noah. That's a good sign."

"I am, sir. It took me a little longer than I'd originally anticipated, but I believe it was worth the extra effort." He paused to hand over a thick manila folder to the older gentleman.

"Well, we've found our man. His name is Locke, sir—Jonathan Locke. The envelope contains information about him."

"And have you conversed with him?"

"Indirectly. For the moment, he knows nothing of our intentions. As you will recall, we both agreed that it would be best that way in the beginning. I've arranged for him to come into a unique opportunity within the next few months—an opportunity he will expand."

"With our assistance?"

"I prefer to think of it as *discrete guidance.*" Noticing the fruit bowl on the old man's right, Noah realized that it had been a long time since his last meal. "May I, uh . . ."

"Of course, Noah. Help yourself."

He selected a deep red apple from the basket, and began to polish it against the sleeve of his white jacket. "I believe that the company Locke will develop will become a perfect platform for us to operate from."

"From a distance, of course."

"Until the time is right. At that point, Mr. Locke will be informed for whom he is working . . . and why." He paused now to raise the shiny apple to his mouth. But before he could take a bite, the old man interrupted with another question.

"What if Locke begins to move in a direction contrary to our plan?"

"He'll be watched carefully . . . and given a gentle nudge from time to time to keep him on track. Properly guided, the plan will become as important to him as it currently is to us."

"Noah . . ."

"Sir?"

"I'm glad you're on *my* side."

Noah smiled at the compliment. "There's also a gentleman in California with political aspirations I'll soon be working with. Oh, and there's a woman in the East—coincidentally not far from where Locke is. Her name is York . . . Mariana York. She's not quite ready yet. But as her situation becomes increasingly difficult over the coming months, I think she'll become more receptive."

"Interesting. Perhaps it would make it easier if you arranged for the young lady and our Mr. Locke to . . . shall I say, encounter one another?"

Noah chuckled. "You've always been a matchmaker. However, I would prefer not to become involved with the affairs of the heart. It could make for a rather delicate situation."

The elderly man looked at him with a sly grin. "And pray tell, Noah, where would any of you be today if we were not concerned with the affairs of the heart?"

The younger man smiled as he polished the apple against his white jacket, then slowly held out the red apple with his left hand.

"I go now, sir, to share the fruit of ideas with those who will listen."

"My blessings upon you, Noah," the old man said, a twinkle in his eyes from the silvery star whose light reflected off the swelling tears.

In twenty-four steps, the younger man disappeared, and his senior companion and wise associate sat alone.

The conspiracy was about to begin.

CHAPTER ONE:

The Abyss

Y ou've always had trouble with the truth," Aaron remarked.

"What do you mean?" she shot back, the anger showing in both her eyes and her voice.

"You know what I mean, Mariana . . . then again, maybe you don't. Maybe you even fool yourself."

She knew better. She knew with total clarity that she had difficulty with truth, especially where someone's feelings or emotions were concerned. She simply found that distortions of the truth were easier to live with than the full disclosure of the accurate facts. She found it easier to speak the words and develop the ideas that the other person wanted to hear—to spare them from having to deal with the consequences of the truth. That had been her pattern for as far back as she could remember, and it had caused her more difficulty and regret than she could ever begin to recall or imagine.

"Aaron, if you're going to make an accusation, finish it. Don't just leave it hanging there."

"For heaven's sake, Mari. Just because there's something you don't want to hear, you don't have to label it as an accusation."

"Get to the point, Aaron." She looked away from him as she spoke the words, knowing within herself that she would defend against whatever he was going to say.

He stood up and walked to the red brick fireplace, then turned to face her, folding his arms as he began to speak.

"I think our love affair has fallen on its face, Mariana. I think we've got ourselves a marriage—an existence of two people who can't figure out their own individual feelings, let alone the other person's. Deep inside your soul, Mari, I think you've accepted the fact that the roses have faded, that it's all over, and that the only hope for either of us lies in going our own separate ways."

There was but a half second of silence before she responded, and her words were instinctive and defensive.

"Speak for yourself, Aaron. Is this your way of telling me you want out of our marriage?"

"Mari, please . . . don't shift the blame. Don't even look for the blame. The question is, do *you* want out?"

There was silence. He was opening the gate for her to step outside and regain her freedom. He was removing the pain and the discomfort for her. All that was necessary was a simple response: a yes, a no. But not a maybe. Not silence. Not childish pouting used to camouflage her engulfing fear of the consequence of an affirmative answer. If there was any desire on her part to end this relationship, then this was the time and this was the place. Circumstances had afforded her the convenient moment. If only she knew for sure what she wanted. There was the fear of ending the marriage and there was the nagging, ever-present awareness that its end was neces- sary if either she or Aaron were to ever be fully free to make something of their lives. She was, for the moment, frozen by indecision, and she looked away from him as though his suggestion was totally without merit and not deserving of any form of response.

Aaron York knew the truth, and in spite of his many weaknesses, he chose to deal with it rather than hide from it. For him, the uncertainty of a future without his Mariana was not nearly as painful as was living with the agony of the current and deepening hostilities prevailing between them.

"Mariana, I've asked a simple question of you, and you insist on silence as your response. Must I remind you that even silence speaks its own answer?"

But the habit of hiding from the pain of truth continued. She had always needed to be pushed toward decisions, especially decisions that had pain as a companion on either side of the issue. Now Aaron was providing the push, and deep within her soul, the still, small voice provided her with an emerging awareness of what her final answer to his question would have to be—unless, of course, her silence would cause him one more time to withdraw from the confrontation. Aaron was good at dealing with adversity, but he had never learned to deal with her silences and she knew it. It had become her chief weapon in escaping the many final confrontations that had occurred between them.

She sat silent and motionless, staring out the bay window with an expression on her face that was almost without emotion except for the slow and deliberate breathing that he knew to be symbolic of her anger.

"Mari, I'm not letting you off the hook—not this time," he said watching her. "Either you're going to make the decision and inform me of that decision, or I will let your silence be the confirmation of the fact that it's all over between us. In either case, I'm going to get a decision from you. You're not going to run from *this* one."

Her eyes slowly shifted toward his and she looked at him, but the silence continued. Only the eyes spoke, and their transmitted message was one of pain and fear.

Mariana York had often thought that her marriage to Aaron had been a mistake. It was one of those commitments made between two people for all the wrong reasons and at an age of immaturity when neither knew of the importance of compatibility or the need to find *oneself* before finding someone *else*. But only in her private moments and within the silent confines of her own mind did she entertain these thoughts, for they were thoughts that one should not ponder. She had been raised to believe that marriage was of the greatest importance—more important, more sacred perhaps than the individual lives and spirits of the married couple. That implanted belief had not let her permit herself to consider that the single human life should be of equal importance to the union of two individuals. Even at this moment, Aaron was offering to sacrifice that marriage, that solemn oath sworn before man and God, and his suggestion was nearly beyond her ability to consider or comprehend.

Finally, and without thought as to what she would say, she began to speak.

"Aaron, why are you so quick—so anxious to make our marriage a sacrificial lamb?"

Aaron looked toward the ceiling as a signal of his disgust, then looked back at her.

"I am not making it a sacrificial lamb, Mariana. We're the ones who are being sacrificed—you and me! We're arguing more often than not. The people we owe money to are hounding us day and night. I don't like what I'm doing to earn a living, and you're giving up a teaching career because you're tired of fighting an antiquated bureaucracy. I find interest in things that are of no interest to you and vice versa. You blame me for the mess we're in, and when you do, I blame you for your lack of support. We're in a negative spiral, Mariana."

"And your method of correcting it is a divorce?"

"No, *the* method of correction is a divorce."

"Aaron, I think it is *you* who wants out of the relationship." She spoke as though she had just made a discovery.

"If that will make you feel better, Mariana, fine. But now that you've come to such a conclusion, I'm going to ask *you*, just once more, do *you* want out—*you*, Mari. Forget me and forget the reasons. Forget all the superfluous incidentals that we could discuss for the next ten years. The question is, would *you* welcome your freedom from the mess we're in?"

"Aaron, how could you . . ." She looked toward the window.

"Yes or no, Mariana. Yes or no. Would you welcome your freedom to rebuild your life?"

There was but a millisecond of silence before she exploded into anger. Her words shot at him like projectiles, her eyes piercing into his own as if to give emphasis to her words.

"Yes, Aaron. Yes!"

His eyes closed slowly, but his expression remained fixed. He was hearing the words his mind wanted to hear, but his heart did not. Yet he accepted her answer with relief.

"Mariana, are those words from your heart, or words spoken in anger?"

She sprung from where she had been sitting and spoke as she walked away toward the bedroom.

"Oh God, Aaron. You've pressed me for an answer. Let's not start analyzing *that*, okay?"

There was a finality to the tone of her voice that, with reluctance, he would accept as he watched the door close behind her.

Inside the room, and alone, Mariana York fell onto the bed in a flood of tears. There were no thoughts or anger. There was only an overwhelming sense of aloneness in the midst of the pain.

She would not know that the door behind her opened and that Aaron had, in a moment of regret and indecision, stepped inside for a final appeal for one last attempt to preserve their marriage. But the sprawled body and the flowing tears had given him the last bit of confirmation that he needed. She had painfully accepted the inevitable. She had finally admitted to the defeat that had been so hard to express. He could not now, in a single moment of weakness, pull her body across that line of demarcation. The pain would subside. The tears would stop.

The truth had been spoken, and truth, as it should always be, had made the decision for them.

Slowly and unnoticed by Mariana York, her husband stepped back, closing the door behind him. Outside and a half block down the street, the bell of the church clock announced the hour. For just a moment, Aaron York remembered how, in the early years of their marriage, Mariana had loved the sound of that chime. Then—and he couldn't remember when—they stopped noticing the sound at all. It was as though it had become a part of the emerging silence of things too familiar to notice. Tonight, and for the first time in more months than he could remember, he heard the slow and rhythmic toll of the bells, and it was as though the tolling was symbolic of an ending.

Mariana had also noticed the sound, in spite of her own sobbing. For a moment she too remembered. But while she felt the sweeping uncertainty of her future, the tolling bells seemed to signify not an ending, but a beginning.

✦   ✦   ✦

"You can have more than you've got because you can become more than you are."

The words of the book seemed to provide assurance that all would be well for Mariana York in spite of her current circumstances.

"Everything changes," the author had written, *"which should give pause to the rich and hope to the poor."* The words continued to flow across the page in a silent but symphonic rhythm.

"Humans, in spite of their current circumstances, must be prepared to accept both the promise as well as the peril of all of life's situations."

The blue eyes of the woman scanned the pages, extracting the messages from the well-written words and filing the thoughts away into her mental library. They were words of reassurance and encouragement, but for her they had not yet worked. There seemed to be constant conflict between the life she had dreamed of as a child and the world she now lived in as an adult. One remained a desirable dream, the other existed as a horrible nightmare.

Across the room, the voice from the television spoke. Though it triggered thought pictures that frequently penetrated her desire to give her full concentration to the book, she needed the strange companionship that the television brought to the room. The book, combined with her own existence and presence, was not enough.

"The present administration is literally destroying the economic fiber of the nation," the woman on the television was saying.

"Learn to look for the miraculous hidden among the common and to detect the unusual opportunities intermingled with the routine," the book said.

"Our prisons are crowded, our courts are congested, our national unemployment rates are staggering, and our leaders try to convince us that America is on the mend," the television voice continued.

"There are but subtle differences between sophistication and arrogance, and you must constantly stand guard at the door of your mind, for the voices of doom and pessimism speak far louder than the voices of hope and reason," the author had written.

"This nation stands on the threshold of collapse—look at the interest rates and the growing number of people filing for both unemployment and bankruptcy. This government must create jobs, I tell you. Jobs!"

Mariana York fought to read on. *"The human tendency is to engage itself in the study of effect, but give little attention to the cause behind all effects. While the crowd shouts its boisterous proclamations that treat only the effects of life's challenges, become the silent seeker of cause and bring your human ingenuity to treat that cause, and effect will then treat itself."*

The woman on the television was becoming angered at the man on the program who seemed to be asking questions.

"If the American people elect Robert F. Reardon to the presidency, it will be the final blow to an economy already out of control. Reardon has already proven himself to be the rich man's politician, and this country needs someone who will get counsel from the poor," the hostile woman said, tapping her nails loudly on the table to give emphasis to nearly every word she spoke.

Mariana York gave her attention now to the heated debate between the man and the woman on the television screen. She recognized the man to be Senator Elliot Brendis, but the woman was unknown to her.

"Mrs. Simon, if you were interested in seeking the best advice on matters of business, would you not visit with those who are successful rather than those who are not?"

"The rich and powerful are the minority, Senator, and this nation is supposed to be a democracy where the majority govern. We need a president who will give assistance and attention to the poor."

The debate was interrupted for a commercial on the wisdom of investing in a new money market fund. Mariana York returned to the open book.

"To endure what is, we must remember what was, and focus our dreams and our imagination on things that will one day be, for indeed our thoughts of today produce the circumstances of tomorrow."

Mariana read as quickly as she could while the commercial continued on. But then, she had often mistaken motion for progress.

She leaned back after a crammed sixty seconds of reading and ran her fingers through her long blond hair. The hair that once glistened and curled was now dull and straight, for there seemed to be little reason lately for wanting to look the way she had always looked when her life had meaning and purpose. Mariana York needed the money that would come from being employed again, but she had a fear of beginning anything that might lead her into a rut that would perhaps be deeper than the one she was already in, and yet she could not go on letting her roommate handle all the expenses the way she had the past few months.

The coffee was gone when she set the cup and the book on the table and stood up for the first time in nearly an hour. She walked to the mirror on the wall in front of her and removed the robe that had kept her warm. Underneath, she wore blue jeans and a tight turtleneck sweater that revealed a figure that had not deteriorated, as had her attitude and self-image. She brushed the hair back from her face with her hands, and with a deep sigh, walked away from the framed glass that revealed more than she wanted to see. More important than what she saw was what she felt. Her attitude about life and people was becoming pessimistic, and her determination of earlier years to make something of herself was waning. Not only had she failed to achieve her ambitions of earlier years, she now couldn't even remember what most of them were. Life for Mariana York had become a process of maintaining an existence rather than of designing and living a life of substance. Most of her time was occupied with reading newspapers, watching television and thinking about what she didn't have. She was now sleeping later each morning and staying up later each night. She was even now abandoning one of her greatest enjoyments—the enjoyment of reading the books that had meant so much to her. Even her writing was no longer important. The journals that she had worked on so meticulously were now in a cardboard box in the closet of her bedroom.

Instead of collecting her creative thoughts and philosophical insights, those journals were now collecting only dust.

It was exactly six o'clock when the foot kicking the outside of the apartment door reminded her of the existence of another human being. The voice of Mikki Thomas followed the kick on the door.

"It's me. I can't reach my key."

Mariana removed the chain on the door and released the dead bolt, swinging the door open to reveal two large bags of groceries hiding most of the red-haired female who held them.

"We never thought about carrying groceries when we decided a high-rise apartment would be better than a garden apartment, did we?" The voice of the redhead was slightly angered as Mariana grabbed one of the bags and stepped out of the way.

"It's colder than a well-digger's butt out there," she said as she walked into the kitchen.

"It isn't much better in here," Mariana answered. She set her bag on the counter top and went to the living room that was directly across the breakfast bar from the kitchen and switched the TV set to another channel, raising the volume so she would hear the news over the conversation that was sure to follow.

The announcer's voice blasted through the apartment as Mariana leaned forward to readjust the excess volume.

"On Wall Street today the Dow-Jones fell nearly twenty points, the largest one-day decline in fourteen months. Analysts say the recent announcement by OPEC Ministers on a proposal for another one dollar a barrel increase in crude oil prices triggered the slide.

"Elsewhere, the Labor Department said the unemployment rate jumped almost a full percent last month. That, coupled with the announcement earlier in the day that inflation rose to an annually adjusted rate of twelve percent, sent investors scurrying as over ninety million shares were traded on the New York Stock Exchange.

"And finally, three major eastern banks raised their prime interest rate today another full percent, making borrowing almost an impossibility for most Americans. We'll have more on these and other stories after these messages."

Mariana turned the volume lower and walked back around the counter and into the kitchen. "By the time you listen to the first minute of the news you feel like you want to crawl into a hole and stay there," she said.

"Yeah, everywhere you go these days you hear the same things. People are hurtin', sweet things—it's a sign of the times. Maybe if everybody just stopped talkin' about it, it would go away."

"Sometimes I wonder if it'll ever get better," Mariana answered, staring down into the unpacked bag of groceries.

"Listen, life is a big circle," Mikki said, putting a carton of milk into the refrigerator. "The longer I live, the more life seems to be like the seasons. Right now, it's the winter, in more ways than one. But springtime is out there. It'll come back, you'll see. My intuition tells me there's a light at the end of the tunnel."

"With my luck, it'll probably be on the front of an oncoming train."

Mariana picked at the grapes that were lying on the counter top.

"Mari, the only thing you need to do is change your self-image. You're becomin' more negative by the day. You're still moanin' about your marriage that didn't work and the school system that wouldn't let you use your talent. That's the past, Mari. You've got to shake those things off and get on with it." Mikki Thomas' anger was beginning to show and Mari sensed it. She began removing the groceries from the bag sitting next to her as a gesture of acceptance of Mikki's remarks.

Mikki felt Mari's hurt and eased her tone of voice.

"Hey, at least we've got a roof over our heads. We could be like a lot of folks I see on the street every day. It's one thing to lose your marriage, or be out of money and out of a job, but some of these people are out of hope—that's the bottom, Mari, when you lose your hope, and a lot of folks are lettin' that happen to 'em these days. That's what *you're* doin'. You're cooped up in here twenty-four hours a day with nobody to talk to 'cept that TV and those newspapers, and the stuff they throw at you will kill you if you listen to it long enough."

She didn't know whether to continue or let what she had already said sink in. Mari was a loving, kind, sensitive person, and her nature required the care that one would give to a piece of fine crystal. She required that kind of special handling because she was really that kind of special person. She required care and gentleness because she always gave care and gentleness to others.

Mari stopped unpacking the brown paper bag and leaned her arms onto the counter top, her eyes staring off into another world that only she could see. Her voice was barely audible.

"Do you know how bad it really is for me right now, Mikki . . . really?"

"I think I do. I also think that most of what you feel right now comes from worry—it's fear painting pictures in your mind. Look, you've got your health and your education and that's more than a lot of folks can say. What you need to do is step back and take an objective look at yourself. Get yourself a job. Get yourself involved in somethin'—*anything*, for now."

Mari continued to stare. "There's something about a job that scares me, Mikki," she said. "Somehow, somewhere there is something out there that will let me use the natural talent I have and will let me earn an income at the same time." Her eyes turned now to Mikki, looking for understanding.

The redhead leaned back against the counter and folded her arms. She wanted to give understanding, but her smile showed pity and her head nodding from side to side showed confusion. "That could take a while, kid," she said.

Mari understood the reality of Mikki's remark. The real issue was the fact that the world often is impatient with those in pursuit of the undefined. Left to herself, Mari would never allow herself to settle for something less than what she wanted. But now, her inactivity was placing the full burden of existence on her friend, and the cracks in the friendship were beginning to make their appearance. It was a repeat of the historic battle between dreams and necessity.

"I suppose you're right." She turned completely now to face her friend. "The pain of watching you carry the full load is worse than probing inside myself for the answers to what I want to do with my life," she said with a forced smile.

"I know what you're feeling, Mari—really I do."

"Then you know more than I do. I feel only numbness, Mikki, and confusion."

"You'll find yourself. Just give it a little time."

"I know." Her words had the sound of a courteous response rather than an accepted fact.

The two looked at each other, valuing the friendship that had withstood a thousand tests or more. Mikki put her hand on Mari's shoulder.

"Listen, I just heard today that they're going to be hiring a few people where I work. Most people I know would love to work at Camelot Productions, and I can get you in to talk to Walter, this guy I know who works in Personnel. It may not be something you want to do right now, but the people are great and it'll get you involved in something."

"I don't know, Mikki . . ."

"Hey, c'mon. After all, I work there, so it must have somethin'."

"What kind of people are they looking for? What jobs are they—?"

"I don't know for sure . . . probably secretarial. Heck, it won't hurt to check it out. I'll call Walter as soon as I get into the office. You get yourself out of bed before I leave in the morning and be ready to come down if I call you."

"You sure?"

"Would I kid a friend?"

Mari stretched her arms over her head and stood on her toes, stretching her small five-foot-and-one-inch frame as a gesture of relaxation and acceptance.

Mikki had finished with the groceries before either spoke again, and it was Mari who broke the short silence.

"I wonder if I'll ever get out from under this mess?"

"Will you stop!"

"What?"

"Are you aware that most everything you say these days is a put-down?"

"No, I wasn't—putting down on you, I mean."

"Not on me, sweet things, on yourself!"

"I guess I'm a mess, huh?"

"Yep."

"Maybe I should have stayed married to Aaron. Maybe I ended it too soon."

Mikki ran water from the faucet into the red metal teakettle and placed it on the gas range, lighting the burner at the same time.

"I thought that was all over. You mean you still love him?" Mari removed the jar of instant coffee from the pantry shelf behind her.

"Love him? I think I *needed* him. I guess I had a selfish kind of love. Remember, we were married at eighteen, Mikki. How can you really be in love at eighteen? I wonder if *anyone* really knows what love is about?"

"Listen, sweetie, if you married Aaron because you needed him, then that was your first mistake. You need him right now—no doubt about that—but why even think about such a thing?"

Mari walked to the living room and picked up the coffee cup she had used all day and returned to the kitchen where Mikki was folding the brown paper bags for stowage under the kitchen sink.

"I know, Mikki. I remember reading something in a book once—one of the many I started and didn't finish. It said 'Beware of someone who seeks to take care of you—lest your caretaker become your jailer.' I never forgot that. I read it when Aaron and I were still together and it hit me like a thunderbolt. Without being aware of it, I had surrendered my freedom and the ambition I had once had for the security of a marriage and a job, and both nearly killed me."

Mikki pondered her comment while she washed Mari's coffee cup.

"So why would you even think about going back with Aaron?"

"I'm not *seriously* thinking about such a thing. I guess my current situation is so shaky that *anything* looks good."

Mikki took Mari's cup and dried it with a partially used paper towel and began putting coffee creamer and sugar into the two cups.

"Strange how the past seems to always be better after we've left it," Mikki said, almost as though she were speaking to herself.

"That's good, Mikki. I didn't know I had a philosopher for a roomie."

"Listen kid, one thing that helps me accept life is Camelot Productions. That's why I think it would be good for you to work there, at least for a while. The people down there make it their life's work to study people and help 'em become more than they are. You learn so much about yourself just by working there, Mari."

Mariana picked up the spoon her friend had used and scooped a spoonful of instant coffee into each of the cups. The sound of the spoon scraping on the bottom of the glass jar caught Mikki's attention and she wrote the word "coffee" on the clean pad of paper that would become her new grocery list.

"Well, maybe I'll look into it. Who knows what might happen."

"Can't do no harm," Mikki responded.

Within minutes, the hot water had been converted into two cups of steaming, hot coffee, and the two women now sat on the living room sofa. Mari resumed where she had left off with the newspaper earlier in the day and Mikki watched the remainder of the six o'clock news. Neither spoke a word until the first commercial interrupted the newscast.

"What's this country comin' to?" Mikki said, making a statement more than asking a question.

"It's going to hell in a handcart," Mariana said without looking up from her paper.

"First we're bein' taxed to death," Mikki said. "Then it's inflation. To get *that* under control, we gotta have a recession, which somehow affects unemployment . . . all of which has something to do with high interest rates brought on by too much money. Shoot, I don't have too much money . . . you don't . . . my friends don't. It don't make no sense."

Mari listened while turning the pages of the paper. "That's one problem you don't have," she said.

"What's that?"

"Being unemployed."

"Well, sweet things, bein' employed don't give no immunity to the rest of those problems. Those groceries today cost me thirty-two dollars. Two bags—thirty-two . . ."

Mariana interrupted as she closed and folded the newspaper. "Hey, I'll get a job and do my share, okay?" Her words caused several moments of silence before Mikki finally responded.

"Gettin' a job, Mari, is just the beginning, and you'd better prepare yourself for it. You've been sittin' in this apartment feelin' sorry for yourself for so long you've lost touch with what it's really like out there. Your job, whatever it turns out to be, will allow you to get by, just like most of us are doin' these days. Some of my friends are losin' their homes 'cause they can't afford the payments. They've charged their credit to the limits. Some good marriages are goin' on the rocks because of what's happenin' to this country. The durn subway costs almost a dollar—a few years ago it was a quarter. All I want you to do, Mariana York, is quit whinin' about your circumstances and quit gettin' hot with me every time I say somethin' that rubs you the wrong way. We're supposed to be friends, remember?"

Mari sat back and folded her arms. She glanced at the television and then turned to face her friend who was looking directly at her from the far end of the sofa. She is a good friend, Mari thought, and she felt a rush of emotion as the tears swelled in her eyes. Purposely turning to the television that was resuming its daily commentary of national gloom and local doom, she pinched her nose slightly with the thumb and forefinger of her left hand then rubbed her left eye slightly, consciously pretending to hold back a sneeze. She chose to let her silence be her apology and Mikki knew her well enough to interpret her actions and accepted the apology without words.

The weather report began as Mari spoke again. "Remember Beverly Burke?"

"Sure—Beverly. I haven't thought about her in years. She was more of a troublemaker than we were," Mikki said, with a laugh that confirmed that the two were again on friendly terms.

"I ran into her last week—I forgot to tell you. Do you know what she's doing now?"

"Last I heard she was an executive secretary."

"That's what I find interesting, Mikki. She was no more serious about school than we were. All of us were having too much fun chasing the boys."

"Yeah, I always wondered about that. How come they never chased us?"

"Be serious. Did you know she's driving a new Corvette?"

"You're kidding!"

"No. And she's living in a new condominium . . . and she dresses well, too."

"Beverly?"

"Beverly."

Mariana York leaned forward to pick up her hot coffee cup with the penguins on the side. The penguins were lined up in single file, marching along toward the other side of the cup. The penguin in front was slouched over, its head toward the ground as if weakened by the burden of its obvious role of leadership. The ninth penguin back—the last one—skipped along, its wings outstretched and a smile painted on its face, knowing not of the responsibilities to come when one day he would move by experience and longevity to the front of the line.

She stared at the cup as she held it with the thumb, forefinger and index finger of her right hand. Why did growing up have to be that way? she thought. Why was the fifth penguin back also bent over, looking toward the ground as the leader was? Had he once led? Was his dejected, slothful appearance a mark of the burden of leadership or the burden of mediocrity? Why was only one of nine showing signs of happiness and contentment? Is that what life is all about—relinquishing the excitement and dreams of youth for the wisdom and maturity of an adult? Her mind posed questions, but it supplied no answers, and she studied her mental questions as she sipped at the contents of the cup with the philosophical message.

Mikki's voice interrupted her thoughts. "Luck—pure and simple," she said.

"Nonsense," Mari responded.

"What else can it be?" Mikki asked. "We graduated together, didn't we? We're the same age . . . took most of the same courses in school. We grew up together, fooled around together . . . what else can it be but luck?"

"I don't have the answer, Mik, but the answer is there. Why some people do well and others don't has little to do with luck. Giving credit to luck is an excuse that people like us use every time we see someone doing better than we are."

"Well, Einstein, if you find the answer, let me know. I'm tired of having too much month left over at the end of the money." There was silence throughout the television report on inner city crime and its movement toward the suburbs.

This time it was Mari's remark that broke the silence. "Mik, I'm not going to live this way anymore." Her remark seemed to be more than just conversation. It had the ring of a solemn vow—of one who had deliberated over an issue for a lengthy period and upon consideration of all the facts had reached a final and irrevocable decision.

"Live what way? What do you mean?"

"This—this—being uncertain . . . being lost. I'm moving in a bad direction. You were right . . . earlier, I mean, when you said I needed involvement in something. You were right and I'm going to somehow change things. I don't know how just yet, but I will not go on like this anymore. It's not fair to you and it's not fair to me, either."

Mari swallowed the rest of her coffee in one gulp and looked at the last penguin, remembering how she, too was once carefree and excited about the future. Her eyes moved across the cup to the first penguin, and for a fleeting moment, had become aware that in the story painted on the cup that now dangled from her finger was the story of Mariana York—twenty-eight years of a human existence depicted by an unknown artist in the form of nine penguins on a coffee cup.

The two sat silently now, captivated by the hypnotic effect of the electronic instrument in front of them. They sat through a deodorant commercial, an oil company commercial, and a public service announcement on the dangers of drinking and driving. The repeat of the story on the woeful economic situation ended before either of them spoke again.

"Mikki, do you know what's probably worse than being in a position of looking for a job—when you don't have one, I mean?"

"What?"

"Doing something you don't want to do. Something you hate, I mean."

"Maybe," Mikki responded. "Unfortunately, not everyone can just sit at home and . . ." She stopped short, knowing that what she was saying sounded like a direct attack on her. "What I mean is that you can't walk out on something, Mari. That would be a bit irresponsible."

"Sure it would, Mikki, but staying with something you don't like and not actively looking for something better is a bit irresponsible, too, wouldn't you think?"

"Yeah, but things are tough, Mari—durn tough, they really are."

"You don't have to tell me, remember? I'm the one who has spent months searching the job market, and . . . Mikki?"

"Yeah?"

"Remember when you were sixteen or seventeen years old?"

"That's too long ago," she said, reversing her legs on the tabletop.

"C'mon. Remember how you just knew that someday everything would turn out well?"

"Sure, but that was back before we grew up, Mari . . . before we discovered what *real* life is all about. *That's* the real life, kid," she said, pointing her finger at the television showing pictures of the truck drivers carrying their picket signs.

"Is it, Mikki? *Is it* the real world, or is it something that the media pushes on us because it's sensational? Are you aware . . . have you ever thought that maybe, just maybe . . . oh, forget it!"

Mari moved forward onto the edge of the couch as a signal of her intent to end the conversation.

"No, none of this 'forget it' stuff. Maybe what?"

She didn't move off the couch, but sat silently for a moment, obviously collecting her thoughts, then spoke again.

"Does the *system*—the things you see on that tube every day—does *that* control humans or do humans control *it*? Is it really *that* bad, or do those people at the station just blast us with that crap because they know that it's human nature to want to watch blood and guts and poverty?"

"What are you saying? What are you asking?"

"I'm saying . . . I'm saying that maybe we're making our own problems, or at least most of them. It seems that the more we talk about how bad it is, the worse it gets."

"But it's *reality*, Mari," Mikki said. Her legs came off the table now and she sat directly upright. "You asked if I remember being a kid. Sure I do. But that's what I was—a kid, and kids don't know about responsibility or about finding a job or paying bills. Kids live in a world of dreams. But they'll learn too, someday. They'll mature just like we did and find out the hard way what reality is all about."

"Oh reality be damned!" Mari shot back. "Reality once was a man riding on a horse, but dreams gave us the car, the plane and the stuff that you and I take for granted. Behind every great movement was a dream, Mikki. Free people living in a free country was once a dream before the dreamers got to work. Reality—yes, reality is *that*, Mik," she said, pointing again at the television. "But is that what we want? Maybe *that's* my point. Reality right now says we've got to conserve energy or, by God, we're going to run out. Even the president is telling us we've got to conserve. Thank God we'll at least have a new president soon. Where are the politicians who inspire people . . . who say neat things like . . . like . . . 'some people see things as they are and ask why and others see things as they could be and ask why not?'

"Listen to me," Mari continued. "You're my friend and I love you, and I know I'm a bit of a mess right now, but I'm not insane. I'm . . . I'm saying that somehow, some way we should dream more and get excited more about how things could be. What's wrong with that?"

Mikki stood up. "Okay, Mariana, what's *your* dream?"

Her question brought a silence as Mari paused and looked down now at the floor. Her eyes moved up to meet her friend's. With deep concern in her voice, Mari uttered the words that filled the blue eyes with tears. "I don't know," she said.

One of the tears overflowed from her left eye and rolled quickly down her cheek, leaving a moist trail behind it.

"I don't know," she said again, shaking her head slowly. Mikki saw the head bow and saw the second tear follow the path of the first.

Mikki grabbed the tissue box from the end table and dropped three of the yellow tissues in Mari's lap as she sat down next to her, putting her left arm around her shoulders. "You dingy," she said. "You're too serious about life sometimes."

"I'm sorry," Mari said, putting a single tissue to each eye. "My life is in a bit of a mess and I've let it get that way by sitting around feeling sorry for myself, I guess."

"Why don't you just grab your jacket and come with me? I'm going to meet Charlie Livingston for dinner and a show."

"No. You go ahead. I'd make bad company tonight. Anyway, I'm not hungry. Go on, enjoy yourself. I'm okay."

Within another two minutes, Mikki had made her final appeal that Mariana again rejected, and once again Mariana York found herself alone with her thoughts and the now barely audible voice on the television that seemed to say something about being back with more updates at eleven.

She sat down at the dining room table and propped her head up with her right hand, the right elbow resting on the tabletop. Her left arm lay limp across the table in front of her, the fingers tapping on the wood surface to the tune of "Days of Wine and Roses" that came out of nowhere and danced through her head. It would be another evening alone with her thoughts and with the ever-present world of make-believe spilling out of the television.

Tomorrow would soon become today and perhaps with it would come a new opportunity. Tomorrow had gradually become her great escape. Everything of value seemed always to be held in reserve for tomorrow. She would start tomorrow. She would try tomorrow. She would be better tomorrow. But something always seemed to happen in the transition of the tomorrows becoming today. It was the *present* she had trouble with.

Mariana York was a capable woman ready to be touched with the power of an idea . . . an idea that could be either good or evil. It was a turning point . . . a threshold leading to change. Her mind was not yet capable of comprehending the magnitude of change that was being planned for her. Somewhere, an observer sat waiting for her exact moment of readiness. The plan was ready. The nation was ready. The wheels of implementation had long ago been set in motion, and one more of its intended participants would soon call out for help. It would be the cry for help that would unlock the treasure chest of answers.

CHAPTER TWO

The Search

I t was two minutes before ten when Mariana stepped into the reception area of Camelot Productions. The bus trip from Springfield had taken just under two hours, and had provided her with the time she needed to mentally prepare herself for a confrontation with the world of people and business. It was a world she had not been a part of for many months, and she was apprehensive not only about her ability to deal with it but also about her ability to sell herself and her talents, which had become rusty through lack of use.

Mikki sat just inside the door and to the left. She had been the receptionist for Camelot for just over a year, her bubbly personality making her well suited for the position. Mikki noticed the approaching figure and looked up. Her preoccupied expression changed instantly to a warm smile.

"Hi, sweetie," Mikki said. "Are you ready?"

"Is fear an indicator of readiness?"

Mikki chuckled. "Grab a chair over there and I'll buzz Walter in just a second."

Mari turned in the direction of Mikki's gesture and walked toward the two sofas positioned at ninety-degree angles to each other against the wall. In front of each was a coffee table with the customary assortment of magazines. A man in his fifties was on one of the sofas. His eyes met hers for a brief second, but no words were spoken as she seated herself on the unoccupied sofa. She placed her handbag next to her and reached forward to pick up a magazine. *Success Unlimited*. Her eyes looked back at the table, examined the selection that remained, then at the magazine in her hand. Success seemed to be what she lacked most so she began the ritual of thumbing through the pages. Her act was typical of those uncertain of their future and dissatisfied with their present—always searching, but seldom seriously enough to find the ever-present answers. Her eyes scanned the pictures, the advertisements, the titles, but never looked long enough at any particular page to absorb the messages that she needed to hear. It was a trait of the weary and downtrodden to flip through the pages of a book as they would flip through the years of their lives.

The bold red title caught her attention as the page flipped by, and she reversed her process instinctively as though she had pressed a non-existent rewind switch.

Do You Know What You REALLY Want?

The words had a special significance and she subconsciously increased the level of her concentration.

"Opportunity is best seen from a distance, aided by the telescope of desire," the small print said. *"Before progress may be achieved,"* it went on, *"progress must be clearly defined, for unless it is, we will continue to mistake motion for progress.*

"Waiting for things to change is delusion. The future, at least for the single human life, will be a duplication of the past. Things change when people change. Otherwise, things remain unaffected."

"Miss York?" Her mind switched from the world of ideas to the world of reality. Mikki sat smiling, signaling Mari to come to where she sat.

She closed the magazine and dropped it on the table as she stood up. At the reception desk, Mikki spoke in a hushed but friendly voice though her face wore an expression of one stranger courteously addressing another.

"Walter will be down to get you in about five minutes . . . and smile a little, sweetie. You look absolutely horrible."

Mariana widened her eyes, showed her teeth in an artificial smile and thrust her tongue outwards toward Mikki. The redhead's eyes rolled upward in a pretended gesture of disgust, then she turned away to resume her duties. Mari returned to her seat on the unoccupied sofa. The eyes of the man on the other sofa flashed away from his newspaper and toward her as she crossed her legs.

"What company are you with?" The unexpected question caught Mari by surprise.

"I beg your pardon?"

"What are you selling?"

"Nothing. I'm here for an interview." She tried a friendly smile, but wondered about his intentions. He was not well dressed and his oversized briefcase, worn shoes and white socks reminded her of the stereotypical unsuccessful traveling salesman.

"You look scared," he remarked. "No job is worth gettin' scared over."

She reached forward to pick up the magazine and thumbed again, but this time with a purpose.

"I'm really fine, thank you," she said.

She found the article again, but felt too uneasy with the man staring at her to concentrate. She knew the conversation had not ended.

"I've had too many jobs in my time to let another interview scare me," he said.

She courteously laid the magazine in her lap, folded her hands over it, and looked directly at him. "Are you here for an interview, too?"

"Not me, lady. I got a job already. Not much of a job, but these days who can be choosy?"

"What do you do?" she asked.

"I sell artificial plants."

"Artificial plants?"

"Sure. The commission is good and the product is simple. No worries about over-watering, bugs or fertilizing."

"What else have you done?"

"Sales of one kind or another—for longer than I care to think about. You name it and I've sold it, lady. And I'm here to tell you no job is worth gettin' upset over. If I don't like somethin' I get out, and that's the best advice I can give you."

"Are you happy now—with your plants, I mean?" She gestured toward the large briefcase she imagined to be filled with plastic samples and colorful brochures.

"Happy? I don't know anybody that's happy these days. The country is fallin' apart, you can barely keep up and—well, you know what it's like. Happiness is for the kids, lady, not you and me. I pay the bills and I make enough sales to justify the company keepin' me around. The rest can take care of itself."

"But is that what it's all about?"

"What?"

"Life—humanity, I mean."

"Let humanity figure it out for itself. I used to care about such things, but I don't see anybody worryin' about me, so I long since quit worryin' about them."

"I suppose you're right," she answered. She didn't need the conversation, not now especially. She picked up the magazine from her lap and pretended to read the article, hoping the man would withhold further comment. There was silence, except for the tapping of the typewriter keys from behind Mikki's desk.

"*Let humanity figure it out for itself.*" The words echoed in her mind for several minutes after the man had spoken them. Her eyes looked at the page in front of her, but her mind pondered the pessimistic remark. She wondered how he might have been when he was younger. Surely at the age of five, in response to his father's question "What do you want to be someday?" he didn't respond with "A pessimistic artificial plant salesman," she thought. Somewhere in his past there had been a spark— a moment of hope and excitement. What had happened between then and now? She forced herself to resume the article.

"*Most people die at thirty but are buried at seventy,*" it said. Her thoughts drifted again toward the shell of the man, and then to herself. Where he was, she could be headed, she thought. Or was she already there? Is it possible to become pessimistic and unaware of its very existence? Her own doubts now beckoned at her consciousness more than the words on the page.

"Hey, lady. Here's an interesting article," the plant salesman said, laughing as he spoke. "'The Twentieth Century Fails in Greenland.' See, I guess it could be worse. We could be in Greenland."

"The twentieth century doesn't seem to be working well anywhere," she answered, then paused to think about her own remark. Perhaps her pessimism *was* as bad as his, she thought.

✦　　✦　　✦

The two were separated by a metal desk. Walter, the director of personnel, sat in a vinyl office chair that rocked slowly backward and forward as he read over her brief resume. Mari sat with her legs crossed, in silent apprehension. Her eyes scanned the wall behind him. The many plaques and pictures were his own accumulation of past events. He appeared to be a happy and confident man, as much in person as he was in most of the pictures. Despite the formality of the office, Mari sensed that he was not typical of one in the position of placing human personalities in business structures. He was courteous and sincere, and not at all pretentious.

He laid the resume on the top of his desk and smiled at the woman in front of him.

"What exactly are you looking for?" he asked.

"Well . . ." She cleared her throat and changed her position in the chair, a certain sign of her discomfort. "I'm not really sure—I mean . . ."

Walter leaned forward now, his arms folded on the desktop. "You were referred by Mikki Thomas."

"Yes."

"I gather that income is more important to you than opportunity."

It was a rather odd question for him to ask, she thought. She struggled to fight an overwhelming sense of hopelessness. The director of personnel placement looked briefly at the resume then back at her, and she barely tolerated the silence. "Miss York, have you ever considered that opportunity may be more important than income?"

"It depends."

"On what?"

"On whether you're broke and behind on your bills when opportunity knocks," she replied. "Sometimes opportunity knocks, but you may find that your financial situation is so desperate that you're chained to the chair and can't respond to the knock."

Walter laughed. "I don't see any chain marks on your wrists," he said, pointing to the hands that were folded in her lap. "And I don't believe I hear any knocks," she countered, smiling and staring directly into his laughing brown eyes.

He reached for the manila folder lying open in front of him on the desktop, then looked back at her.

"Miss Thomas tells me you're excellent with people—in communicating your ideas."

"Yes, I believe I am if it's an idea I believe in."

"Have you ever been in sales?"

"No, other than as a young girl selling Girl Scout cookies. My resume shows that my profession has been teaching. I don't believe you read it completely, did you?"

"The resume?"

"Yes."

"No, not really. Forgive me, Miss York, but I try not to give much attention to resumes."

"Oh, that's unusual. How else . . ."

He knew her question before she finished asking it. "Resumes are often exaggerations of the truth designed to enhance our experience and possibly even our value. I prefer to judge the individual both on their past performance and the reasons for their lack of performance. Frankly, I'm more interested in potential than experience."

"I see." She felt uncomfortable with his answer, and it showed more than she wanted it to.

"Are you sure—that you understand my answer, I mean?" His head was directed downward, but his eyes raised to look directly at her.

"Mr.—" She hesitated, not remembering his last name or even if anyone had ever mentioned his last name.

"Please, Walter will be just fine," he said reassuringly.

"Walter, normally I would be intrigued by your question. And yes, I do think I understand the difference between having a job and having an opportunity. But frankly, for the moment all I need is a steady source of income and the chance to get back into the routine and responsibility of a job again."

"Do you object to something involving sales?"

"Somehow I don't see myself as a salesperson," she answered, with a shrug of the shoulder.

"What then?"

"I'm really not sure. Perhaps something in training. I've thought somewhat about that, since I have a teaching background, I mean."

"You do realize that training is what we're all about?"

"No, I don't really know that much—only what I hear from Mikki— uh, Miss Thomas, on occasion."

Walter took his eyes from hers and opened a desk drawer to pull out a brochure that he handed to her. He leaned forward again as though he had made some sort of decision.

"Miss York, I'm going to do something here that you're probably not going to understand, or entirely agree with just yet. But I want you to go along with me in the beginning."

She didn't answer, but smiled in courteous acknowledgement of her willingness to listen.

Walter became intense now, as though he were a close friend giving serious advice to one who might not be willing to take it. He quickly wrote a few words on a slip of paper, then continued.

"I want you to go upstairs to see our director of sales. Here is his office number and his name. The name will be on the door just to the right after you step out of the elevator on the fourth floor."

The word "sales" gave her a twinge of anxiety that immediately transformed her attitude from hopeful expectation to resigned indifference.

"I understand your interest in a position in training. But after reading that brochure, you'll understand that our very products—the books, tapes and seminars that we sell to the public—are a form of training. The men and women who conduct and author the seminars and products that you would be selling have learned to implement our philosophies into their own personal lives . . . *before* they're allowed to teach them to our customers. Most of the group who provide the training began their careers with us in sales and became—well . . . what you might call a product of our product."

Mari York shifted her position in her chair again. "May I ask you a question?" she asked.

"Of course."

"Wouldn't it be just as difficult to sell or represent a product that you don't completely understand as it would be to teach that product to others?"

"Good question," he said, nodding his head in agreement. "It would appear that either would be a bit hypocritical. But believe me, we've considered that and you'll understand that there is a difference after you've gone through our internal training program."

Walter studied her response, but said nothing. Mari gave a brief smile and then spoke.

"You can tell that I don't exactly get excited over a sales position, can't you?"

This time Walter laughed and sat back in his chair again, crossing his legs and tapping a pencil on the desktop with his left hand.

"Sure, but it's your fear of the unknown that's giving you that feeling. There isn't a single person on our sales staff that really wanted to sell when they came here. They had read our books, heard our seminars and decided that they'd like to work for a company like ours."

She took a deep breath, looked toward the ceiling and momentarily closed her eyes. Finally she looked back at him, shaking her head from side to side to add impact to her statement.

"You're a great persuader, Walter. You almost make sales sound attractive."

The conversation had ended quickly and Mariana York watched now as the elevator lights lit up in sequence—one—two—three—four. The chime sounded in synchronization with the opening doors. As she looked ahead, she saw a reflection of herself as she stood motionless in the elevator. She stared almost hypnotically into the mirror-covered wall, pondering the interview yet to come and the conversation she had just had. There was the quiet but persuasive urging to remain in the car until again the doors closed on the uncertain possibilities ahead. The elevator would take her back down and she could avoid the confrontation and the uncertainty of the impending interview. But then, deciding that the uncertainty of the future could be no more distasteful than her current circumstances, she stepped out.

Mariana glanced at the note Walter had written. In spite of the legibility of the instructions about turning to the right, she turned almost instinctively to her left. Her mind had somehow taken a strange mental picture of where she was to go. Fate and the instinctive human response to the quiet urgings of the mind often contribute as much to the human drama as do planning and deliberate conscious effort. Without thinking, she entered the door on the right—the first office just down the hall from the elevator.

The name in gold block letters on the door was distinctive. There was no title—only a name: Jonathan Locke.

The office inside was obviously a reception area, but whoever should have been sitting behind the reception desk wasn't there. The furnishings were elaborate, with a sunken conversation pit at the far right end of the large room. Two of the three walls surrounding the pit were filled with books. The third wall, at the very end of the sunken area, was a fireplace. The flames danced warmly and invitingly as the burning logs snapped and crackled, spitting multi-colored sparks upward like miniature fireworks. Centered in front of the fireplace was an immense coffee table made of wormy chestnut and ebony wood with a smoked glass top. Wrapping around the table on three sides was an off-white sectional sofa facing toward the fireplace. The entire office was filled with growing plants, and the place had a charm that gave Mari the feeling of being in a home where great care had been given to detail and coordination.

To her left, she saw the large double doors obviously leading into the quiet refuge of an inner office. She stood quietly, almost afraid to make a sound that would invade the peaceful charm of the surroundings. The soft music that held back the silence was from another time, adding to the effect of this unique office and making her wonder about the person who worked from within those walls. Her eyes moved toward the wall to the left and to the picture of the ocean. It was a painting she had seen only twice before. It was the captivating scene of the open sea during a storm with the hint of sunlight reflecting gently on the swells of the water. Thirteen gulls flew in formation, suggesting peace and hope amid the turbulence. It was a reproduction of a painting by George Moran titled *Ocean, Highway of Nations*.

The walls behind her that surrounded the door through which she had entered were covered with framed letters, pictures and what appeared to be writings and quotations, their significance perhaps known only to the one responsible for displaying them. Mari turned slightly to her left to read some of the messages.

"The thing or circumstance of tomorrow is the thought of today."

"Learn to take the greatest joy from the endeavor of labor rather than from the harvest. Learn also that the intensity of the work determines the quality of the harvest."

"The greatest deterrent to success is the lack of understanding, acceptance and appreciation of your own self-worth."

One frame displayed a somewhat puzzling article. It was only an envelope, but it was strangely unique, its paper having a soft glow as though it were luminescent. On the envelope itself was an inscription written with a broad-point fountain pen or a quill.

"A Gift, To Be Used and Shared."

She wondered what the envelope might have once contained and why it was the envelope and not its contents that was displayed on the wall.

Behind her, Mariana detected a slightly audible click. As she turned her head slightly from the mystique of the framed envelope, her peripheral vision caught sight of a figure entering from the doors of the inner office. She felt a strange strength—a charisma—even before she turned to look at the person.

The well-dressed man was studying a file as he closed the door behind him. He stood for a moment, the papers in his left hand, while his right hand removed a gold pen from his jacket. He was older than she, perhaps by ten years or so, but seemed to have a maturity and confidence about himself that went beyond his years. However, the tailoring of his expensive dark-brown suit revealed the youthful body of an athlete. The gold watch around his left wrist reflected the light from the ceiling above him, and the momentary reflection of light on gold flashed a yellowish beam that penetrated her eyes. This was the man who was behind the personality of the office itself. She knew it and she felt his strength and sensed somehow that this man was not the person Walter had referred her to. Her mind instantly recalled the handwritten instructions. The name—the director of sales—was . . . it was Stevenson

. . . something *Stevenson*. Her mind again flashed stop-frame pictures of the past few moments and she saw the name on the door of the office she was in. It had said Locke—Jonathan Locke. She was in the wrong office, and felt her cheeks grow warm with a blush of embarrassment.

The man wrote a quick comment on the papers he held as though he had made some decision. He looked up now for the first time since entering the room, and his eyes met hers. The eyes were a penetrating, piercing blue that made her almost want to look away. A courteous smile parted his lips as he spoke.

"Good morning." His voice was vibrant and warm. He glanced at the empty chair at the secretary's desk, then made an obvious deduction.

"Is Miss Lincoln helping you?"

"Well, no . . . I've only been here for a minute, and—well, I'm afraid I've stepped into the wrong office by mistake."

She felt more uncomfortable now, and it obviously showed. There was once a time when she would have felt equal to anyone, but not now, and she looked away from him knowing that his eyes were still on hers.

"It's quite all right," the man said. His smile broadened as he moved toward her and extended his hand. "I'm Jonathan Locke."

She moved her purse from her right hand to her left and took his hand in hers. His hand squeezed slightly to suggest an inner strength, but there was a gentleness that subordinated the strength.

"I'm Mariana York," she said, looking at his eyes but not into them. "Walter—downstairs—sent me to see Mr. . . . ," she hesitated.

"Mr. Stevenson?"

"Yes." *How would he know that?* she thought.

"You turned to the left instead of to the right when you stepped out of the elevator," he explained, almost as though it were a common mistake. His voice and his smile made her feel a bit more at ease.

Often people say more by their behavior and their appearance than with their words, and for Mariana York this was one of those times. Her discomfort and lack of confidence were the enemies within her. The well-dressed, confident man standing before her was symbolic of what she wanted to be. Though she had the capacity, she lacked the intense ambition that comes from activity and well-defined purpose.

The man studied her for a moment and then spoke again as she began to turn toward the door.

"Are you here for an interview?"

"Yes, but I'm really afraid I've made a mistake—other than entering the wrong office," she added, as her eyes moved in an arc from right to left.

From the short sigh and shrug of finality he sensed something about her feeling of uncertainty. He doubted that their paths would cross again, and understood the need she had for some sort of direction.

"You have an appointment you've decided not to keep." He had made a statement rather than asking a question.

"Yes, I think so. Walter, the personnel director, felt I would do well in sales and arranged for me to see Mr. Stevenson, but I'm afraid it's just not for me."

She stood with her hand on the door latch. "You're right," Locke said.

"Oh?"

"Yes, if that's what you think, then I would have to agree with you."

His remark surprised her, and she sensed either that the man was being courteously agreeable or was about to become philosophical.

"I'm sorry to have disturbed you," she said, opening the door of the office.

"Just a moment—please."

She stopped hesitantly in the doorway. The man walked to the secretary's desk and returned to her holding a book in his hand. "Please—take this with you and read it when you have time. I think you'll enjoy it."

She took the book from his hand and glanced at the blue and yellow cover. *Make Something of Yourself.*

He spoke again. "Please, the title doesn't mean I'm suggesting anything. It's just that impulse tells me that you're ready for what the book has to say. It's a gift, and I hope you enjoy it."

"Thank you." Her tone suggested both gratitude and confusion.

She repeated herself. "Thank you very much," she said, looking again at the book and back at him. She smiled once more and left, closing the door behind her. Her mind was more on her decision to skip the interview than on either the book or the man who had given it to her. Her emotions had quickly switched from hope to uncertainty, from resolve to frustration.

Once again, the day seemed like those of the past. She stopped at the elevator, torn between walking the few short steps to the waiting sales interview or leaving. The fear of failure is often a more powerful emotion than the desire for progress, and responding to the feeling within her, she pushed the white plastic circle with the arrow pointing downward. The chime sounded instantly, as though the elevator had anticipated her decision to walk away from a possible future to return to a predictable present.

The ride downward is often convenient.

With tears in her eyes, she walked past Mikki Thomas, who smiled at her instantly. Seeing the look of dejection on the face of her friend, however, the smile gave way to a sympathetic look of concern.

"What happened?"

"I got a free book," she said, pausing at the desk where Mikki sat.

"Who?"

"Locke. Jonathan Locke."

"What? How did you see him? Do you know—"

"I went into the wrong office, Mikki. I was going to see someone about a sales job, if you can believe that."

Mari York was speaking, but it was almost without thought as to whom.

"Mariana, you wouldn't know a real opportunity if you got hit with it in the face. You're too busy feeling sorry for yourself." Mikki went back to her work, and Mari went back into the coldness of Philadelphia in winter.

CHAPTER THREE:

The Gift

I t was nearly six when a weary and dejected Mariana York returned to her shared apartment. She was greeted by the ringing phone. The voice on the other end belonged to Mikki, who laconically informed her that she would be home late. The conversation was short and polite, and Mari knew the reason for it.

Mariana chose a TV dinner at random from the freezer and placed it in the oven. Forty-five minutes later, feeling somewhat refreshed from a long, hot shower, she carried the tray into the living room. The balance of the evening went to watching a documentary on unemployment and welfare, an analysis of the president's address on the state of the economy, and the ten o'clock news. Occasionally, she reflected on her day and the morning interview at Camelot Productions, as well as the four hastily arranged interviews that had followed. One was a major appliance sales position with J.C. Penny. Another was for a manufacturer's representative for deep-sea fishing equipment. The other two turned out to be life insurance sales. In all four cases, she felt that the greatest attraction was the advertisement, and none offered her the challenge or the income she felt she deserved.

By ten-twenty the voice from the television was becoming redundant with its commentary on how bad things were, so she lowered the volume but left it just loud enough to provide her with what seemed like company. For the next ten minutes, she wandered throughout the apartment aimlessly, looking for something to fill the void she felt within her. She thought of playing cards, but remembered the missing Jack of Hearts. She thumbed through the latest magazines as though in search of a subject, but could neither define or find it. Twice, she picked up the newspaper, only to lay it back on the dining room table without reading a word. She was being drawn toward something.

She stood at the window now, parting the curtains to look down upon the snow covered-swimming pool in the illuminated courtyard. The limb of a tree hung across the outside of the window only two feet away, and the light shining outward from the apartment revealed two leaves, dead now, but tenaciously clinging to the limb as though a spark of life might still somehow remain.

Her eyes looked away from the window and her mind blocked out the thoughts that the television voices were causing her to think. The blue and yellow swirl marks on the front cover of a book caught her attention. It was the book the man Locke had given her. She thought of him now. She could still see the eyes and feel the inner strength they reflected. Her memory was painting thought pictures that became suddenly attractive. The man. The office. The envelope . . . that strange glowing envelope. Why would it occupy such a position of importance? What could it have once contained?

"A Gift, To Be Used and Shared."

The thought of the man came back and locked itself into her consciousness. Were this another time, were she a different person, she would want to know him more. But there could be no mutual attraction. She was of a different world and her mind provided for her only thoughts of existence and thoughts of anxiety and uncertainty for what tomorrow might bring—or not bring. She could only imagine what it could be like to live a life with a man such as he was. Jonathan Locke was a man of achievement and stature and Mariana York belonged to the world of the confused and of the lost. Her thoughts were not his thoughts, nor were his in the same realm as hers. She could only dream. She could only fantasize. She could imagine, but she would never experience. She could wish, but she would not have. Deep inside, she wanted so much to free herself, to be equal to those of accomplishment. What was it that made him what he was and that made her what she was? Where did his lucky break occur? she thought. Was it being in the right place at the right time? Was it an inheritance of some sort that made this man Locke what he was? Was the world really an unjust place with the cards of success, wealth and happiness falling haphazardly into the laps of a fortunate few?

The eyes of Mariana York drifted again to the book lying on the table next to her. With the vague image of the man still in her mind, her hand reached out now and pulled the book toward her.

Make Something of Yourself.

She examined the cover closely for the first time. Jonathan Locke. The name on the book brought her from her slumped position on the sofa, and she felt her blood run warm with the excitement of this unexpected discovery. She had been too preoccupied with her own feelings to take notice earlier.

Of course. Jonathan Locke. He was Camelot Productions. Mikki had told her that countless times, but somehow it had not registered. The words that Mikki had spoken to her in anger and disappointment earlier in the day now came back to her.

"You wouldn't know a real opportunity if you got hit with it in the face. "

She had wandered into the office of Jonathan Locke by mistake. The collage of mental pictures flashed again, and she saw his face now just as she had earlier. She relived her moments as they had occurred and recalled now how he had given the distinct impression that he really wanted to continue the conversation with her, at least for a moment longer.

His words replayed themselves on the tapes within her mind. *"Just a moment—please."* There had been a sincerity—almost a plea—when he said the last word.

Her eyes scanned the back cover of the book, where she found his picture and his biographical sketch. His picture brought him there into the room with her and the words that told of his past, although brief, were as though he were speaking them.

He was twelve years older than she. He had experienced personal difficulty and tragedy, but had benefited from both and had used his past to create and enhance his present and future. Born in a small town in the East, he had neither the opportunity nor the money to attend college. Instead he had gathered up experiences from the classroom of life, it said. Locke was a fresh voice amid a world in need of hope and reason.

On impulse, the young woman, her interest rekindled, took the book to her bedroom. Within moments she had prepared herself for bed and snuggled beneath the covers, two pillows behind her head, the music playing softly in the background, and the written words of Jonathan Locke speaking to her in silence.

His book was on philosophy, but not like the philosophies of a Plato, Aristotle, or Socrates. It was a philosophy for the current generation—a philosophy of hope, of challenge, and of encouragement. He wrote of many things she did not understand and of some that she did, but he wrote of nothing that she did not find fascinating. As she read long into the night, her mind asked questions and occasionally the following sentence would answer her own mental inquiry or clarify her confusion. It was as though their minds were intermingling—she mentally inquiring, he mentally explaining. His book sought to give hope to the hopeless, encouragement to the timid, and mental strength to the weary. She wanted to believe, but her mind would often wander back from the world of philosophy to the world of reality and she would become confused for a moment or two. Her strength and confidence grew and receded like the ever-changing swells of a turbulent sea as her awareness of reality told her conscious mind how life was and his words from the printed page told her subconscious mind how it could be.

The words written by Jonathan Locke were eloquent and his style was unique.

"*A life full of adventure is a life full of many decisions and many challenges,*" he wrote. "*Do not ask for 'things' to get better; ask instead that you might become stronger.*"

The words continued on, page after page.

"*The great benefit of adversity is that it always provides an opportunity to grow; and the great curse of adversity is that it gives us a tangible excuse to withdraw into mediocrity.*"

"*The great value of the past is how you choose to invest it in your better future.*"

"*We all need a certain amount of security so that we may live. We also need a considerable amount of challenge so that we may grow.*"

Within the pages of his book, Jonathan Locke had written as though he had lived her life, for his experiences were similar to her current circumstances—even worse in many respects. He had experienced the real world and had an obvious understanding of disappointment, tragedy, self-doubt, and the other human emotional maladies that lead to nowhere. Interspersed with his commentary on failure were his assurances and encouraging insights into the coming of the better future.

"*The great tragedy of life is not poverty, or hunger, or even death. The great tragedy is that we could, but we don't; we should, but we won't. Within us all exists the capacity for uniqueness, for accomplishment, and for freedom from unwanted obligation. Beginning at this very moment, you need never be the same again—except by choice. But again, the great tragedy speaks loudly. We could, but we don't; we should, but we won't.*"

Her mind wanted to absorb the remaining unread pages of the book, but her body wanted more to sleep. And, as is often the case, the needs of the body overcame the desires of the mind. The book slowly slipped from her grasp. The pages flipped quickly together and the book of hope fell onto the bed next to the now limp hand that had held it but a moment before.

Mariana York was in the twilight zone between thought and sleep. Slowly, imperceptibly, the conscious mind stepped aside and that other mind—that mysterious source of thought that never sleeps—went to work, filing away the assimilated thoughts of her last few moments of consciousness into her mental computer.

The young woman did not know that her roommate would not return to the apartment—not this night. The events that were to come were in a sense predestined, and would require both the remaining hours of the cold windy night as well as the stage that had now been set. It could permit neither interruptions nor spectators. The events that had touched her life from the moment of her birth until now had brought her to this time and place.

Within the confines of her mind, she heard the door click as though someone had slowly turned the knob so as not to disturb her. Through the closed lids of her eyes, she saw the figure moving from the door to stand next to the bed where she lay. It was happening and yet it was not happening. She was aware of the presence of someone, but she was *not* aware. There was no fear, no terror, nor cause for either, and she remained still and asleep.

The voice that spoke was a voice not of this world. The distinct masculine tones were mellow and reassuring though the words were heard only within her sleeping brain.

"Mari—Mariana York. Are you asleep?"

She stirred slightly, her head shifting on the pillow, unconsciously facing toward the direction of the voice.

"Mari." Her inner mind responded to the second call, and the words were spoken by the woman, though not with her lips.

"Who—who are you?" She was inquiring, but without alarm, as though knowing that a special stranger had come upon her in a place where danger does not exist.

"My name is Noah. But for us, names are not important." The inner eyes of her mind were open now and she was fully alert. Unlike the state that exists in dreams, she clearly saw the figure standing before her as well as the familiar details of the room. He was dressed in an unpretentious white suit and shirt. Even the tie was white. The face was rounded and cheerful, but partially covered with a well-trimmed, black beard that gave him a stately appearance. He had an air of sophistication and elegance, although not of this world, and his voice suggested both total trust and supreme authority. The only thing of this world that seemed to be part of him was the apple he held in his right hand. It was a deep red, more so than any she had seen before, and he began rubbing it slowly against the sleeve of his left arm as he spoke again.

"Things don't seem to be going well for you, little one." Speaking with a smile, he continued. "You seem to have difficulty accepting truth."

Their strange mental conversation had begun on a note that caused a sudden but somewhat subdued flash of anger within her. His remark reminded her of Aaron and her response was short.

"I beg your pardon?" she said.

"You're surrounded by truth, my dear—the truth of what it takes to be happy as well as what it takes to be prosperous, but you've not been listening."

From someone else, such words would have been unnecessarily harsh, but this man spoke with a deep sense of caring. His accent had a slight English flair and his mannerisms were calming. She put aside her anger of a moment before and posed a question again, but in a more courteous tone of voice.

"I feel as though this must be a dream, but you and . . . this whole thing seem so real. Where are we . . . who are you?"

"Neither the 'where' nor the 'who' is as important as the 'why,' Miss Mari. The truth is that I am here and so are you—here in your room. *How* I managed this somewhat unorthodox meeting may be an interesting question, but not nearly as interesting as *why* I've come."

"All right then, uh—Noah, *why have* you come?" She saw herself ask the question and she saw herself give him a somewhat confused but interested smile. It was an odd sensation, this event. She was engaging in conversation and, at the same time, witnessing the entire event, as though she were two people, of separate minds—one *participating* in the exchange of thoughts and words with this strange man, the other observing and evaluating that dialogue. She was both participant and witness.

"Ah hah! You have asked the right question. Are you listening?"

"Yes."

"With both your mind *and* your heart, little one, for this shall be singly the most important conversation of your life, you know."

"Well—given the unusual circumstances . . . yes, I'm listening."

"Good." The man, still holding the apple in his hand, held it up slightly and out to his right as if placing it upon a pedestal. "What is this, do you suppose?"

She looked at the deep red object in his hand, at his eyes, then back again to the apple. She felt like a schoolgirl, convinced of the obvious answer to his question, yet reluctant to give the wrong answer.

"An apple?"

He smiled. "True—to you, an apple. To us, a good deal more. To us it has become a symbol of free choice . . . or selection, if you will."

"Who is us?"

He looked upward in slight disappointment, then back to Mari as though he were forcing himself to be patient with her. She felt uneasy, knowing he was looking for something other than the question she had asked him.

"Who, Miss Mariana—"

Her mind quickly caught the flow of his thoughts and she interrupted.

" . . . is not as important as the 'why'."

"Correct." He smiled again to show his pleasure at the fact that she had caught her own error.

"For the sake of our conversation, we shall call this—this object—an apple. Now, I pose to you an interesting question." He glanced down now at the apple, up at her, and with one single smooth-flowing movement, tossed it toward her. She responded instinctively, catching the apple after its five-foot flight across the distance that separated them.

"How do you tell an apple to grow?"

She sat staring at the apple that was now in her cupped hands. The combination of her surprise at his unexpected act and the brilliant redness of the apple itself caused her to only partially hear his question, although she knew one had been asked. After a momentary silence she looked up to find the strange visitor staring at her, patiently waiting for an answer. "I'm sorry—what?"

"I said, how do you tell an apple to grow?"

Again she felt confusion and a twinge of discomfort at not knowing how to answer the unusual question.

"I'm not sure what you mean," she said.

"Do you tell an apple to grow or does it just—*grow*?" Confidence returned to her voice as she spoke again. "It just grows—by itself."

"Do you find that at all interesting?"

"Not particularly. Should I?"

He laughed and his brilliantly white teeth showed themselves fully for the first time. His laughter was infectious, and she joined him with her own.

"You ask rather strange questions," she said.

His laugh subsided into a broad grin. "And you give some rather humorous answers, little one."

He became serious once again, the smile now more in his voice than on his lips.

"The apple grows, Miss Mariana, because it is nature's intent for it to grow—from seed, to blossom, to final fruit. It need not go to school. It endures cold, heat, rain and wind. It clings to the very limb that gives it life and purpose until, finally, it becomes what you now hold in your hand . . . what you call an apple."

He waited for a response, but on seeing only interest in her eyes and silence from her lips, he continued.

"It's not nature's intent for the apple you hold in your hands to evolve as a pear. All things have their own worthy purpose, whether it be an apple or a pear with *their* purpose or a nation—such as yours— with *its* purpose, or even the individual human being with *its* purpose. Do you understand?"

She was listening intently now to the words of this strangely fascinating man and her response was both immediate and honest, without the earlier fear or apprehension.

"I think so—although it's a bit philosophical . . . *deep* might be a better word."

In the twinkling of an eye, the part of her that *watched* the dialogue taking place merged with the part of her that lay on the bed engaged in conversation, and they were one. The event was like that of passing into the next world, and her facial expression mirrored her surprise.

"Is anything wrong?" he asked.

"I—I don't think so," she said. "It's just that I had the strangest sensation just now."

"It's nothing, really," he said. "Merely the coming together of your conscious mind with your subconscious mind—a rare occurrence for humans, yes, but quite necessary for you, Miss Mari."

She heard him, but her mind was more on the strange sensation she had just experienced—one similar to those she had experienced as a child when, on occasion, an event would give the sensation that it had happened before—somewhere in time. The French had a name for it—*Déjà vu*, she thought.

Her right hand moved to her eyes, and she rubbed them gently, pondering for the moment the sensation that lingered still. A millisecond later it was over and her mind instantly focused on his remark. She replied now as though nothing had happened.

"Necessary for me—why?"

"That comes later, little one."

She became conscious of the apple, which she held in her left hand, and looked down at it, then up at him.

"And about the apple—you were talking about its purpose."

"No, I was merely using the apple as an example. I said that all things have their purpose, particularly humans, and even more specifically, Mariana York—YOU!"

"Right now, my purpose is to stay alive—to survive in this confused world."

"My dear young woman," he said with a smile, nodding his head from side to side. "That is the *occupation* of many, I will admit, but it is the *purpose* of none."

She smiled in return, but said nothing.

"You have all the attributes of those who are successful, Miss Mari. You have a normal human mind and body—more normal than *many* whose achievements exceed your own, in fact. You have the gift of creativity, of sight and insight. You—and all humans, actually—can envision things that have never existed, and as if by magic, you create them. And then, you have something else, too, that most of your friends on this spinning blue-white sphere do not have."

He paused purposely, shifted his weight to the left foot, and folded his arms.

"And what is that?" She asked the question because he obviously expected it of her.

"Your freedom. You have the freedom of speech and of thought. You have the freedom to agree or disagree, to try or not to try. You have the freedom to succeed and the freedom to fail. With the freedom of deciding not to try, you attract your own failure, and by trying, you have the chance to succeed. But the freedom of *choice* is yours. You—you Americans, are even free to honor your country, or to speak out against it . . . something that *most* of the rest of the world cannot do. In our world, my dear, this thing *you* call freedom, *we* call free agency. It was given to you as a birthright, as an automatic means of separating the strong from the weak. Actually, you *humans* are free to select your own destiny. Have you ever thought of that?"

"No—no, I haven't—at least, not in a long time."

He took a single step closer to the bed, lowered his voice slightly, and peered at her with his piercing blue eyes, his arms still folded.

"My dear, it has been said that what you don't use you lose. You, as an example, were given many talents, most of which still remain untapped by you. Either you stop feeling sorry for yourself and use what you have or it shall be forfeited through what we call the 'Law of Familiarity.'"

His voice carried a note of almost divine authority, and she listened to him closely, neither agreeing nor disagreeing. Mariana York studied the man himself almost as much as the words he uttered.

Noah paused for a moment, searching her eyes for signals that would tell him something of her response. Satisfied that she listened with both her mind and her heart, he continued.

"Mari York, my dear young woman, do you know of the Law of Familiarity?"

"No, I don't . . ."

"Then it's time you did. There is a law, irrevocably decreed in Heaven from the day of the very foundation of the world, that is known in *our* world as the Law of Familiarity. You, my little one, and many others, are seized by the consequences of falling victim to this infallible law. In essence, the law is simple, although the full explanation is rather complex. For now, however, I shall reduce it to a simple phrase."

Noah stood motionless, the slight but ever-present smile gone from his mouth now as he spoke with a saddened authority.

"All things of value will, with the passage of enough time, be taken for granted."

He said nothing more, but once again studied her response as she let the words float on her conscious mind for several seconds, her eyes fixed upon his. There was a meaning—a deeper meaning than she could grasp, and he sensed the need to continue.

"I want you to think of things of value, Mari—real value, I mean. The value of choice—you all have it, but seldom use it. In the country in which you are a citizen there is the value of freedom and of nearly boundless opportunity—in spite of the present economic and political turbulence. There are values of love and friendship, and of talent—both learned and innate. Think about values, my little Mari . . . about values, not about circumstance. Think further for a moment of what happens when values are confronted with adverse circumstance, for therein lies the great human dilemma. Adverse circumstance combined with the passage of but a little time auto-

matically diminishes the worth of our values until at last we can see
them no more."

Noah's folded arms separated now. He cupped his hands in front
of him and the smile made a faint reappearance. "Mariana—my dear
Mariana . . . you already are all that you need to be to achieve and to
experience all that you want. You need not look for new discoveries. You
need only to look within yourself. You need only to—to *rediscover*. Time
has stolen away your greatest value, the gift given to you as a birthright,
and that is your *excitement* and your *faith* in yourself and in your future.
You had it in abundance as a child, Mari, but time—the passage of time
and your search for knowledge and prestige and position have stolen
away your greatest asset. You exchanged excitement for intellect and
traded belief for skepticism. You came to anticipate failure rather than
pursue success. You fear rejection rather than command respect. Not
only have you failed to achieve your dreams of earlier years, Mari, you
can't even remember what they were."

Despite a smile on his lips there were tears in his eyes, and within
his heart there was a genuine love and caring. She leaned forward now
toward the man whose words and emotions were affecting her. She
did not fathom all that he said, but she *sensed* all that *he* felt, and an
uncommon communication formed between them as they stared silently
at one another, each fighting to hold back tears that made spoken words
nearly impossible to utter.

A single teardrop flowed down her cheek, and her head turned
slightly away from him.

"Oh, Noah, I feel so terribly lost inside." She swallowed with difficulty and placed her clenched fists against her temples, her forearms
resting on her knees that were raised in front of her. The white handkerchief landed on her left forearm and her blurred vision could barely
perceive the monogrammed "N." The man who had tossed it to her stood
silently, his superior control and discipline forcing back his own emotion.

"I do not wish to bring you tears, Miss Mari, only answers. But I
suppose the prelude to self-discovery often requires tears," he added.

She unfolded the handkerchief, wiping her eyes and blowing her
nose. The stately appearance and mannerisms of the man in white
standing before her made the act of blowing her nose into his handkerchief seem almost irreverent.

"I'm sorry," she said, laughing slightly as she spoke the words.

"Don't be," he responded. "On the subject of the Law of
Familiarity, Mari—"

"Yes?"

"When the novelty and uniqueness of a given situation or circumstance give way to the commonplace, often the only thing that remains is responsibility reluctantly assumed."

"What are you speaking of?"

"Your recent and unsuccessful marriage to Aaron, little one. You've felt guilty since it ended, and that guilt is another factor that limits your present and future possibilities. You've been building walls around you to keep out the weeds of life, and that's foolish. You will succeed in building the walls, but one day, as you try to relax in your tormented loneliness, you will find the weeds of loneliness and despair growing inside the walls next to where you sit. You may escape many of life's *circumstances*, but you cannot escape all of life's *emotions*. Most of life's emotions—good *and* bad—should reside where they occurred—in the past. Remember, the greatest value of the past is how wisely you choose to invest it in the future."

"You make the difficult sound so effortless, Noah. It isn't, you know."

"The difficult is never effortless, Mari, but it is nearly always necessary."

"It's not just my marriage, Noah. There are a lot of things right now that I just can't get clear . . . what I want to do with my life—I just . . . I don't know how to explain it, I suppose."

The man watched her closely as she spoke. Both remained silent for a full minute. Finally the young woman shrugged her shoulders as a gesture of confusion and sat more upright in the bed again, folding her arms around her knees and looking up at the staring and patient visitor. The move she made with the blanket flipped the forgotten apple to the edge of the bed where he stood. Noah reached down with his left hand and picked up the red fruit, staring at it as he spoke.

"I understand, and that is why I've come to you this night. I have a mission, and you are part of that mission. I come to you with more than conversational philosophy and well-intentioned humor—that alone is not enough to change the course of the human direction. There are many among you who earn their living by seeking to provide outside motivation through their shallow humor and irrelevant and antiquated experience."

He reached into his jacket pocket and with his right hand removed an envelope—an envelope with an unusual quality that made her scan backwards several hours. Her mind flashed a picture of an envelope in a frame, but the image was interrupted by his words.

"I bring you a gift, Mariana York. It is not the sort of gift normally given to one human by another, but one with a uniqueness of power and potential. The moment that you should have it is now, my young woman."

He leaned forward slightly to offer her the document. She took it from his hand without removing her eyes from his. He neither smiled nor blinked an eye, but watched her with a solemn dignity as though this were a moment of monumental significance to him.

The envelope was not unfamiliar, for it was the second time this day that her eyes had seen the unusual item. It was similar to the first one she had seen in the office of the man named Locke. The texture of the paper suggested that care be used in its handling, as though it would crumble if misused. A one-inch wide ribbon held the envelope closed . . . a red ribbon whose unusually rich color caused her to glance at the redness of the apple that Noah was again rubbing against the lapel of his jacket. The two reds were identical. The envelope was not sealed, nor was there adhesive around the edge of the flap. The front of the envelope bore an inscription written, as in the case of the earlier envelope she had seen, with the gliding strokes of an unusual pen. The faint light from the lamp on the table to the right of her made the message difficult to read. But when she focused her eyes and turned the envelope slightly to pick up more of the light, the message was clear.

"A Gift, To Be Used And Shared"

She slid the ribbon gently across the envelope until it fell onto her lap, and she carefully removed its contents. The twice folded single sheet of matching beige parchment inside contained a message that filled one side of the paper, written with the same unusual scroll handwriting as appeared on the outside of the envelope itself. She paused now to look toward Noah once more. He stood motionless, his right elbow cupped in his left palm, the glistening red apple in his right hand resting against his cheek, while his eyes remained fixed on the letter she held in her hands.

His eyes shifted quickly to catch hers, but his expression remained unchanged.

"It is the greatest gift that one among you could receive," he said softly. "Read it slowly, Mari, and let each word and its message touch the very depths of your soul, for from this night forward your life shall be one of movement toward greatness and toward extraordinary accomplishment."

Suddenly her mind flashed an earlier recollection. "A Gift, To Be Used and Shared," she remembered. It was the same envelope, or one like it. It was the same handwriting, and even the strange and indefinable glow of the paper was the same.

She moved her body slightly toward the light and began absorbing the message from the page. As her eyes scanned the words, it was as though a voice were speaking within her brain—not her own, but that of another.

Mariana York—

Many are called, but few are chosen. You are among the chosen few—chosen to master and to share a message. The message, once understood and applied, has the capacity to irrevocably change the attitude and the circumstance of those whose lives are touched by it.

First—become aware that humans have the remarkable capacity of achieving that which they must achieve. Discover what you must do, your grand obsession, and commit yourself to both its pursuit and its achievement, in spite of all obstacles that shall confront you.

Second—develop an understanding that any value you pursue requires two things before it becomes yours. The first is the discipline to follow your personal plan in life. The second is the passage of time . . . and it is not given to you to determine how much time is finally enough. Clarity of purpose and the passage of time, combined with intensity of effort will produce the achievement of that purpose. It is automatic.

Finally—a warning. As all mankind is given a blessing at birth, so are you given a curse. The curse is behind most stories of human failure and mediocrity. Be certain that you, too, will encounter the curse as you pursue your new objectives in life.

From this night forward, and throughout all the days and nights of your existence on earth, your life shall become increasingly unique, and you shall forever look upon yourself as a masterpiece of creation, aware of your purpose in life and the true value of that life.

He who has handed you this message and who stands before you will stay with you a while longer and be visiting with you from time to time. He shall, with your assistance, restore both your life and your land to the intended posture of greatness.

May you become all that you were intended to be.

CHAPTER FOUR:

The Obsession

Mariana looked at Noah for the first time in several minutes. She had read the words on the page a second time but was still very confused.

"I don't quite understand," she said, looking down again at the letter and back at Noah.

"I didn't think you would—not now, anyway. A full understanding of anything almost always takes a conversation and a little pondering. Tell me, what don't you understand?"

"This letter—where did it come from? I mean—this whole thing, you—"

"Mariana, will you never stop looking for ordinary answers to extraordinary events? The 'who' or the 'how' is seldom as important as the 'why.' Reasons must *always* precede answers, as cause must always precede effect."

He looked at her as she continued to struggle with events beyond her comprehension.

"Mari, do you want to change yourself and how you feel about your existence here on earth . . . do you *really*?"

Her confused mind flashed from the current moment to her real world—the world that she somehow knew was still there waiting for her once this strange dream ended. But then, *was* this a dream? The clarity of the objects around her made it difficult to accept this strange conversation to be merely an imaginative excursion through the wandering fantasies of the sleeping human mind. The book lay at her side. Its blue and yellow color was vivid as the very moment in which she had held it in her hand, just before sleep became more demanding than her search for answers within its pages. Next to her on the night-stand were the clock radio and the tissue box, all in explicit detail. No, it could not be a dream, she thought to herself. For a few seconds she closed her eyes and reopened them to find the bearded visitor still standing before her, the red apple in his hand. Finally, her mind repeated the question that had been asked of her—did she really want to change herself? How many times had she wished she could or said she would.

Mariana York was haunted by the emptiness of having no purpose or obsession or human activity of any kind. The disappoint-ments of a love affair gone astray, and the horror of divorce and its subsequent loneliness and hours of readjustment and reflection merely added to the growing void. She recalled all the times she had felt inferior—even to those of lesser ambition and education. She remembered the fear that often seized her when the phone rang and she felt once again the agony of having to lie to friends about why she would often choose to stay at home rather than go out for a dinner or a movie when the real reason was the inadequateness of her financial situation.

What had happened to the dreams and ambitions and excitement of the young woman who had always believed that life and the process of growing up would be a grand adventure? What had become of the spirit and vitality of the young woman who knew no such words as "impossible" or "can't." Her mind drifted for several seconds more into the world of reflection and recall before slowly returning to rejoin her motionless body in the dimly lit bedroom where the man in white stood patiently awaiting her answer.

"Noah, I am confused by all of this . . . by you, by this—this letter. But believe me, whoever you are and wherever you came from, I say to you that . . . that I *must* change! My life is slipping away and I find myself not even caring about it. I *want* to change myself, Noah . . . Can you please . . . help me?"

The tears streamed freely down her face now, and she made no effort to stop them and felt no embarrassment.

"Good," he said, the smile beaming once again. Mariana laughed openly now; amid the tears of sorrow were the emotions of joy.

"Good," he said again, laughing with her as she wiped her eyes with his handkerchief. "Now, about that letter—what don't you understand about it?"

"Other than who wrote it and where it came from?"

He shrugged his shoulders and shook his head to signify the unimportance of the question. The young woman, accepting the strange situation, looked briefly again at the letter then read aloud.

"It says here that humans have the remarkable capacity of achieving that which they must achieve."

"That is correct."

"That doesn't make sense."

"Why not?"

"Well, it would seem then that everyone would have everything they could want. There would be no poverty . . . everyone would be wealthy . . . they would only need to establish what they *want* and they would have it."

"Wrong."

"But that's what it says."

"That's what you *think* it says, foolish child. That's what *everyone* thinks it says."

She read it again, slowly this time, enunciating every word, her finger tapping at the paper with each uttered word in succession.

Noah folded his arms, the apple still in his hand. "You've missed the emphasis on the key word, Mari."

"Which key word?"

"Think, Mariana—think!"

"Ability?"

"No."

"What, then?"

"It is there, Mari—like the sunrise it goes unnoticed except for those who will open their eyes."

She looked again. Nothing.

"The word is *must*, Mari. MUST!"

She thought for a moment. "But as I said before, if that were true . . ."

" . . . they would only need establish what they want and they would have it?"

"Yes."

"Has it occurred to you that there is a world of difference between *wishes and wants* and something that is an *absolute, imperative MUST*?"

"I suppose so, but . . ."

"Mariana! There is untold magic in that phrase if you will only try to understand the message. When you *must* do something—whatever it is—when it becomes an uncompromisingly urgent matter, what do you do, most of the time?"

"I do it?"

"Is that a question?"

"I guess it is."

"Let us suppose that through your negligence, the—what do you call it—the phone company threatened to discontinue your phone service at noon tomorrow unless you paid your outstanding debt. What would you do—assuming of course that you are a normally intelligent and responsible person?"

"I'd pay it."

"Suppose you didn't have the money?"

She thought for a moment. "I hate phones anyway," she said smiling, "so I suppose I would let them take the thing away."

"Mari! All right. Suppose it were your electricity. There would be no lights, no power for your refrigerator or your television, and—"

"That would be different," she said. "That's rather necessary, Noah, really."

"What would you do?"

"I'd pay the bill."

"You have no money."

"I'd get it—somewhere!"

"Why?"

"Because I have no choice. The phone may be one thing, but—"

"Ah ha!"

"What—ah ha?"

"That is the emphatic 'must' I am looking for. Let us call it a sense of urgency."

"But not everything in life is *that* important."

"I know."

He paused and looked carefully at her, but her quizzical eyes told him she had not yet understood the message.

"If your building were afire right at this moment and you had only seconds to escape, leaving all your possessions behind, what would you do?"

"I'd leave."

"You would?"

"Of course! My life would be at stake, and some things you just don't replace."

"Mari, suppose—just suppose—that with that same sense of urgency, suppose you simply *had* to earn a large sum of money. Suppose your standard of living absolutely demanded that you earn, uh . . . what would be a large monthly wage, in your opinion?"

She thought for just a second. "Oh, two—no—five thousand dollars a month."

"Suppose you *had* to earn that much—with the same seriousness— the same urgency that you would have to escape a burning building or pay an overdue utility bill?"

"I suppose I'd earn it," she said.

"Why?"

"Because I would have to—according to the picture you're painting."

"Exactly! And I pose an interesting question, Mari. Why don't you, or more people out there just like you—people of talent and ability and health, and some degree of ambition—why don't more of them earn five thousand dollars each month?"

"Because—because they don't have to."

"Precisely! They don't have to—and that is *your* current dilemma. You don't at this very moment *have* to do anything. Tell me, what do you *want* to do?"

"I don't understand."

"As an occupation. As a means of earning a living."

"That's my problem, Noah—I don't know. I could find lots of—of *jobs*. That's not what I want."

"What *do* you want?"

"I don't really know."

"Then find out, for until you do you will sit idly, slowly losing your ambition and whatever talent that still resides within that body of yours. Discovering that talent and how to take it to the market place is as urgent as your need to escape from a burning building. In both cases, little one, your life depends on it, believe me."

"How do I find it?"

"You might begin by seriously searching—by giving the matter some very serious thought. By the way, do you know why more of your kind, you humans, don't do well in life—by that I mean achieve more, prosper more, laugh more, and enjoy the blessings of life?"

"No, why?"

"Because they don't know *what* they want to do. As a result, they end up somewhere in some assignment, some occupation that simply came by when they needed to earn a living. Finally, with the passage of enough time, their *job* becomes their *necessity*, and their hope for a grand human achievement becomes merely another unfulfilled dream and they cease the search for a better life. It is tragic, but it is commonplace, and what I am describing is happening to *you*. You are both wondering and wandering, and you will soon, of necessity, settle into something not of your deliberate choosing but of absolute necessity, and you will live out your remaining years forever reflecting on what you *might* have done."

"Are you predicting or are you warning?"

"You, Mariana York, will determine that. Your failure to heed my warning will make my warning a prediction. Well, that is not *entirely* true. The fact that you have been selected as the recipient of the letter you hold suggests that it shall be *you* who both predicts and warns."

"Oh?"

"Yes, you will not see the magnitude of the gift you have received instantly, but you will soon see it. And when you do, you will understand its blessing to you and the great responsibility that comes with it. But first, I must be certain that you understand the essence of the subject we've discussed. Do you?"

"You mean regarding people getting what they have to get?"

"Yes."

"I understand your point—intellectually, I do, but I'm not sure that I *feel* it."

"Can you see how it *may* be true?"

"Yes, your point is interesting. In fact, it's almost *too* simple."

"Precisely!"

"What you're really saying is that I'm too comfortable, is that it?" She smiled pretentiously.

"Partially. But more, you've lost your spirit and excitement about life, especially regarding your occupation. You see, within all humans lies a sleeping talent that, if tapped and applied, would make work a totally enjoyable experience. That's why you must first discover your talent, and then learn how to take it to the market place."

Her mind began wandering when Noah mentioned that she had lost her spirit and excitement about life. Mari recalled those moments earlier in the day when she had sat next to the plant salesman in the lobby of Camelot Productions. She thought of his pessimism, and of something he had said: "Let humanity figure it out for themselves," he had told her. She recalled the shallow look in his eyes, the absence of anything of value worth pursuing. When had he lost it? When had the dream and the thirst for becoming somebody given way to ambivalence? Was it at her age? The fear of doing virtually nothing with one's life other than staying alive, paying the bills and handling the problems created a fear greater than any of those that she would have to overcome in order to do something with her life.

She remembered something she had read somewhere:

"Life should be more than a birth certificate and a grave marker, with a half million dollars in consumed goods and services as the only evidence of your human existence."

Noah's words called her back to the current moment.

"Pray to God, Mari, that you discover your talent and learn how to apply it, for in that discovery lies the key to fortune and value."

Without thinking, she responded. "Noah, if I could do what I *really* want to do . . . I mean *really*—"

He smiled and clasped his hands together as though in a gesture of inner joy, and interrupted her.

"That's what I want to hear, Mariana."

"How do you know? I haven't told you yet."

"What it is doesn't matter. It's how you said it . . . It's the sparkle in your eye as you spoke. But go on, please. What is it? What *would* you do?"

"I would write, Noah. I would write, and I would teach." Her words rang with an inner excitement and enthusiasm.

"Then why, in the name of all that is good, are you not doing it?"

"I did for a while—teach, I mean."

"Why did you stop?"

"The educational system was too confining—too bureaucratic, I suppose. I don't know."

"Why did you start, then?"

"Because I love sharing things—thoughts, primarily—with other people."

"Then your love for teaching should not have been abandoned because of the reasons you've stated. There are many forms of teaching, you know."

"Oh?"

"You said you had a desire for writing. Why don't you write a book? That's a form of teaching."

"Noah, who am I . . . to write a book, I mean. After all, if I had accomplished something or experienced something worth writing about . . ." She deliberately left her own sentence unfinished.

"I'll pretend I didn't hear that," he said with a flash of disgust, turning his head slightly away from her.

"The fact is, you love teaching and you love writing. That is all the reason you need for beginning. And by beginning, you will discover along the way all that you need to succeed at it."

"It's that simple, is it?"

"It's that simple."

"Who would publish it—or buy it, Noah?" She spoke not with a tone of pessimism, but as one asking unnecessarily foolish questions as he or she searches for additional encouragement.

"Many people bought and read your Mr. Hemingway's last book—and Ayn Rand's—as well as hundreds of other successful authors. But what about the *first book* written by any of these great men and women? In order for there to be a last great creation, there must first be an initial attempt . . . perhaps several," he added.

For half a minute she thought and Noah watched, until finally he spoke again.

"There are many ways to teach. Find a worthy idea or a useful or valuable product and learn how to sell it. Such a calling will create two things for you: first, an income, and second, it will give you experience in teaching others how to use it and why they should have it. The sales profession is an excellent forum for developing the great human virtues, you know. It—"

For the first time, Mariana broke into open laughter, interrupting the well-intentioned Noah in the middle of his thought. "You're joking," she finally said. "You're the second person to make that suggestion in the same day. You wouldn't know a man named Walter by any chance, would you?"

"I beg your pardon?"

"Nothing. I'm sorry, Noah." The laughter resumed, but was more subdued this time, and he waited for her to stop before continuing.

"Think what you will, Mari, but it is true. Confronting the public with an idea of value will teach you the virtues of discipline, independence and commitment. It will also sharpen your skills at persuading and communicating. You might seriously consider it as a beginning."

Her facetious laughter was subsiding now to a lingering and slightly serious smile.

"Perhaps," she said.

"Whatever your grand obsession may be, you may find that you will have to follow many strange paths along the way before you at last arrive at your final destination. Better to follow paths leading to a well-defined *somewhere* than to linger in ruts leading to *nowhere*."

There was silence as they studied one another—she, his wisdom—he, her sparkling eyes and serious expression.

"Noah?"

"Yes?"

"I'm laughing—not at you—but at myself. You're making me see something . . . something I don't fully understand, but something inside. It's more of a feeling, I suppose, and it's a good feeling. It's something I must ponder, but I'm glad for it."

He smiled jubilantly. "Good," he said. "Good."

A flash of white filled the room through the window behind where Noah stood. The full moon had peeked out through a momentary break in the thick clouds filling the night sky. Its brilliance was magnified by the newly fallen snow that had fallen throughout the evening.

The unexpected event seemed to Mariana York to be symbolic of a major self-discovery.

"Noah, I don't have all the answers yet, but I've captured the feeling."

"Then you have all that is necessary for the moment. The answers will automatically reveal themselves as you learn to apply the second step in the letter before you."

She had nearly forgotten the letter that now lay next to the book beside her, and she picked up the single sheet:

Second—develop an understanding that any value you pursue requires two things before it becomes yours. The first is the discipline to follow your personal plan in life. The second is the passage of time . . . and it is not given to you to determine how much time is finally enough . . .

Noah waited until she looked up from the letter before speaking. "Do you understand?" he asked.

"Yes, I think so," she answered. "Once you decide on your—what you call your 'grand obsession,' then you must work at it until you've somehow succeeded."

He laughed. "I think you have the feeling."

"I'm doing better?"

"You're doing better. Almost better than we thought you would."

"We? What do you mean 'we'?"

"Please, not now. The answers to your questions will come in time."

"Noah, you're not fair. How much time?" She knew almost what his answer would be before he finished his sentence.

"It is not given to you to determine how much time—"

"—is finally enough," she said.

"Correct. You may understand the words of the second step, but I'm not certain that you comprehend their full meaning."

"Much of this is difficult," she admitted.

"Mariana, let me elaborate just a bit. You see, to a very large degree it is impatience that is the great killer of many talented people in search of a better understanding of life. They often commit themselves to a worthy endeavor, but the obstacles of life soon discourage them from their course and they become lured to new adventures. They wander, talent in hand, from one place to another, building foundations but never completing their projects. Even the task that you shall soon accept will test you from time to time. In spite of its worthiness and the promises of a rich and bountiful life given to you in the letter, you will have times of sorrow, despair, and discontent, and you will expect results and response in your time, rather than in due time. Remember this, little one, all things in their own due season. The farmer who plants his crops in the spring must wait until the fall to reap the final harvest. His storehouse of food may be exhausted, and his children may cry out for relief from their hunger, but he must endure those trials and wait for nature to work its own predictable magic. You cannot ask the soil or your future for an advance. The same magic that converts the seeds into a rich harvest will convert your disciplined and consistent efforts into results, Mari. You must remember that . . . above all things, remember that."

She listened like a child hearing a fascinating adventure story and marveled at the storyteller's unique ability to paint word pictures and to stimulate her feelings of awareness and understanding. Noah stood before her now, not as a strange intruder into her private world of dreams, but as a welcome guest into her inner world of thoughts. She was no longer trying to evaluate how the event was happening, but was now massively assimilating all that was happening. Here was a man who made no effort to impress her with either his word or his manner, but whose ability to express was so captivating that he made her see things she had not seen before, and imagine herself to be worth more and capable of more than she had ever imagined.

"I had somehow not equated the—the 'passage of time' to mean 'patience,' Noah, but it's making more sense now. When I think of it, I had plenty of patience with the children I once taught, but I've never given patience to myself."

"Then, teacher, begin by teaching yourself. Those who listen will learn as much from your example as they do from your words. I've noticed that we often teach best those things that we ourselves most need to hear."

"So you think that teaching and writing is the course I should pursue?"

"It's *your* life, Mari. What do *you* think?"

"It's what I want. The question is how I can best get started again."

"Then the *want* will produce the *how*—it always does, you know. That is fundamentally what I want you to see. But you must see it. You must see it from within you own soul, because no one person can give to another that final magic spark of an inner awareness and understanding."

"I know," she said, looking past his eyes to the wall behind him.

"But I am pleased that you want to pursue your occupation of teaching through the written and spoken word again. It is the choice we *thought* you would reach and knew that you must reach in order to fulfill the promise given to you this night. I have a few thoughts on your role as teacher, my little one."

"Yes?"

"By teaching ideas to others, you truly do affect eternity, for rest assured that there will be no limits to where your influence stops. By touching another life and changing the direction of that life through your teachings, you have the capacity to alter events. You see that, don't you?"

"Yes . . . yes, I do."

"And as you go about your teaching, do not seek only to teach people the things that they do not know, but seek to teach them to live and think as they do not live and think. Teach them virtues and pursuits, Mariana. Teach and write on truth and discipline and ambition. Teach and write on the value of setting worthy goals—both in personal and business life. Teach and write on the value of good communication, on the skills of leadership, on integrity, and on the rewards of consistently applied labor through clearly defined thought. Teach and write that humanity may learn to replace anger and hostility with love and forbearance. Above all, Miss Mari, as you teach so must you become, for to teach one thing and live another is the height of hypocrisy. And finally, on this subject of teaching, learn the art of teaching your fellow humans how to decide firmly those things that they will *not* do, so that they may one day soon be free to do those things that they *should* do. Do you understand, Mariana?"

"I do, Noah. And what is more important, I *believe*."

"Then it is your belief that will serve as the magic catalyst to bring about all that you dare wish for. Have faith—believe that all things are possible. Assume the impossible is within your grasp, and believe that you shall achieve and you will achieve. Learn to use your imagination for developing concepts, then learn to convert your vague concepts into a plan. With that plan or goal, combine the intensity of desire, the execution of skill, labor and practice, along with patience and consistency of thoughts and action, and no power or influence on Earth will be greater than yours—provided that undeviating faith is your constant companion."

Mari heard not only the words, but also she captured the full meaning of those words, and their value became etched upon the depths of her soul. She was hearing the truth spoken as she had never before heard it and feeling possibilities emerging within her imagination that she had never before experienced. Her mind moved from glimpses of the future to recollections of the past and back again, without missing a single word as he spoke. His concepts, urgings and warnings created thought parallels in her mind and made her see her own weaknesses without regret or pain, and her own strengths without excessive pride or vanity. She was seeing herself and her attitude changing with an inner eye of confidence and clarity, and the swells of joy from deep within her were now becoming clearly apparent in her twinkling eyes and in her confident smile.

"What else do you not understand, Mariana?"

She paused only briefly before answering. "The letter speaks of . . . of . . ." She glanced back at the document and then back to his eyes. ". . . of a curse, Noah, but it says nothing specific—nothing beyond a vague reference."

"And it must remain that way, my dear. As the document states, the curse will manifest itself in its own time. It always has and always will. To converse on the subject now would be premature and fully ineffective. We shall deal with that in its own time. Beyond *that*, have you other questions? If so, now is the time to bring them to the surface, for our time grows short."

"Just one thing. Must we end on such a negative—I mean, your words give me hope, but just now you planted a seed of negativity and fear about this—this *curse*."

He smiled an understanding sort of smile. "You are indeed right, little one, but you must remember that reality is the best beginning. In spite of what many of your—your 'positive thinkers' may say, there is virtue in reality, and the fact is that life is designed to be mostly negative. The negative side of life needs little attention, Mari. It feeds upon itself. Only goodness must be nurtured if it is to survive. Doubt, worry, and fear will intercept your efforts to succeed—you can count on that. The curse will come in many forms. The curse is the tool of the adversary—he who seeks to discourage and dethrone goodness. He has many colleagues, Miss Mari, some of whom you shall surely meet. Just be prepared for reality; that is all I ask. Prepare yourself for impending adversity and you shall overcome it. But do not ignore it. Such is the behavior of fools."

"May I ask questions of a non-philosophical nature?"

"You may ask, but I cannot promise an answer to *all* questions you might pose."

"Whoever you are, Noah, wherever you've come from, however you've entered my room, I want you to know that be this a dream or some other unique occurrence, its value to my understanding of myself is immeasurable. I suppose my question is, is this a dream, Noah?"

"To some degree, Mari, but only in that I am visiting a part of your mind that is seldom visited—not consciously, anyway."

"When you're gone, will I remember what—what happened, and all that was said . . . and how I feel at this moment?"

"Not consciously, although the feeling about yourself and your future will remain."

"Will I see you again?"

"You will, but at a time and place of my own selection."

"And the promise made to me in the letter, Noah . . ."

"The promise was meant to be honored fully on the day and moment it was prepared for offering to you."

"Noah—" She hesitated now, but the question had to be asked. "Why me?"

"The answer to that is partially found on the reverse of the envelope next to you."

She picked up the envelope and turned it over. In her haste to open it, she had not noticed the scroll writing across the center of the back of the envelope.

> *Behold, I have chosen thee—I have refined thee in the furnace of affliction.*

It was as though a soft, reassuring voice spoke each word as her mind scanned the phrase. This moment, this second in time and the voice that she heard in her mind were of such extraordinary importance as to defy description, and the single, obscure and indescribable event seared the words and feelings she had heard and sensed this night forever into the depths of her inner mind and soul. She felt nothing but warmness and an assurance of peace and contentment.

"Your past few years have been but moments of accumulated preparation, my little one. Each disappointment, doubt, and moment of despair and loneliness was for this night," Noah said in softly spoken words.

"But I still must ask, Noah. Why me?"

"I cannot answer, for to do so would reveal events that at this time are beyond purpose."

"What am I to do next . . . in the morning, or whenever?"

"You need not be concerned. The events of this night will dictate to your conscious mind what you should do. As one who was once among you has said, 'The die has been cast.'"

The apple had been hidden by his cupped hand, but now made its glowing appearance once more as he began polishing its already brilliant redness against his sleeve.

"Is there anything else?" He raised the apple toward his face as if ready to bite into the red fruit.

"What has *really* happened tonight?" she asked.

He lowered the apple away from his face and spoke. "We've uncovered the excitement of childhood that once was yours—that once was the gift of all humans. Also, we've merely helped you determine what your own great talent is—which will now become your obsession. Your talent, dear Mariana, will create a place for you. You need not search for a position or a job, not any longer. Remember, *your talent will create a place for you.*

"Be aware that what you have experienced this night can be experienced by anyone, without the necessity of my presence. The rediscovery of an inner excitement, confidence and attitude, and the discovery of one's innate talent combined with an awareness of the fact that all humans have the promise of being able to achieve what they must achieve, these things lie within the grasp of anyone who makes the decision to begin their own search for a better life. For reasons that cannot now be revealed, that discovery has been nearly forced upon you, Mari, as gift. But all mankind can summon up their own gifts, with the same promises and the same rewards. Its discovery lies in the pages of books unread, of conversations unheard, of classrooms and seminars unattended, and of thoughts not yet pondered.

"And now, I give you a single requirement, my dear. You must, in order to fully experience all the rewards reserved for you, commit yourself to the service of others, that they might in great numbers be led to their own self-discoveries. You must fully commit yourself through speeches, books, conversations, or whatever means possible, to become the servant of many, for it is written that as you sow, so shall you reap. Giving and sharing and helping is indeed the beginning of receiving, and your full reward shall be in proportion to your full effort directed at helping others."

"What you're saying is not new, Noah—"

"Of course not, Mariana. The promise you have received as a gift is the same solemn promise given to all mankind generations ago. But only a few have learned to use it. To the masses it is an antiquated philosophy having no place in the new competitive and liberated lifestyle. Your people are looking everywhere except within themselves for the answers to peace, harmony and abundance. It now becomes *your* responsibility to affect the masses so that they might see where the answers are—within *themselves*. You must teach them cause and effect, and you must teach them the effect of thought on circumstance. How to teach, and what to teach will come to you as you diligently read, search, grow and help others with the knowledge you currently have, and with the knowledge you've gained within the past several hours.

"And—heavens, it seems that there is so much to say and so little time to say it, my little one . . .

"*If you would plant for days, plant flowers. If you would plant for years, plant trees. But if you would plant for eternity, plant ideas.*

"That is your calling, Mariana. That is your talent, your obsession, and indeed your gift. As a friend once said, 'If you give someone a fish, you feed him for this day; but if you teach a man to fish, he will feed himself for a lifetime.' Teach, Mari, with all that is in you and for the sake of mankind, your country and yourself, teach—with all your heart, might, mind and strength. Do you understand?"

The confident smile was enough, but her words gave additional confirmation.

"I am ready, Noah. I am ready for something . . . terribly important."

"I know," he said, "and when the student is ready, the teacher will appear." He began polishing the apple on his sleeve again. "Don't forget the apple, Mari. You don't tell it to grow, because it's nature's design that it should do so. It is likewise nature's design that you should prosper and find happiness. Goodbye, Mariana York."

With that, he was gone, with the same quickness that he had appeared in the room. The re-emerging moon flashed its light across the snowy whiteness, and once again the dimly lit room came alive with a soft-white brilliance as if to announce the parting of this strange person whose presence, purpose, and origin still remained ambiguous.

Once more, the woman was alone with her thoughts, but they were not thoughts of fear and apprehension. There was confusion, but mingled with renewed hope and confidence. Her conscious mind was returning now to rest, aside from the subconscious. Where before she was nearly unaware of the sights and sounds of things around her, she now detected the music playing somewhere in the distance. Her eyes were closed now and her awareness and clarity of the events that had just occurred were fading. It was as though she were moving from one world into another . . . from a world of peace and total harmony into a world of reality and complexity. Her eyes opened slowly, the music now closer and louder. Her thoughts were scattered, and she felt a strange but relaxing numbness inside her own head. The eyes focused on the window across the room, and the whiteness beyond the window.

She turned her head to the right, feeling the softness of the pillow beneath her head. Before her was the clock radio—the source of the music that had brought her from sleep. It was seven o'clock and a new day was beginning.

Mari opened and closed her eyes twice to bring the surroundings into sharper focus. Her mind was clear and her body felt fully rested, and she sat erect with the sharp movement of an athlete beginning sit-ups. She moved her head from side to side to loosen the muscles of her neck and raised her arms over her head, arching her back and yawning simultaneously. It was then that she saw the sunrise, and it represented more, somehow, than merely the beginning of a new day. Her eyes saw the sunrise, but her mind and heart saw the sunrise of new possibilities.

She sat for just a moment looking around the room. Her eyes caught the cover of a book lying at the foot of the bed. It was the book she had been reading before falling asleep the night before. She thrust herself forward toward the book and her right hand pulled it back toward her. She must have kicked it somehow during the night to move it that far down on the bed.

But she did not have time now to look for the explanation. There was a bus to catch. She had a purpose this day, an almost instinctive urging that drove her body quickly from the bed and into the shower. She would not wait for Mikki to call. Beginning this day, she would pursue her own better future, rather than waiting for it to find her.

Within an hour, a newly emerging Mari York was opening the door of her apartment to begin a special mission. There had been no television and no news programs. The morning newspaper remained unopened at the entrance to the door. On this day, her mind would remain uncluttered by information designed to distract the ambitious.

At the end of a two-hour bus ride through early morning rush hour traffic, the neatly dressed young woman walked through the doorway of Camelot Productions with a renewed purpose.

CHAPTER FIVE:

The Beginning

Mikki looked at her as though she recognized her, but then wasn't so sure. Mari further confused her by walking past her desk, saying nothing, and flashing only a quick wink. She went directly to the elevators and pushed the button.

It was not the same Mariana York who had stood at this same place yesterday. There was no apprehension or disillusionment. She had a purpose, and in her mind there was no question as to whether the purpose would be achieved. It was a fait accompli.

She wore a white skirt and matching white jacket. Under the jacket, she had selected a red blouse with ruffles down the front, and her handbag and shoes matched the blouse. The long blond hair had been carefully brushed and the brilliance of the locks hanging over her shoulders seemed to add an even greater sparkle to her eyes. Her appearance was indeed striking.

What had happened to the woman on the outside was merely reflective of what was happening to her on the inside. Somehow, deep inside the confines of her own mind, there was a friend speaking to her—reassuring, guiding, and suggesting. But the conscious mind of Miss York was aware only that a firm and uncompromising decision had been made to do something with her life. It was as though she had very simply and resolutely changed her mind about herself. There was no awareness of the mental seeds placed in her subconscious in the hours just before the dawning of this new day.

The ring of the bell signaled the arrival of the elevator and as the doors swung open, she stepped inside. In seconds, she emerged at the fourth-floor level, glancing momentarily at herself in the mirror-covered wall that only yesterday reflected an image of bewilderment and doubt bound up in the five foot, one-inch frame of an unemployed and disillusioned ex-school teacher. Today, the reflection bore a relaxed smile that was not artificially painted on to make herself look better. It was there naturally because inside she smiled from the way she felt about herself.

She turned left and walked directly to the first door on the right. The gold block letters seemed different today, she thought, as though they had been polished the night before. Without hesitation, she opened the door and stepped inside. The interior of the office was just as yesterday, but somehow a bit brighter. The music was still playing softly in the background. The only new addition to the office was the dark haired woman seated behind the reception desk.

"Good morning. I'm Miss Lincoln. May I help you?"

"Yes, my name is York—Mariana York. I'd like to see Mr. Locke for just a moment, please."

"Do you have an appointment, Miss York?"

"Actually, no. I was visiting with Mr. Locke for a few moments yesterday and there was something I failed to do—properly, I mean. It'll only take a moment."

Normally, the secretary would have been reluctant to interrupt Mr. Locke for someone without an appointment. But for an unexplained reason, she smiled warmly and rolled her chair slightly toward the intercom.

"I'll see if he can take a moment," she said, and Mari smiled warmly in return.

"Thank you."

Mari removed the book from the red purse and looked down at its cover.

"Mr. Locke, a Miss York to see you. She said she saw you yesterday and had forgotten to take care of something."

Mari could not hear his response, but she detected a hesitancy and whispered to the secretary.

"He gave me a copy of his book yesterday—here in the office," she explained, holding the book out for her to see.

Miss Lincoln spoke into the phone. "Sure. Would you like some coffee brought in when you're ready for Miss York?" There was a pause. "Fine, I'll look after it."

The remark was self-explanatory, but Miss Lincoln confirmed it.

"It'll be about five minutes. He's just finishing up something. Can I get you some coffee, or would you rather wait until you meet with Mr. Locke?"

"I'll wait until then, thank you."

"Okay. Why don't you just have a seat . . . perhaps in front of the fireplace?"

"Thank you. May I browse a bit? The wall there is covered with so many interesting things."

The secretary smiled. "Of course."

The gas-burning fireplace gave added warmth to the cozy atmosphere of the office, but for the moment Mariana was drawn to the collection of pictures, plaques and assorted memories filling the wall behind her. She had had but a moment yesterday to find fascination in what others might find merely commonplace.

There were book jackets, framed and dated, most with the same author's name—Jonathan Locke. There were awards and, of course, photographs—all of people she had never seen before. Some of the items she recalled from yesterday. Among them, one quotation that seemed more special now:

"The greatest deterrent to success is the lack of understanding, acceptance, and appreciation of your own self-worth."

Yesterday, it was but another catchy slogan with little or no personal significance. But today, it somehow reaffirmed a feeling that she had about herself.

Her eyes drifted toward the center of the wall and there, as it had been yesterday, was the envelope—that strange, glowing envelope of unknown significance. Yesterday, it seemed odd only that it should be there. Today, it caused feelings to emerge within her that reminded her of the feelings she used to experience as a child—the sensation of having been there before. And the words themselves:

"A Gift, To Be Used and Shared."

Surely the familiarity of that simple phrase was because she *had* seen it before . . . just yesterday, here in this very office. And yet there was something more than just that. For some inexplicable reason, seeing the envelope gave her a sensation of inner confidence and reassurance unlike anything she had experienced in many years.

Mariana York would not know or be able to recall the details of the night before. She was unaware that just hours before she had held a similar envelope in her hands and that its contents were meant for *her*.

At this moment there was an odd familiarity, but the feelings within her were related to no particular incident, conversation or strange visit in the night. There had been no gift and no promise.

But there *was* a new woman—both inside and outside.

"Miss York?"

"Yes?"

"Mr. Locke has just finished his long-distance call. He said to bring you in then." She moved toward the doors to the inner office and opened one of them as Mari approached. "I'll bring the coffee right in," the secretary said.

"Thank you," Mari answered.

While her meeting with the man only twenty-four hours ago had been brief, he had made such a distinct impression on her that she immediately recognized him as she stepped inside the office. He was moving out from behind the large cherrywood desk to greet her.

"Miss York?"

"Yes, Mr. Locke. Thank you for seeing me. I seem to be developing a habit for interrupting your day."

They both extended their hands at the same moment in greeting.

For several minutes, the man went through the process of showing the woman some of his books that he had collected on the subjects of personal development, psychology, history, and government. His bookshelves completely filled the walls of his office. When Miss Lincoln arrived with the coffee, they exchanged remarks on the beauty of the light covering of snow that had fallen during the night. Handing her a cup, he guided her into a soft chair across from the table from where he now sat in a large leather chair. Each had taken their first sip of coffee before Jonathan questioned her about her purpose in visiting.

"I assure you that I'm not lost again, Mr. Locke. I'll admit that yesterday I was—in more ways than one—but not today."

"Did you interview for a position at all yesterday?"

"No. No, I didn't."

"I didn't think you would, actually."

"Oh?"

"Forgive me, Miss York, but—well, if I may be very honest, I would find it difficult to believe that the woman I see here in the office today is the same person I saw yesterday. I know that isn't very complimentary, but . . ."

"I would prefer accuracy to compliments."

He smiled as one would who had just found something warm and relaxing about another person.

"Either yesterday was a particularly bad day or something dramatic has happened to you overnight. In either case, the change is most unusual. But no, I didn't think you were ready to sell your talent to anyone yesterday. Today, however, I can tell that you've decided on a specific purpose. What can I do for you?"

"I know you're busy, Mr. Locke, so I'll come right to the point. I very simply wanted to drop by and personally thank you for the book. I suppose I looked like I needed it."

He smiled and crossed his legs. "Let's just say you looked as though you were in need of some answers. I know, because I've been there before. The look on your face was what a friend of mine used to refer to as the 'death rattles.' Did you—have you had a chance to read it yet?"

"I started it last night. To be honest, I fell asleep reading it. But I finished it this morning on my way to your office."

"You're a fast reader."

"I've taken a course in speed-reading and, if I might anticipate your next question, yes—I most thoroughly enjoyed it. Some of the things you said hit me rather hard. In fact, I believe I dreamed about some rather interesting things most of the night . . . things that your book caused me to consider . . . things I had not thought of in years."

"Then it's been of some help?"

"Far more than you may know, Mr. Locke. By the way, are the ideas in the book fairly typical of the things that you teach in your seminars and in your cassette tape programs?"

"The theme is rather consistent, yes. That's because most of the important and valuable lessons in life have a certain consistency of thought. It's not easy answers or catchy answers that we should be in search of, but truthful answers, don't you agree?"

"Of course."

"What did you most enjoy in the book? Was there something in particular?"

"People have the remarkable capacity to achieve exactly what they *must* achieve. *That* is the essence of the gift, Mr. Locke."

"What?"

"I said—"

"No, what I mean is . . . where did you hear that?"

"In your book."

"It isn't in my book, not as you just stated it."

She blinked her eyes just once and glanced for a short second at the floor and then back again. She was certain she had read it last evening—

just before falling asleep. He saw her look at him with a slight hint of confusion, which quickly disappeared.

"Well, I find the thought rather intriguing, if you look beneath the surface. Perhaps you should explore the thought in one of your *future* books."

"Perhaps I shall," he said, leaning forward slightly to take another drink from his cup. He was overwhelmed at the remarkable difference in the slender woman from what she had appeared to be the day before and yet he hesitated at making an excessive issue of it, for to do so might well sound like shallow flattery. He chose to savor his admiration rather than express it. He sat for a moment listening to her comments about his excellent taste in office furnishings, but his mind was actively studying both her beauty and her mannerisms.

She spoke deliberately, but with a hint of genuine excitement. Even her light conversation about the decor was handled with style and elegance. Her clothes had a professional air to them, but revealed enough of her feminine contours to suggest an above-average figure.

"Mr. Locke, I'm terribly sorry," she said glancing at her watch. "I meant only to step in for a moment, and my moment has become several. Your appointment calendar is going to be behind all day, I'm afraid."

"Don't worry," he answered, as she took the last drink from her cup, "I've been in since seven and have everything in the morning calendar finished—unless Miss Lincoln has added something I'm not aware of."

"Do you always start that early?"

"Not always, but I do always try to make each day a full one—either by staying up late or beginning early."

"Is that one of the secrets for becoming successful?"

"It could be. But for certain, it *is* one of the secrets for avoiding *poverty*."

They laughed together.

"Would you like another coffee?" he asked.

"I really shouldn't. I have two objectives today, this time with you being the first."

"And the second—or shouldn't I ask?"

"Of course—I'm going to visit your sales office and convince them to let me bring my powers of persuasion to Camelot Productions."

"Isn't that where you were supposed to be going yesterday—when you were lost?"

"Yes, but then I wasn't ready."

"And now?"

"Now, there's no question about my readiness. It's something that I decided last night, and on waking this morning I was even more convinced."

"What changed your mind?"

"Your book played a major role in my decision. I'm interested in two things, Mr. Locke: what I can learn here, primarily, and then what I can earn here. Each is important, but one without the other provides only an existence."

"Are you suggesting that money is not your biggest incentive in considering . . . or keeping . . . a job?"

"I would never suggest that it isn't an important consideration, but in fairness to both sides, I think earnings—or the opportunity for earning—should be in proportion to results, and that results produced by a person should be recognized by earnings. But more than that, I think a person should constantly work on him or herself first . . . he or she should become *worth* more. I think if *that* isn't the first consideration, then you may find that your income has exceeded your value—which at best is a precarious situation.

"It seems that *you* should be the authority on that, Mr. Locke. Didn't I just see something on the wall of your outer office about—how was it—'Make certain you always grow up to the level of your income, or one day your income will shrink down to where *you* are'?"

He smiled at her ability to quickly recall a quotation at the exact moment that she needed it, and he made that remark. "There must be a place for my ability to do that," she said.

"There is—if you're consistently good at it."

"Here?"

"Here. What is your present occupation, Miss York?"

"I *was* a teacher—tenth graders. But that was some time ago. I've been living on savings since then, and trying to find myself. It's time I became serious. Necessity has a way of forcing us into action, doesn't it?"

"That's the way the system works," Jonathan agreed. "Just last evening, I wrote a few notes in my journal about the two sources that bring about changes in people. One is inspiration, and you'll admit there's plenty of that—the books, the libraries, seminars, advisors, ministers, friends—inspiration is all around us, but we seldom respond when it speaks. It usually takes the second source to get our attention—"

"Desperation."

"Exactly."

"How accurate." She laughed and changed her position in the chair.

"Isn't it? The difference is that inspiration whispers and desperation shouts. And we all know that if someone shouts at us, it's usually because we've failed to listen to the calmer voice, which suggests we're probably in trouble."

They laughed together, not as one *because* of the other, but as one *with* the other from mutual enjoyment of one another's contribution and response. The courtesy and reservation of two people who had met only moments before was quickly being replaced by a genuine pleasure at the sincerity of expressed feelings.

"Listen, one more coffee—okay?" He jumped out of the chair and headed toward the double doors before she could answer. A moment later the efficient Miss Lincoln had refilled the blue cups with fresh coffee this time leaving the pot behind on a tray with a knowing smile.

"She has a wonderful personality," Mari said.

"It takes people like Miss Lincoln to make our business work properly," he answered. "It's not what you *know* about our business that makes the difference, it's what you *are*. "

"Isn't that *always* true?"

"Yes, but here it's essential. We're selling more than just hope and encouragement, and what some would call success principles—we're selling people on themselves."

His next remark, after a moment's pause to stir his coffee, sent a strange sensation through the woman to whom he spoke. "Rekindling the human spirit has become my grand obsession," he said.

The silver spoon Mariana had been using to stir her own coffee slipped from her grasp and rattled on the saucer.

"Excuse me," she said. He watched the event, but made no comment, filing it instead into his mental library as something he said that had touched a sensitive spot. She felt him mentally dwell on the event, which added to her bewilderment.

Suddenly, her mind heard the faint echo of a voice—"You must find your grand obsession . . ." But in a moment the voice was gone and she continued as though nothing had happened.

"There's nothing like having a well-defined purpose, Mr. Locke, and it's clear that you have yours. I admire that, and I'm going to find my own—what you call 'grand obsession.'"

"Good for you. Any ideas yet?"

"Absolutely! I'm committing myself to selling my abilities here first, and from what I learn at Camelot, I'm going to somehow create a reputation as a teacher—a lecturer and writer. You're going to be reading my books one day, Mr. Locke. You can *count* on it."

"Your ambitions are admirable. It isn't going to be easy, you know."

"I'm prepared for that. But I have a promise . . . one that won't permit me to fail."

"You have friends in high places?" he said jokingly. "Better than friends in high places is being in high places," she said with a short laugh, which brought a longer laugh from him. "No, my greatest asset is that my talent will create a place for me." She said it very matter of factly, as though it were a foregone conclusion.

"Miss York, how many of my books have you read?"

The question seemed strange—more than just a casual inquiry, more like someone probing for necessary information needed for answering serious questions.

"Just the one you gave me yesterday. Why?"

"Nothing, really—just that something you said just now has a special significance to me. In fact, we've been together perhaps . . ." He glanced at the gold watch on his left wrist and back at her. ". . . less than a half hour, and you've made two separate remarks, both of which are seldom quoted, and one of which—unless I'm mistaken— hasn't even found its way into my books yet."

"Well, perhaps I heard it somewhere else. What did I say? Perhaps I'll remember."

"Your talent will create a place for you—and it's quite unlikely you would have heard it quite that way before. I've only heard it once."

The strange sensation returned again, as though her mind were taking her back into a long forgotten experience. Mari hesitated slightly before answering.

"I—somehow I . . . I must have picked it up, but I honestly don't recall where. You're certain it isn't in your book?"

"Positively."

"Well, I don't recall using it before—ever. What's wrong, do you have copyrights on it . . . am I guilty of plagiarism?"

He smiled warmly, but his eyes were serious. He crossed his right leg over his left and placed both arms on the armrests of the leather chair, looking directly at her.

"You're guilty of only one thing, Miss York," he said. "Not using your talent."

"You're right about that. And if I don't get moving, I'll talk to you all day, making you an accessory."

She moved forward on the chair and picked up her cup, her movements confirming that her remark about leaving was not just conversation, "Mr. Locke, just one thing about my visit here today . . . "

"Yes?"

"It occurs to me that you may wonder about my real purpose, and I want to assure you that I sincerely felt an obligation to thank you again. I also wanted you to know that it's my intention to work with your company. I wanted you to know of my presence. However, should the thought occur to you that I might be seeking special consideration—assuming that I'm accepted, and I believe I will be—I'll not take advantage of what I feel has been a mutually rewarding meeting with you for getting any . . . let's say 'special treatment.' I've thoroughly enjoyed this time with you, and thank you again for being so kind."

She stood up, placing the cup on the tray in the same movement. They stood across the table from one another as he responded to her remark.

"Miss York, we have several good policies here regarding the sales staff—one of which is called the President's Club. Those who achieve well are invited to special events in recognition of our combined and our individual accomplishments. I trust you'll do well so that we might have the opportunity of spending some time together again."

"You'll be there?"

"Well, it wouldn't look right if the president failed to attend a President's Club function, now would it?"

As when they had first greeted this day, both extended their hands. This time the handshake was significantly more meaningful, for more than words had passed between them. There was a genuine respect, a warmth for one another that had quickly developed in the limited time they had spent together.

Jonathan reminded her of the directions to the sales office, they repeated their goodbyes, and she was gone. Both would pursue their own responsibilities, but neither would forget this day, for each had been deeply affected by the other's presence.

In the weeks that followed, a new woman was emerging to replace the wandering and uncertain former school teacher named Mariana York. She was added to the sales staff of Camelot Productions, and was placed in the eight-week training program to prepare her for a calling whose true purpose even she did not fully understand.

She had indeed struggled for nearly two months as she studied the products and read books long into the lonely nights. She studied those who had achieved success, and carefully noted the common thread interwoven among them all—the ever-present battle with overcoming adversity. Whether it was Lincoln, Disraeli, Churchill, or Sadat, all had been given more than enough reasons for remaining average citizens in their own time, yet all had risen above the pull of mediocrity. She sought out the stories of the great men and women of all ages; she studied good as well as evil, pondered present events as well as past events, and observed and learned from the stories of success as well as the tragedies of failure. She studied intently the subjects taught by Camelot Productions—subjects such as the qualities and fundamentals of leadership, the value of communication, the art of setting goals, and the importance of tapping the full human potential.

For her, it was a reliving of the childhood experience—the discovery of things never before seen and the rediscovery of things long since forgotten. Her world was alive again, and her potential increased and her horizons broadened with each book she read, every attempt she made, every dream she dreamed, and every tear she shed, for the rebirth of her life was not easy. Finally, she entered the world of human confrontation where ideas are sent into battle against ideas, philosophy against philosophy, and old ideologies against new insights.

CHAPTER SIX:

The Battle

To a large extent, Mariana had compromised some of her wants for some of her needs by accepting the position with Camelot Productions. Although she still had reservations about a long-term career in sales, she had enjoyed enough early success and satisfaction to be convinced that she was at least headed in the right direction.

More than anything else, Mariana York had needed a cause to believe in, and the products of Camelot Productions provided that beyond any doubt. For the first time in her life, she had found something to feel strongly about—not because it seemed expedient to do so, but because if felt right.

Her new career was also offering her the opportunity to explore the weaknesses in her character. She needed to develop the discipline that comes from getting up early when there is no clock to punch. She needed the discipline it takes to work a full day when the freedom of a commission-paying sales position allowed her to quit whenever she wanted. She needed the discipline for calling on potential buyers when the fear of doing so was paralyzing. And, above, all, she needed the discipline for putting into practice the very concepts she was selling—working harder on *herself* than anything else.

Like so many, Mariana York had unwittingly fallen into one of life's dangerous traps. She had found security in paid vacations and annual raises, and solace in free hospitalization and retirement pensions. She had also found comfort in the knowledge that should any unexpected curves be thrown her way, her husband would be there to look after her. It did not matter that her paychecks and raises were both predictable and inadequate, or that the time and duration of her vacations and eventual retirement were dictated by the needs of someone else. She was being looked after—by her job and her marriage; she had no reason to doubt that either would be taken from her. As a teacher, she had forgotten that she still needed to learn. As a wife, she had not recognized the fact that her dependence on Aaron was gradually leading her into a perilous situation. With security comes the natural inclination to stop. Where there is too much comfort, there is no desire to change. If current plateaus are met by current needs, there is no reason to grow.

When fate had finally pulled Mariana York out from under the blanket of security and into the cold light of reality, she had been unprepared. Though it had been difficult to understand at the time, Mariana now realized that she had indeed been fortunate not only to have finally left her career in teaching, but also to have been forced into making a decision to leave Aaron. Every tear she had shed during those long months of loneliness and indecision had had its value. Never again would she be content with where she was or what she was. For Mariana York, there would always be one more mountain to climb.

There were certainly a number of mountains to climb in *this* new career; some days the disappointments and uncertainties seemed unending. However, *having* to produce results before getting paid gave her more satisfaction than she had every experienced when she was *always* getting paid merely for trying.

But the discovery of the *true* value of difficulty is seldom easy. The appearance of challenge can crack and eventually break the human will to succeed. Though she had been warned of the response that many would have to programs designed to make people more than they are (especially when so many were so content with what they currently were), she was certain that the opinions and objections of others could never affect *her* beliefs in the philosophies and products that were becoming so important to her own growth . . . and her own income. She had had confrontations with many people from a wide variety of backgrounds over the past few months. She had lost on a few occasions, but had won on many more. She was beginning to feel confident in her abilities. She was beginning to feel right about what she was doing and what she taught. She was beginning to relax. She was beginning to feel secure . . .

Charlie Livingston, who had become an almost steady companion of Mikki's, had referred Mari to a friend of his who owned a large real estate firm. Mari had called the man, spoken to his secretary to arrange the appointment, and was now waiting in the reception area outside the door of his office. The ten o'clock appointment was already fifteen minutes behind schedule. As she sat reflecting on how she would approach the man, voices from the office floated through the open doorway.

". . . and in the last three months you haven't brought in a dime!" The man's voice was harsh and the tone threatening. "But Mr. Culpepper," a woman's voice responded, "I've been trying to explain to you. I've been under a lot of pressure lately. My husband and I are in the process of getting a separation and it's been very hard on my children . . . and on me. All I'm asking is that you give me another month to get my personal life straightened out so I can get back—"

The woman was interrupted in mid-sentence.

"I'm not interested in personal problems. I'm interested in professional results. And in the last three months I haven't seen any. As far as I'm concerned, you're takin' up valuable space in this office at my expense. This isn't some charity I'm runnin' here. This is a Real Estate office."

The woman replied with dignity, but the emotion added a strained quality to the words.

"I'm not asking for charity. I've been with this office for a year now. In the first six months, I produced more sales than any other—"

Again the male voice interrupted her. "You're talkin' past history. I'm talkin' about today. If you've got problems at home then keep them there. You aren't going to work them out on my time and in my office."

A chair scrapped across the floor as though the occupant had risen quickly. Mari's view had been blocked when the secretary returned with a cup of coffee for her, so she did not see the woman who left.

"Thank you," Mariana said reaching for the cup. "I appreciate—"

She got no further for at that moment the man stepped into the reception area. Though he was only in his early forties, he was completely bald. The clean-shaven head was set on a thick neck and broad shoulders that looked as though they belonged to an ex-linebacker for the Steelers. Ignoring Mariana, he stormed to the secretary's desk. Jerking his thumb toward the sales offices behind him, he said in a voice that hinted of victory, "She's leavin'. Get her papers ready." As an afterthought he added, "And make sure she doesn't take any thing that doesn't belong to her."

Wheeling about now, he turned to face Mari. "You must be Livingston's friend. Come in." There was no welcome in the voice and the cold eyes were almost as intimidating as his appearance.

"Shall I hold your calls, Mr. Culpepper?" the secretary inquired.

"Not if they're money calls."

Without glancing behind him, he proceeded through the office doorway and seated himself behind a massive desk. Undaunted, but a little shaken by his abruptness, Mariana followed behind him and stood before the desk.

"Good morning, Mr. Culpepper," she chirped brightly as she handed the man her business card.

"Have a seat, Miss . . ." he paused to look at the card, "York."

She seated herself in the restaurant-style chair against the wall, which he had indicated with a wave of his hand.

"So, Charlie said you had some training programs of some kind."

"Well—Yes, I suppose you could say that, although our programs are a bit different than—"

He interrupted without apology and without a smile. "Charlie also says that you're new with this company, this . . . Camelot Productions, and that you could probably use some help." He looked at her over his glasses.

"Yes, I'm new with Camelot, but I wouldn't want to say that I need your help. Well, perhaps I do, but not at the expense of your buying something that wouldn't be of benefit to you."

"Don't worry. If I don't want it or believe in it, I won't buy it. Okay, what are you selling? What's your pitch, Miss York?" There was something about the way he spoke that made her flinch involuntarily. Both his arrogance and rudeness made a surge of anger difficult to control. Struggling to maintain her composure, she explained the benefits of the seminars, videotape programs, and books of Camelot Productions. She spoke with sincere enthusiasm about the need for goals in life and the value of one's attitude.

"You see, Mr. Culpepper, it's not so much the selling that counts. More important than technique is how you feel—about people, about your product, about yourself. It's—"

"Is this some of that motivational hype you're peddling?"

"I beg your pardon?"

"My people don't need motivation, Miss York. They need instruction. They need to know how to make calls, how to get listings. They need to know how to close a sale—that's what they need. You got anything on how to close sales . . . on how to become a better salesperson? You're talking motivation, Miss York; I'm talking Real Estate." He spoke the last two words as if he had just named the only thing in life that mattered. Glancing at the barren walls of the office and the hard lines of the man's face, she began to realize that she was probably not far from the truth.

"I wouldn't begin to suggest that I have *all* the answers you're looking for, Mr. Culpepper, but my limited experience tells me that before you become what you call a *better salesman*, you must first become a better *person*." She hesitated, almost knowing that what she had said would be as far as she would get before being interrupted again, and she was right.

"Hold it," he said, leaning forward in his chair and clasping his hands together on top of the desk. "I think you missed something, lady. I'm not interested in, and I ain't got time for teachin' people such foolishness. If they're not what you call a *better person* by now then it's too late for me."

She smiled at him and spoke the words from somewhere else in time. "Let humanity figure it out for themselves?"

"That's it."

"Suppose—suppose some of your salespeople out there needed only to believe in themselves . . . suppose they needed only that. Suppose just a word of encouragement from you had the capacity to double just one individual's production. Wouldn't you want to give it?"

"My people are all grown up. Let 'em go to the shrinks or the preachers for that kind of help, not me. They're supposed to be professionals. They all got their license to sell real estate, and that's their job. Maybe I'll consider some ideas on how they can learn to sell more, but none of that motivation rot. I don't believe in it."

Mariana fought with herself not to become argumentative or defensive. She struggled desperately for a response that might make some sense to him. However, in conversations of this type, there is little time for pondering what one might have said or could still say. The heat of conversation is often like the heat of battle—thoughts and words must be spontaneous. There is no time for practice or training, no time for evaluation or consultation on procedure or how to improve. There is only the event itself. Only one view will prevail in the end—the view of the one who feels strongest about the matter. It is this unshakeable belief that provides speed of thought and that helps the individual to maintain poise and restraint even when his view is under attack. There is no time during battle for practice. Practice produces its own opportunity; it is a time to prepare, to anticipate, to perfect and to analyze. Battle produces only a segment of time for performance before quickly producing the victor and the vanquished.

Mariana York was now reeling from the verbal blows her opponent had dealt. Her early successes with less formidable opponents had had a dangerous effect on her training: she had not gotten better, she had merely maintained her status quo. That she was failing now was not the result of a lack of belief in her products—it was a lack of belief in herself to convey her ideas to the non-believers.

"I don't believe in motivation either, Mr. Culpepper." Her voice was strained with tension. The smile had long since left both her face and her voice. "We've both been to seminars where the one conducting it told entertaining stories or funny jokes and managed to get most of the people pumped up over an unrealistic or unattainable idea. But when these people return to their real world," she explained, making a sweeping gesture with her right arm, "the hype doesn't work."

"Let me see if I've got this right. You don't teach people how to sell, right?"

"No, not directly. We—"

"And you don't motivate people to sell, right?"

"No, our seminars are—"

"Then what *do* you do?" He hurled the last sentence as a challenge.

Mari responded to the challenge. Before she could be interrupted again, she launched into a rapid explanation.

"We talk about life and the human tendencies we all have. The seminars cause people to take a closer look at themselves—at the direction they're moving in and the ultimate consequences of that direction so that people can find their *own* solutions. And it's these solutions, their *own* solutions in response to their *own* desire to change themselves, that will produce better results."

"Is this one of those weird cults or some kind of therapy session? My brother-in-law went to one of those jobs. They kept him locked in a room for a whole weekend and he came out like a zombie . . ."

This time it was the woman who interrupted. "No, nothing like that. It's very simply a three-hour seminar that covers such things as how and why to set goals, and the things we can all do—both in our business lives and our personal lives—to produce better results."

The man stared at her as she spoke, showing no emotion, no sensitivity, no interest. He threw his right arm over the back of his chair, then turned slightly away from her so that his body faced the door while his head remained turned toward her.

"You keep mentioning that these seminars help people with their personal lives, Miss York."

"Yes, and their professional—"

"I really don't care about what my people do with their personal
lives. To me, that's their business. I'm only interested in what my
people produce."

"But Mr. Culpepper, very often what your people produce is in direct
proportion to what's going on in their personal world. If they're having
problems at home, if they're having trouble with the children—"

He interrupted again. "I can't afford, Miss York, to waste time figurin'
out somebody's family problems. I'm runnin' a business here. I insist on
discipline and I insist on results. These people are professionals and my
job is to give 'em any support I can that will help 'em make more money.
I'm not runnin' a rehabilitation program . . . a half-way house for wayward
real estate agents. That just isn't my job. I own fifteen pieces of residential
real estate. I think that if you sell real estate, you oughta invest in it, and if
you don't, you're a bit stupid 'cause all you're doing is working for your
clients, makin' them money and settlin' for the crumbs—commission. I've
always said it's not what you earn, it's what you do with what you earn.
I believe in that. I run this business and make decisions solely on profit.
I'm financially well off, and I did not get that way by tryin' to figure out
the personal lives of my salespeople. Now, if you've got somethin' that
will teach my people more about sellin' property, believe me, I'm more
than willin' to listen. Charlie asked if I could help you—and you're a nice
lady—but I'd be stupid to ask my people to spend money on somethin'
whose value is hard for me to see, now wouldn't I?

The man had made a good argument. He had thrown a punch that
wasn't covered in the training program. There had been no practice on
what to do when your opponent lays you on the canvas, reeling from the
effects of a blow that was logical and supported by strong feelings.

Her eyes scanned the office for a clue, a sign, something that might
tell her how to reach the man. But they were of two different worlds.
Mari's world was built on a philosophy that the development of oneself
produced an automatically proportionate amount of material reward.
Culpepper, on the other hand, believed that financial results were the
bottom line and that all else in life was incidental.

As she continued to search for an answer, Mari's eyes came to rest
on the credenza behind his desk. It was filled with an assortment of
trophies, each signifying his achievements over the years. In the midst of
the awards was a picture of his wife and four children. The frame was all
but hidden behind an enormous trophy in the shape of a dollar sign that
bore the inscription *"Top Producer of the Year."*

On impulse, she asked a question. "Are you happy Mr. Culpepper?"

"Sure I'm happy." His response was immediate, his tone defensive. "And what about you, Miss York? Are *you* happy?" Mari did not answer immediately. After a moment of reflection, she answered him. "Yes and no. I'm happy with my *direction*, but not with my level of achievement."

Her answer brought the first sign of emotional response from him that she had seen since the conversation began ten minutes before. His eyebrows lifted slightly and he turned his chair directly toward her once again, folding his arms and leaning backward.

"Interesting," he mused, smiling for the first time. "Perhaps *I* am happy with my achievement, but not so happy with my direction," he concluded.

For a moment she felt that she had succeeded in attracting his interest, that she had made a point that had finally reached through the wall she had been unable to penetrate. But her joy faded as quickly as the smile on his face.

"Miss York, let me be very honest with you. I agreed to give you some time because our mutual friend, Charlie, said you had something that would be of interest to me. I've listened to what you are offering and now I have a comment or two. I said that I'm happy with my achievement—which I am. I also said that I'm not happy with my direction—which I'm not . . . I've lost fifteen minutes of valuable time. It's fairly obvious that you're new in your business . . . this *success* business of yours. I'm sure you believe in what you're doing, but I'm a bit concerned about somebody selling success who admits that she's not successful. It's success that interests me, Miss York. Happiness does not enter into Real Estate or this office. I don't believe in the stuff you're peddling. I've got no time for personal problems. Let the people who need sympathy get if from somewhere else.

"You can't change people, lady—winners are winners and losers are losers, and I've got no time to mess with the losers. If you had any good sense, you'd find somethin' more legitimate to get into. You've got potential, Miss York. You ever think about gettin' a real estate license?"

She was so stunned by his words that it took a moment for her to answer. Her eyes were filling with tears, but they were tears of anger and frustration. Her answer, when finally she spoke, was barely audible.

"No, no I haven't."

"Then maybe you should. *I'll* teach you how to sell and you'll get yourself into somethin' where you can make some *real* money. *I'll* give you success, Miss York."

She stood up now, looking away from the man.

"Mr. Culpepper, thank you for your time. I'm sorry you think it was wasted—and no, I think I'll pass on your offer."

He made no effort to stand or to extend any goodbye courtesy. She did not walk toward the door but turned instead at the edge of his desk and went directly to the credenza behind him. She picked up the picture of his family and placed it in front of the dollar sign trophy. He turned to watch her, but said nothing. Mari looked down at him through misty eyes for an intense second, her expression saying what her voice could not. Finally she left the office, closing the door behind her.

As she walked along the hallway toward the front door, she noticed a woman with something in common with herself—she, too, was on the verge of crying, her lower lip quivering as the large brown eyes filled with tears. As the woman lifted a cardboard box from atop a desk whose empty drawers were hanging open, Mari glanced at the nameplate that now rested on top of the pile of miscellaneous items filling the box. *Janice Alexander*, it said.

Their eyes met and for a brief moment they were friends bound together by the common thread of heartbreak. Mari paused to hold the door open for her. With a courteous "Thank you" and "You're welcome," both headed in different directions in the parking lot, each with dreams as delicate as lead crystal that now lay shattered at the feet of the same man.

CHAPTER SEVEN:

The Reassurance

It was late afternoon when she lowered her body onto the bed. She had driven aimlessly for several hours trying to make sense of the event that had shattered her composure earlier in the day. Now, alone in the safety and security of her apartment, her mind played the tapes of the encounter, rewound them and played them again. She thought of what she should have said to the man who had robbed her of her dignity. She let herself be hurt by living over and over again the words he had spoken that had left her shaken and defenseless.

Perhaps she was right about her initial reluctance to enter the sales profession. She had read once that the rewards of a sales career are so great because so few people ever really succeed. Now that she had had her first experience in dealing with intense objections that cannot be overcome, she understood why.

Finally she relaxed enough to allow the hurt to subside, and there lingered only the less intense feelings of self-doubt. Mercifully, sleep slowly came to a mind that was emotionally exhausted. The blinds of the windows across the room were drawn, and only a faint glow from the light of the setting sun shone through them. Her thoughts slowed down to single-frame pictures of faces and places. Soon there was the grayness and then the blackness of sleep. Both the body and the mind were motionless, and the only sound in the room came from the tapping of tree branches against the window as a slight breeze gave them a gentle nudge. Her sleeping mind gave the tapping of the branches the form of footsteps and part of her mind made fuzzy images of imagined events. The breeze outside grew with sudden intensity, rustling the branches with the fierceness of a winter storm. Slowly the howling of the wind took the form of a deep human voice calling for attention.

"Mari—Mariana—" The voice of the wind became more human-like, and the eyes of her mind became alert.

"No one has the capacity to make you doubt yourself, Mari. No one. Only *you*."

"What?" It was her mind that spoke to the voice, or so it seemed. "Are you—?"

Either her mind *let* her see him or her mind *made* her see him, but once again the man dressed in white stood before her, casually tossing the red apple into the air. The 'tap-tap' sound broke the silence each time the apple came to momentary rest in his palm.

"Noah?"

"Did you hear my admonition?"

"You said that only I can make me doubt myself."

"Yes, but in spite of your knowledge to the contrary, you seem to be insistent that *others* should, by their words and deeds, control your mood and your self-confidence."

"Are you referring to what happened today?"

"I am."

"The man was rude, Noah. But in spite of his rudeness, he made me do some thinking."

"Wrong!"

"Why?"

"You say that in *spite* of his rudeness, he made you do some thinking. I say that because his side of the argument was more *forceful* than yours, he made you *stop* thinking. You chose to make yourself lose control, and all that you had learned was lost in anger and humiliation.

"You must be controlled by your interest in *progress*, Mariana—not pride. Today you allowed negative emotions to overcome your positive intentions. The ancient Chinese have said, 'In all things, success depends upon preparation; without it there is only failure.' Today you encountered one who, by life experiences, was more prepared than you. Much of what he said was inaccurate, but his inaccuracies were interwoven with enough truth to convince you that your cause—your *beliefs*—were unworthy, and you cast them aside. Moreover, you allowed his doubts in your *product* to cause you to doubt *yourself*. "

"What would *you* have said, Noah?"

"Your question is as foolish as his opinions about the value of learning how to sell."

"I don't understand."

"You want to take what I would have said and file it away? For *what*? Do you expect that very same situation, that same set of circumstances, to occur again? Do you not understand that every conversation, every confrontation, every circumstance has its *own* personality? The man today, Mr. Culpepper, he was seeking a set of answers . . . of *procedures* that would make his—his *people*, as he called them, armed with responses, insights, and methods that would make them more effective in the sales profession. Even if you, or if Jonathan—Mr. Locke—were master salespeople, you would be incapable of transferring your knowledge of sales procedures *to his people*! *Your* knowledge would be based on your collections of life's experiences. Your words would stem from your past encounters. It is the sincerity, understanding and perception of your *own* experiences that will bring about *your* success. Anyone can be taught to speak memorized dialogues and clever phrases, but unless the words have their root in strong emotion that is born from the personal experiences of the one who speaks them, the words are meaningless.

"Here is one of the great truths, Mari. Learn to experience life—both the successes *and* the failures. Gather in all that you can. Practice your profession and ponder your results. At the end of each day, examine what was thought, said or done; then ponder what *might* have been thought, said or done. Let life touch you. Continue trying through the failures, little one, *all* the failures. In moving toward your grand obsession you will encounter many Culpeppers who will cause you to question yourself, but you must not allow them to cause you to *doubt* yourself *or* your purpose. Question your purpose thoroughly *before* you embark upon the journey toward it, but *never* doubt it once the journey has begun. If you listen to every voice that beckons as you wander through the dark forest, you will soon find yourself hopelessly lost, far from the path you had once chosen. Many will call to you, and many of those who call will have arguments of great persuasion. The test is in how deeply *you* feel as opposed to how deeply *they* feel. Are *their* causes and *their* beliefs more worthy than your own? Will you follow blindly every voice that calls for your attention, Mari? When will that which *you* have chosen, through deliberate choice, to be *your* life's work be as important as what *others* think you should do? God has given to you *your* life, with *your* talent, and He has deliberately revealed to you *your* opportunity. How *dare* you allow one among you to speak with a voice so authoritative as to lure you away from that which has been your own free choice? Would you trade freedom for slavery? Would you pursue a career not of your own conscious choice? Would you give yourself license to think little of yourself when your talent gives you cause to think highly of yourself?

"I wish, dear Mari, that I were free to reveal to your wandering mind the latent talent residing within you that only now is coming alive. I wish that you could somehow sense the true magnitude of the gift that already has been given to you and the rewards that will come with it. Already they are beginning to manifest themselves in your life, and you must not cast aside so foolishly the progress you have made at the first sign of adversity."

She listened intently as he spoke. His words were more like thoughts being planted in her mind, and she sensed not only the meaning of the words, but also the depth of his emotion.

"Noah, as I listen to you I feel the message you're trying to convey. When you're here with me, you show me a world that aids in building my depth of character and understanding of life. But there's another world that I live in when you're not here, one that seems designed to *destroy* character and disassemble the understanding I gain when you speak with me. Are you aware—*really* aware—of my world?"

He gave the most understanding smile she had ever seen. "I am aware, Mari," he said, closing his eyes as he spoke the words.

"Then I have a question about *our* world that seems incompatible with what I must confront in *my* world."

He chose not to speak, his silence urging her to continue. "You speak of my—my 'grand obsession'—the thing that I choose to do in *my* world that lets me use *my* talent . . . that lets me do that which I most love to do." She paused to find the right words. "I am engaged in a career that I would not deliberately choose, Noah. I am doing it and elected to do it, because something within my mind said it was right to try. Yet, if I am going to be honest with myself, I do not *want* to do it, and it seems that I will never be fully happy within myself in the role that I now fill. I seem to be off track, Noah, and yet it was *you* who planted the seed that first led me into a sales career, and—well—it's *not* an obsession, Noah. It was *your* idea, not mine."

She felt that her words were beginning to sound rather accusatory, and ended her thought with a question rather than continuing on. "Do you understand?" she concluded.

"Yes, but you must remember that one does not always find oneself simply falling headlong into a grand obsession. We move *toward* it, Mari, gaining necessary experience along the way. Success and happiness take time. To fully enjoy the obsession, when once you get it, takes preparation. I ask only that you take the time to enjoy the *journey* as you move toward the *destination* you seek, or when you finally arrive, you will look back and find that you missed so much of value along the way.

"All things have their own worthy purpose, Miss Mari—even this thing you now pursue—even your Mr. Culpepper!"

They both laughed. "Mari?"

"Yes?"

"Your talent *will* create a place for you; but for now, the talent needs a little work, as do your patience and your self-confidence. But you're coming along quite well. Believe me, we're proud of you."

"Even after today?"

"Even today had its—"

"—worthy purpose?" she finished the thought for him. "Indeed."

"Noah, my life *is* improving. I see it every day, and I'm grateful. Here with you, it is so easy; but there—well, I must work on myself. I'll be okay."

"Mariana, it will be some time before I see you again. I want you to know that."

"How long—?" She knew the answer before finishing the question and quickly changed the subject. "Noah, when you're here, I am aware of your existence, of our conversation, and of our last conversation. I'm also aware of . . . of *there* . . . of what I did today and yesterday. But when I'm *there*, I recall nothing of *here*. Wouldn't it be helpful if I could recall what goes on here? Wouldn't it be *easier*?"

"Don't wish for things to be easier; wish for yourself to become *better*—which is why you are not permitted to remember the 'here.' Well, maybe an occasional, fuzzy flash now and then," he said, smiling broadly again. "Someday, Mariana York, you will discover both the *here* and the *there* are *one*."

"Sort of a Heaven on earth," she said, the comment bringing a smile to his lips again.

"Sort of. When first we met, there were a few things I mentioned that must now be mentioned again to help you to put the events of this day into perspective. First, I suggested that some of the things that you would be called upon to perform would try you from time to time—in spite of its worthiness and in spite of the rich and bountiful life that the gift promised you—that you would have times of sorrow, times of despair, and times of discontent. I also suggested that you would find yourself wanting results and response in your time rather than in due time. Do you remember?"

"I remember. And also I remember what will probably be the second thing that you will remind me of—*all things in their own due season.* "

"Precisely."

"You also said that above all else, I must remember that the magic that converts the seed into the rich harvest would convert my disciplined and consistent efforts into results."

"Then you should understand that what you have just said is actually what today was all about. Even though it was difficult for you, it was nevertheless part of the fulfillment of your promise, of your gift."

"I know it now, Noah. But I want to remember it when I'm alone, when my recall will give me the reassurance I need, not just when you're here to remind me . . . not when the time of crisis is *gone*, but when the time of crisis is *upon* me."

"In my future absence, Miss Mariana, you will have both the challenge *and* the opportunity you need to become worthy of all that destiny has in store for you. Remember, you must master the natural inclination to let others control your moods, for in controlling your moods, you allow others to control your life. You must stand guard at the doorway to your mind, Mariana, for it is your greatest treasure. Do you understand?"

"Yes." He nodded in satisfaction and began tossing the apple again, the tapping of the apple in his palm reminding her of when the conversation began. She found herself losing the vision of the man, as though they faded from the sight of one another. Her mind went from the blackness of sleep to the grayness, the tapping increasing but moving to the window nearby.

The sound was vaguely reminiscent of a tossed apple falling into a hand, but it was only the blowing branches tapping against the window in the fading light of another day, the setting of another sun. Her eyes opened and there was only silence and darkness, and a strange reassurance that everything—including today—had its worthy purpose.

❖ ❖ ❖

In the months that followed the second appearance of Noah, Mariana York slowly gained unusual insights into life, business, and people, but always at a price.

Of all that she learned and was learning, perhaps the greatest benefit came when she discovered a valued and respected friend—herself! It was indeed the dawning of a new life for Mariana York when she learned to accept herself for what she was as well as for what she *was not*.

Mariana also returned to the writing of her own journals, for she had been reminded by Jonathan that the assimilation of information from the mind of someone else has its value, but at some early point in time, one must being to organize and record one's own thoughts. "The great value of studying the thoughts and experiences of another person is what *their* thoughts and experiences cause you to think, feel, and do," he had said. From that wise counsel, she finally observed with clarity that the product of one's *own* mind is of greater value than the concepts from the mind of another.

Her journals began to fill with experiences and knowledge unavailable in the classroom. The ideas came from many sources, but the observation, study and recording of those ideas were her own. The words rang with truth and uncommon style.

October 21, 1980

Some people have trouble finding themselves simply because they don't look high enough.

Many people settle for so very little—perhaps because in comparison to the rest of the world, they have so much.

Through daily experience, I find it is easier to teach and to discuss success than it is to become a success. I must learn to accept that it is sometimes necessary to at least appear to be doing well before my accumulated efforts permit me to do well, and that to do so is not vanity or hypocrisy.

November 22, 1980

Be perplexed by those given to gossip and tale-bearing, but be uplifted by those speaking the truth.

Be puzzled by those who speak lies, but be impressed with their creativity.

Be confused by the worriers among you, but be amazed by their imagination.

Be confounded by those who break their promises, but be considerate of their intent.

Be bewildered by those who waste time, but ponder with interest the possibilities of their unused potential.

Be bothered by those who dissent or disagree with you, but be grateful for their honesty.

Be distraught by those who are insecure, but be glad for your opportunity to provide encouragement.

Finally, at each moment of your life, be aware of things negative, but let the emotion of each event in life, as well as each thought, be of the positive and uplifting side of life.

November 21, 1980

I find a new lesson in each day that passes. I find that seldom are my priorities the same as my clients, and in learning that, I am learning patience.

December 8, 1980

Today I discovered the great difference that exists between presenting facts and logic and persuading emotion and thought. I find that listening has far greater value than speaking, and that I must not allow myself to conclude the whole of what a person is going to say based upon my interpretation of the first few words they speak. I must listen to it all . . .

December 12, 1980

There is, I believe, a three-step process to success. First, conceive an idea through the use of human imagination and creativity. Second, plan the idea carefully and deliberately, using experience and knowledge, letting your goals drive you to a new enthusiasm. And third, execute the plan, using consistency and discipline, and taking the time to review and refine your activities along the way.

December 20, 1980

Get better at collecting accurate facts than in engaging in idle speculation. Get better at giving attention to details than in dreaming of ambiguous generalities.

Become an inquirer of truth, a seeker of wisdom, a searcher of ideas,
an investigator of fairness, an examiner of reason, and an inquisitor
into the relationship of cause and effect.

Examine your thoughts, consider your friends, study your profession, analyze your purpose and ponder your direction.

January 27, 1981

Only by reflecting do we get wisdom from information.
Difficulty and challenge are the constant companions of wealth.

The words flowed on—day after day, month after month. She wrote long dissertations on her failures, describing to herself, for herself, both the cause and the effect. Before, her failures brought only tears, self-doubt and diminished confidence. Now, she used her failures as a classroom and looked upon each event in the same way that a judge would look upon the two sides of an argument—touched by the emotion, but persuaded by cold logic and objective fact. She sought only truth, for from that she could grow. She was the recipient of many personal insults and rejections, but she was not affected by them unless there was a personal lesson to be learned. She studied the weaknesses and unfairness of some whom she confronted, and absorbed the strengths and attributes of others.

Indeed, there were periods of regression, of lingering doubts, haunting fears, and the ever-present uncertainty that is encountered by all who move toward new plateaus of achievement and a future of promise and uncharted opportunities.

Among the opportunities for growth through the encountering of challenge were the moments of triumph and jubilation. She was finding joy in dealing with events from which she would have once sought to escape. A new Mariana York was being born, and she found a fascination in being both participant and spectator in the saga of her own self-development.

With the project prepared for her, she would need to have every extraordinary talent and ability she could develop and master. The seeds of Noah's teaching were beginning to grow, and the life of Mariana York slowly began to change. While she had only reluctantly accepted a sales position because of what she believed she could learn from *participating* in that profession, the true value of that experience was in where it would *lead* her.

There had been many moments of difficulty and many events that challenged her commitment to continue on. She had overcome the event in the office of Hank Culpepper, and the many similar events that followed. While she had no conscious awareness of the words of Noah spoken to the secret chambers of her inner mind, those words guided and directed her thoughts and actions. The voice within her drove her onward in spite of the many occasions when events and circumstances suggested that she retreat to a less challenging occupation.

The major turning point for Mariana York came eleven months after the confrontation with Culpepper. She had been invited to speak at the Delaware County Chapter of the National Professional Businesswoman's Association on the subject of goal setting, as well as to inform the gathering of the value of the Jonathan Locke seminars. Normally, she had always appeared before much smaller groups and had shown a fifteen minute film of Locke speaking on the fundamentals for wealth and happiness. At the end of his film presentation, Locke himself made a brief request for the viewers' attendance at his next seminar, and the role of Mariana was merely to answer questions and finalize ticket sales. As time progressed, she felt more comfortable acting in the role of a sales representative, and she began to answer questions with greater authority and confidence. There had been the challenging occasion when her portable film projector had failed to operate; it was then that she was forced by circumstance to speak the ideas that Jonathan Locke spoke so eloquently on film. After several months, she found herself showing the film only occasionally, and *speaking* the principles of Camelot to her small audiences, with the same results that she had been getting with the aid of the film.

Now, however, her role would be different. The audience was nearly one hundred in number and the setting more formal, suggesting that someone of importance would be addressing the group. She had spoken to groups before from behind a podium—it happened often while she was a teacher—but somehow this was different. Surely the subject material was different from anything she had covered within the educational system. There, goals were only targets for someone to kick a football through.

At first her words came clumsily as she fought the surge of emotion that made her thoughts wander and her words difficult to find. Then, within five minutes, it was as though something inside her began to present her mind with uniquely organized thoughts, and the mind presented her lips with words that flowed with smooth and flawless sequence. She covered the subject of learning to set business and personal goals in a way that captivated her audience.

"Until you know with full clarity what you want to do, what you want to become, and what you want to have, you will always *do* about what you're *doing*, *be* about what you *are*, and *have* about what you've got.

"To effectively change your future, you must begin by knowing what you *are*, and then go to work on writing on paper how you want your future to *be*. Things don't get better by *hope*; they get better by *design*. A life is meant to be built in the same way that an architect would build a structure—first, by written, specific plan. Without a plan to follow, without a sequence of steps designed by *you* to lead you toward your better future, *others* will provide you with *their* plan, and you may find out later in life—perhaps *too* late—that you don't like what their plan has provided for you."

She continued on through the forty-five minutes given to her by the program chairman. She gave both philosophical ideas and practical guidelines, and her audience gave her far more than just courteous attention.

"If you care about your life at all, you must have two simple lists that you keep with you as your constant companions," she said. "The first list consists of those things that you do not now have that you want to achieve. The second list contains those things that you now have that you don't want anymore. I caution you about the second list. It may be necessary to give your attention to this list *before* you go to work on the first list, and it may very well be an agonizing and painful exercise for you to admit to yourself just exactly what you may have to get rid of. Don't permit yourself to escape the pain. It's essential! To try to escape the pain is to try to hide from reality . . . from those things that may be preventing you from becoming all that you were given the capacity to become."

While Mariana York spoke with unusual ease, she had not yet mastered the art of confining her ideas within a limited time frame. As a result, she spoke for twenty minutes longer than she had been asked. While her error was an indication of her lack of experience, it was not noticed by her audience, who remained fully attentive through to her final word.

It was at the end of her last remark that the major discovery of her conscious life occurred. She had grown accustomed to courteous applause, but this was different. As she shook hands with the president of the group who had come to the podium to thank her, the applause continued. She had begun to sit back into her chair at the head table when slowly—a few at first—the group who had been her audience stood. The applause continued into a full standing ovation in sincere appreciation of her persuasive charm, elegance, and unusually well-articulated ideas.

Mari stood next to her chair, accepting the recognition with grace. She nodded her head once slowly, her lips moving to speak a silent "thank you." The event touched at the very threshold of her soul. In the flash of an instant, she saw her future as her conscious mind revealed to her what she now recognized to be her magnificent, all-consuming obsession. It had always been there, but only this event, this moment of sudden and instantaneous awareness, revealed it to her. Indeed, until this insignificant tick of the clock of life, Mariana York had moved from the role of participant to the role of designer in life's grand adventure in achievement.

Somewhere the words of a kindly man echoed in silence . . ."Your talent will create a place for you . . ."

The journey had begun.

CHAPTER EIGHT:

The Emerging

She sat in the cab as it fought its way off Century Boulevard and into the northbound lanes of the San Diego Freeway. She was fascinated by the palm trees lining both sides of the eight-lane, north-south interstate. The driver was an older man who seemed reluctant to talk, leaving her with her thoughts and the sights and sounds of Southern California in late March. She soaked up the beauty of the green hillsides that seemed alive with blossoms that waved in the air turbulence created by the passing traffic. Ahead, the traffic was slowing, and red tail lights were blinking with increasing frequency.

As the cab slowed with the traffic, her eyes scanned the buildings far to the east that appeared between breaks in the hedgerows, and her mind drifted even further to the east—to the Maryland suburbs of Washington, D.C., and to the new apartment that was being furnished in her absence. She had moved now for the second time in two years. The first was from the apartment she had shared with Mikki in Delaware County, Pennsylvania, to a more convenient location near Philadelphia International Airport. The second move was because of her promotion to the position of Washington, D.C., regional manager. In addition to coordinating sales and public relations, Mari was now assisting Jonathan Locke in the production of videotape training programs for use by corporations.

Locke himself had been spending most of his time in recent months in the Washington office, returning to Philadelphia only infrequently.

Mari thought of her friend, Mikki, whom she had left behind in Philadelphia, and of many of the new friends she had made in recent months. Her mind skipped backwards now to the friend who knew her best when things were at their worst. Mikki Thomas had been responsible for Mari's going into Camelot Productions that winter morning just over two years ago. It was Mikki who had encouraged her when she most needed encouraging, and it was Mikki who had paid the bills when Mari couldn't. Mikki Thomas—now Livingston— was currently working as a public relations manager for one of the network TV stations in Washington. If anyone had learned from working at Camelot, it was her red-headed, good-humored friend. Mari remembered a message she had received from her secretary just before leaving. It was from Mikki who had phoned to suggest that Mariana call her the next time she was going to be in the city long enough to arrange some time together, and about some personal items that she had found after Mari had moved out into her own apartment when Mikki and Charlie had decided to get married.

Mari took out her pen and made an entry in her appointment book—a reminder to call her friends. Friends are too valuable to be completely forgotten, even though their own lives and ambitions may move in different directions. She wondered what the personal items might be, and how her friend might be when once they would have some time to spend together. Her mind dwelled on friendships a moment longer.

Her mind flashed now to a picture of Jonathan Locke. He was taking great delight in her growing reputation and had told her just yesterday during their meeting at the Washington office that there were indeed many signs to suggest that the student was quickly becoming the teacher.

The cab driver pulled onto the right shoulder, passing the traffic that had now stopped, and steered off the freeway and down an exit ramp. For another ten minutes they traveled on side streets, turning finally onto a divided drive with an appropriate name—"The Avenue of the Stars." In seconds, she saw on her right what was to be her home for this night. The white exterior of the building curved along its half-block length, forming a slight arch. A larger circular driveway was filled along three lanes with cars being loaded and unloaded. The huge letters across the front of the structure confirmed her arrival at the right destination—Century Plaza—and the cab stopped.

Within ten minutes she had been checked into her room, and she stood at the window of the majestic hotel—the same hotel often used by the president of the United States during visits to California. Her room looked northward, where across the street and below her were the famous Shubert Theatre and the ABC Entertainment Center. The street below her was the Avenue of the Stars, with its two eastbound and two westbound lanes separated by a half block long fountain of water. She was in the very center of Century City, an ultra-modern complex of shopping centers, theaters, and office buildings.

Directly across from her, and towering into the bright sky, were two identical, triangular-shaped buildings, sitting side by side, appearing as monuments to the creative human genius. The panoramic view was utterly fascinating. Beyond the twin triangular Century Towers were the Santa Monica mountains, and as she leaned closer toward the glass window, she looked toward the east where the snow-capped peaks of the San Bernardino mountains were clearly visible. There was little evidence of the California smog, she thought, only stunning beauty and ever-present signs of shoppers on the streets and sidewalks below. She stood motionless, gazing down at the circular driveway where the limousines and expensive cars entered to deposit their passengers in front of the main lobby entrance twelve stories below.

Today, Mariana York stood perched atop the city, a woman who tonight would give advice to others on how to do what she had done. Her war with herself was not yet fully over, nor perhaps would it ever be; but enough battles had been won to give her confidence in herself and in the fact that failure, as she had experienced it, was in full and open retreat. What she used to be, she no longer was; what she had once wanted to be, she was becoming. She had learned from mistakes as well as from successes. She had given herself the permission to fail while she demanded from herself the all-out pursuit of success. It was by giving herself the latitude for occasional failure that she learned how to enjoy the journey toward her successes as well as the ultimate achievements of those successes.

The ringing phone pulled her attention from the window and her drifting mind now was brought back to within the walls. She picked up the white phone on the second ring.

"Hello—Marina York."

"Welcome to Los Angeles, Miss York."

"Boyd, what a pleasant surprise!" It was Boyd Freeman, who had arranged for her appearance. He and his wife, Becky, were among the top ten national distributors of American Products, and were hosting the Los Angeles convention.

"Boyd, how are you?"

"Wonderful! Did you just arrive?"

"Not ten minutes ago," she said. "Where are you? Where is Becky?"

"She's right here. We've just finished the afternoon session and thought we'd check to make sure you made it in. Is the room okay?"

"Everything is wonderful. I was just standing at the window enjoying the view when you rang."

"Would you be up to a short visit . . . maybe some coffee?"

"Of course. I'll start my unpacking. Would you mind ringing room service and ordering the coffee? I'm in room 1236."

"Gotcha. Be there in five minutes."

"Bye."

She began unpacking while her mind recalled her last meeting with Boyd and Becky. It was Chicago in winter, and over two thousand distributors of American Products had braved the wind and cold of the snowstorm to attend. They were one of the most energetic and responsive groups she had ever addressed. They were builders of an independent group of distributors, all having their own organization of salespeople. Mariana admired their ambition and their great respect for free enterprise—for helping people help themselves. She had had dinner with Boyd and Becky following her speech, and it was then that she had been invited to Los Angeles. She remembered the speech in Chicago— She had called it "Free Enterprise, Free People, and Government."

Her mind strangely flashed to a line from that speech—something about the government in the role of the enemy. She thought for a moment, and it came back.

"When a significant segment of the population perceives government to be the enemy, then we must take a close look at our individual and collective direction."

Her mind recalled more of that speech and more of how she felt after it was over.

For a reason that she had never understood, her address to that group of people on that day had awakened a new interest within her—an interest in the preservation of democracy . . . in the preservation of human freedoms. She had not thought much about freedom, because for so many years she had been a slave—to her moods, to her thoughts, to her habits.

But now her progress and her new attitude about life and people had given her freedom . . . more freedom than she had ever known, and she was developing a zeal for life, a respect for liberty, and was becoming an intense participant in the pursuit of happiness. Moreover, she was becoming an avid student of government and was learning to recognize the value of the information taught by Camelot Productions and its applications in solving many of the social, economic, and political problems of the nation. She remembered how, as a student in college, she had often wished she had chosen to study more of government and history, and had occasional visions of being active in government service, and even in pursuing a political career. It had been Jonathan who revived that interest, for he too, saw the need for a new national attitude, and for teaching the young how to perceive and pursue worthy objectives. The two of them would frequently discuss political issues during breaks in their weekly staff meetings at Camelot.

The knock on the door announced the arrival of the Freemans. Becky Freeman was a bubbly woman in her early thirties, with a trim figure, an excellent business mind, and a deep southern drawl—an understandable fact since both she and Boyd were from Tennessee. The combination of Becky and Boyd had created one of those unique blends of personalities, assets, talent, and mutual love and respect for one another. Boyd, with a quiet persuasiveness and gentle charm, compensated for his wife's tendency to overwhelm people with her enthusiasm and almost insistent demand that everyone in the world must become a distributor of American Products.

They had had their warm greeting by the door, exchanged the usual initial pleasantries, and were seating themselves at the round table by the window by the time the coffee arrived. Within ten minutes from their call from the lobby, Boyd and Becky were relaxing in soft blue velour chairs next to one another, with Mariana York across the table from them, the three of them preparing their coffee and reminiscing about the excitement that had occurred at the Chicago convention, and how the convention in this city and this hotel would be even greater.

"How do you manage to get so many people together like this—and so often?" Mari directed her question toward Becky, who had just said that the crowd for the final evening of the convention would be somewhat over three thousand—a thousand more than Chicago.

"It's the magic of having a great opportunity, I guess, coupled with the fact that we have products that everyone needs, so nearly anyone can sell them," Becky answered.

"Does the fact that the economy is struggling affect your business much?" Mari asked.

It was Boyd Freeman who answered her question. "No effect at all. Last year the company did—what, Becky? A little over a billion in sales?" His wife blinked and nodded her head. "You see, Mari, that's the exciting thing about a company like this—in good economic times we grow because the public is buying our product like crazy, and people are joining us because of what they can learn about business. In relatively bad times, people still buy the products like crazy, but they join us then because so many people need to earn extra income just to keep up with things. Either way, we do well; it's just that the reasons change."

"And this year, we'll do somewhere around one point two billion company wide. And," his wife added, "mostly with part-time people. Our organization alone has gone from about seven thousand distributors this time last year to eighty-five hundred now."

"We had to buy a fairly sophisticated computer six months ago just to keep up with the growth of our organization," Boyd commented. "We've been with the company, let's see, going into our seventh year, the first two of which were part-time. Can you believe it?"

"Knowing you two, I can believe anything," Mari smiled, a tone of sincere admiration in her voice and a look of respect in her eyes. "But where in the world did you find that many people in so little time? You do your own recruiting, don't you?"

"Sure, but we didn't find them all, Mari," Boyd said, as he gently ran his hands over the softness of the velour armrests. "We've probably only recruited about two hundred ourselves, but all of those people have the opportunity to build as well, and some have actually done better than we have. But since they're in our organization, we get sales over-rides on their entire organization."

"It sounds exciting," Mariana said.

"It is," Becky answered with a bright smile. "We started seven years ago with almost nothing. We used the products and we believed in them. We told some friends about how we felt, and the fact that we were earning a few hundred dollars extra each month. Some of them decided to join us, some of their friends joined them, and here we are. It's the power of a good idea combined with someone willing to share the idea with others, Mari. That's how you turn a few people into several thousand."

"One tells a few and the few tell many?"

"Exactly!" Boyd smiled at her. "Seven years ago, I was working for the State Roads Commission on a fixed salary and trying to figure out how to keep up with just the simple expenses of raising a family," he said. "Becky's old school friend sold her a big box of laundry detergent. It was inexpensive and it was better than the stuff we were buying in the store. A few months later, things got particularly tough. Our car blew an engine. Christmas was only a few months away and we were getting desperate. Becky decided she needed to do something to help. She found out she could do this business part-time and earn some extra cash. One thing led to another, and here we are."

"Here we are," Mari said. "In seven years, we've all come from somewhere to here. Think of it, you two—you were fighting to pay the bills and today you sit in the Century Plaza Hotel with people from all walks of life that have converged upon this place largely because of your efforts. You deserve to be proud of yourselves."

The couple looked at each other and smiled, each reaching for the other's hand. The gesture was not done to impress, but to express. It was warm and it was genuine. It was an act of love and of mutual respect. Becky looked from the admiring eyes of her husband back across the table toward Mari.

"If you've ever in your life been broke, Mari, absolutely broke, with a week to go until payday, with bill collectors bothering you over debts that you ran up not because of extravagance, but because of self-preservation, then you'll understand how fortunate and how proud we *really* are."

Mariana smiled, but she did not answer. Her mind alone shared a passing thought of their common experiences and their common progress. She remembered the days of diminishing hope, the days of frustration over little things, the anxiety of driving a car with worn tires or watching the gas gauge drop slowly, all the while wondering if there would be enough to get home and knowing that there was no money in the purse in case there wasn't.

Becky's words brought Mari's thoughts back to the present. "But in all honesty, we have to be careful—even now. We're earning well, but one set of difficulties seem to replace another. Before we left home on Thursday, we were discussing some silly remarks made by friends of ours. They felt that Boyd and I are changing all right, but not for the good. They felt we were getting too wrapped up in the pursuit of money. We've had some long talks the past two nights about that, haven't we Boyd?"

He watched her eyes as she spoke with a voice of concern, then smiled when she asked him the question.

"Sure 'nuff," he said, turning to look at Mari. "We found that sometimes the pursuit of fortune can be as difficult as being broke. It's a whole new set of problems, for sure. There's the travel schedule, being away from the kids more than we want, things like that. Every once in a while, I wonder how much is enough."

He thought for a moment, then continued. "Well shoot, you've probably gone through this yourself, Mari. But if I recall from your conversation in Chicago, you don't have a family to worry about. But I'm sure you think about some of the things that we've been thinking on of late, right?"

"Of course, we all have to pause along the road we've elected to travel, to look back as well as forward. What we're really pursuing here, I suppose, is the reason I've come here, and the reason *you've* come here—we're both in pursuit of something. What we may have achieved at this point isn't the issue. What *is* the issue is—first, do we really *know* what we're after and do we really *want* what we're after, and second, are we willing to pay the price?

"Remember, everything has its price. Get a nice secure job, Boyd. Settle down, and learn to live within your income. But when you make *that* choice, be aware that it, too, has its price. You've already experienced what living *that* way is like. On the other hand, do what you're doing—and pay *that* price."

Becky asked a question in a concerned voice. "Do you think what we're doing is right?"

"That isn't for me to answer, Becky." Mari paused to take a sip of coffee. No one spoke because it was obvious that she had purposely interrupted herself before finishing her thought.

"But I do know this. If you think the price of what you're *doing* is high, then go back to being what you were before, and wait until you one day get the bill for being average. Very often we tend to think that the happiness that we're in pursuit of is what we had before. But be careful of that kind of reasoning. As someone once said, *'Happiness is not always something that we experience, but it is often something that we remember.'* We can all go back to being what we were before, but be prepared for the consequences of *that* decision, because once you go back, it will then be just a matter of time until you look back again and find that what you left behind—the business you're now involved in—has become the happiness that you remember."

Mari paused to examine the impact of her words. "What made you two bring this subject up anyway? I don't know you all that well, but it's not like either of you to even be thinking about whether the attempt is worth the risks. What happened—really?"

The couple glanced at one another again, but without a smile. Boyd twisted his mouth slightly and shrugged his right shoulder upward as though giving himself approval to bring out something that he had been trying to cover up but now had suddenly decided to bring out into the open. He looked at Becky who gave him a slight nod of approval.

"Well, we just found out earlier this morning that some good friends of ours, who are among the top distributors of the company, are leaving the business. They told us at breakfast this morning that in spite of the money they're earning, the sacrifices are just too much. They said that between the travel schedule, the constant responsibility for so many people, and the pressures on the marriage, that it had just become too much."

Becky followed his remark with her own. "It's difficult watching someone walk away who has become a cornerstone of the business. It makes you wonder sometimes . . . it makes you just pause a bit to look at yourself and to consider—" She hesitated for just a second and Mari finished the sentence for her.

"Cost versus value?"

"Exactly," Boyd said.

"So far, I've not had that problem," Mari responded. "But perhaps because I haven't, I can be a bit objective with my opinions."

"You mean you've never felt the urge to look back to see if maybe you want to return?" Boyd asked.

"No, the memory of what was back there is still too fresh in my mind. I often play the 'mental tapes' back once in a while, not to see if I want to return, but to recommit myself to move in the direction I'm moving and with greater speed," Mari, answered.

"So you completely love everything about your business?" he asked.

"Of course not. Not everything. Nor do I feel fully satisfied with my progress. But I know what I want to do, and if what you *want* to do is truly what you want to do, then you become obsessed by it. You may have days of frustration and disappointment, but it's never with your project—it's with yourself. I have an interesting question for you to ponder. The question is, if we *could* do better, *should* we? And, to go a step further, if we agree that we should get better, *will* we? Within that question is the story of one of life's great processes."

Becky pulled a brown book from her open briefcase.

"Hold it just a moment," she said, with a smile directed toward Mari, and then passed the same smile on to her husband. "Some of this stuff is too good to miss. I want to get it into my journal. How did that go again? If we could—how was it?" She glanced up at Mari who paused to look upward for a moment, as though the spoken words had floated to the ceiling and were written there for her to read back.

"If we could get better, should we? If we should get better, will we?"

"Got it," Becky said, writing out the last word onto the fresh page in her journal.

Mari continued with her thought. "One of the big questions of life is whether each of us is tapping our own potential. *Could* we earn more, or do more? *Could* we plan better, talk better? *Could* we dress better? Could we be happier? For most of us the answer, I think, is *absolutely*. Do you agree?" She paused. Becky answered in the affirmative, while her husband agreed with a single nod of his head, and she continued.

"Then if we *could* do all of those things, *should* we? For most of us, the joy and the satisfaction and the rewards of earning more, doing more, planning more . . . all of those things would make life easier and certainly more enjoyable. Does *that* make sense?" She paused again. This time both nodded affirmatively though Becky Freeman continued to write without looking up.

"Then if we could, and we agree we should, the next question is—"

"Will we?" It was Boyd who finished Mari's question.

"The answer to that may help you to understand not only yourselves, but also this action of your friends who have decided to leave the business they've built.

"Here is a key phrase for you: All of us could, most of us should, some of us will, but *few* of us do. *That* is the story of human progress. It is sad, I'll agree, but it's the way life seems to be. We can have our opinions about how it *should* be some other way, we can argue that there are exceptions, but in the end that's the way humans seem to behave. The great challenge is to continue doing what *we* feel we should do regardless of what others around us do that gives us cause to doubt ourselves, because there will be many who could but don't, and many who should but won't. There will even be those close to us who have gone as far as your friends have but have, chosen to return. Remember, that is *their choice*. Just make sure that their choice doesn't influence you. Otherwise, if you chose to follow them, then it is not *choice* that has spoken, it is *influence*, and the influence of others may not be in your best interest."

Becky Freeman had continued writing without looking up. Her husband had sunk into the softness of the chair, his legs crossed and his arms laying on the armrests. He was looking directly at Mariana, who in turn was looking at the man's wife as she wrote a final word and dropped the pen onto the open page of her journal. As Becky looked up at her husband, he responded by placing his right forearm on her shoulder.

"What do you think, kid?" he said.

"I wish the Waldmans were here," she said. "That's the name of your friends?"

"Yes," Becky answered.

"They were in Chicago, weren't they? Didn't they sit at the table with us at the banquet?"

"That's right," Boyd said.

Boyd Freeman looked at his watch and sat upright. "Hey, woman! Do you know what time it is? We've got less than two hours before we get started again."

"Oh my heavens!" his wife responded. "Mari, you've got to excuse us. I'm sure you've got things to do, too, but I wouldn't have missed this for the world."

The couple stood up, the woman dropped her journal back into her briefcase, and they moved toward the door with Mariana between them, listening to the instructions on where the ballroom was located, where the registration table was, where she was to sit, and the remaining details they had not covered during the conversation. In another moment they were gone, and Mariana York was alone again, her own words echoing through her mind. She always paused to evaluate what she said to people. It was her way of improving her skills. She was constantly studying her effect on other people—the effect of her thoughts, the effect of her words, and the effect of her thoughts and words on herself. She pondered the process of "could-should-and-will," and how that process seemed to be God's way of reducing the multitude to the minority.

Her thoughts were interrupted by the phone again, which this time was answered on the first ring.

"Mariana York speaking."

The voice was unexpected and welcome, as it always was when she had the occasion to hear it.

"Mariana, how is Los Angeles?"

"Far more beautiful than I imagined, Jonathan. How wonderful to hear from you. How did you know I was here?"

"You work for my company, remember?"

"How clever. Thank you for calling. I just poured some inspiration from my mental reservoir and your call will help me fill it back up. How are you?"

"I *was* doing fine. Then I received a report from the marketing department that hurt me deeply." He was obviously being facetious, but she went along.

"What's wrong?"

"I was advised that requests for you as a guest speaker were greater last month than for me. I never should have allowed you to write your book—not a book as good as that, anyway."

"Well, you're the publisher, Mr. Locke. Perhaps we should consider recalling it on the grounds that it is excessively plagiaristic?"

"Ha!" he said.

"What you said—it isn't really true, is it?"

"What?"

"That requests for me have exceeded the requests for you."

"Well, it was within two or three, I think. Close enough to make me terribly proud of you, Miss York," he said. The jocular tone was gone from his voice, and sincerity took its place.

"Thank you, Mr. Locke," she said.

"For what? You've earned the acclaim you're getting. That book is good, Mari, darn good, and so are your speeches . . . you know that."

"I'm thanking you for saying that you're proud, Jonathan. A lot of people in our business would have their egos smashed when one of their employees challenge the boss in the slightest way. But with you it's different, and I want you to know that the thing that makes me most proud is working for someone like you. We both know that my good fortune is largely attributable to what I've learned at Camelot, Jon."

"Camelot was merely the soil, Mari. *You* were the seed. So who's to say which is more valuable? Only the crop is important. Anyway, enough of this. We've got to watch the overhead, you know. I just wanted you to know that the first ten thousand copies of *The Winter of Challenge* are sold out. You're going into the second printing Monday. Congratulations! And good luck with your speech tonight."

"Thank you, Jonathan. Will I see you soon?"

"Monday evening—when you arrive at National Airport. I'm picking you up."

"You're kidding."

"Flight 509, arriving at 8:25. See you then. Good luck, Mariana."

"Jonathan—" The funny bleep on the receiver was the sound of the long distance relay dropping out. He had hung up. She laughed joyously and dropped her body backwards onto the bed, throwing her arms back over her head, and then recoiling her body forward again with her legs until she stood upright. She sensed the feeling of triumph. There was no wondering why, nor did she feel apprehensive about the reason for the call. She was growing and she was reaching a full realization that her life and talents had no limits.

She wondered only for a second where she might have been had she taken the advice of a man who once sought to influence her with bad advice, and the words of that day rang through the room. "Let humanity figure it out for itself." She laughed and went into the bath to prepare herself for another contingent of humanity in search of their own meaning and purpose. Tonight she would be the principal voice calling out to those many who could, most who should, and few who would.

Somewhere, the kindly man in the white suit smiled with joy. Her talent was indeed creating a place for her.

CHAPTER NINE:

The Speech

The grand ballroom was a sea of excitement. Most of the three thousand were already there, talking together in pairs and groups. Some were laughing, others were planning, still others were engaged in introductions and reacquaintances. The music that played over the noise of the crowd was clear enough to be unmistakable—

"People who love people . . . Are the luckiest people in the world . . ."

It had been appropriately selected, for it was difficult to see a face without either a smile or an expression of hope or confidence. She moved along the aisle toward the front of the room where the fifty-foot banner hung across the top of the elevated stage. Its words were unnecessary—American Products, 1983. Mari moved alone and unnoticed along the edge of the crowd who were either seated or standing at large round tables. A few among the crowd looked at her as though they should know her. Some would whisper to the person next to them and point in her direction. Her appearance alone was sufficient to attract the attention of people. The blue of the gown she wore matched almost perfectly the blue of her eyes. The purse she carried had dark blue sequins that picked up the light from the room and flashed blue-white reflections as she moved. Within a minute, nearly a dozen people circled her, waiting to say hello. One young woman held a copy of *The Winter of Challenge*, which obviously needed an autograph.

Boyd Freeman excused himself from a conversation he was having and moved toward the group that encircled her.

Apologizing to the group that wanted to speak to the smiling blond, he led her to a round table near the podium. He introduced her to those at the table who were already seated. There was a couple from Los Angeles, another from Maryland, and a well dressed man from Austin, Texas. All were friendly and obviously pleased that they had been chosen to sit at the same table with her. The placard on the center of the table spoke a clear message—RESERVED.

"We weren't in Chicago, but we heard a lot about you," the woman from Maryland said.

"Is this your first time in Los Angeles?" the man from L.A. asked.

Both had spoken at the same time. Mari looked first to the man from Los Angeles. "Yes, it is my first time in Los Angeles," and, holding her smile, she turned to the woman from Maryland. "Thank you. I trust at least part of what you heard was favorable."

Within a few minutes a couple from Pennsylvania were seated at the table, and finally Boyd and Becky Freeman joined them. There were a few people still milling about the room when the lights began to dim and the drum roll began. It reminded her of a Las Vegas spectacular. The brilliant, sequin-covered burgundy curtain lifted into the ceiling and a huge motion picture screen was lowered in its place amid thunderous applause from the three thousand distributors who obviously knew something of what they were about to see. For nearly twenty minutes, the film marched through the fifteen year history of American Products. It traced the story from inception to the current moment, and suggested that the chance for individual success was just as great today as it was when the original founders had begun their pursuit of creating an empire years before. The film was well done, both in its quality of production as well as in the story it told. Even for those who, like Mari, were not part of their company, it was inspiring. For those who *had* lived part of this success story, the message held a special significance. Mariana York looked at those sitting nearby who could be seen in spite of the dimmed lights, and saw women crying. She knew about tears, for her past had produced many, but these were tears of joy. Those who shed them knew of the pride that comes from playing a part in the making of a legend, and American Products had indeed become a legend in its own time. For them it was a time to be reminded, a time for reflection, and a time for recommitment to the dream. Even without being a part of the company, Mari felt the emotion. She knew that in this room sat people of unusual character, for they had chosen the pursuit of success and independence through free enterprise. They had all begun as part-time distributors selling the household items manufactured by American Products. By building their own organization of distributors, they were building something for their future. They had chosen activity over leisure and uncertainty over security. The men sat next to their wives. Some of the couples were arm in arm, others were holding hands and exchanging occasional glances and smiles. But there were exceptions. There were those who looked at others with eyes of doubt. There were those who whispered to each other while pointing about the room with looks of jealousy. And there were those who were there, but who were *not* there . . . who had somehow penetrated this unique gathering not to participate and celebrate but to perhaps condemn or ridicule. Such a couple sat to her immediate right. The woman leaned toward the man often, and the expression on her face as she would talk and gesture gave the impression that she was questioning or perhaps even condemning something that had been depicted in the film. It seemed that Mariana had seen her somewhere before. Her black hair was cut short, making her hairline follow the contour of her head. She was a thin woman, who seemed to somehow resent her femininity and yet, were she to smile more, would be a woman of unusual natural beauty. She turned slightly at one point to reach for a glass, and Mari took advantage of the opportunity to glance at her pre-printed name tag. Like all others in the room it said, "Hello, My name is . . ." followed by a single name written in blue pen—"Gloria."

Their eyes met only once. Mariana smiled a short but warm smile. The woman named Gloria acknowledged the smile with a funny twist of her mouth but looked immediately away, her eyes scanning the human panorama as though looking for something of more interest than the film.

When it ended, the film and the story it told generated a human spirit of oneness that brought three thousand inspired people to their feet in a tumultuous standing ovation. It was *their* story that had been told. It was *their* promise that was being offered—to each, individually, and to the group, for its collective pursuit. The spirit that permeated the room was one that every human should experience at least once in their lifetime, Mari thought. Had she not been obsessed with her own driving obsession, she would choose *this* opportunity, *these* people, and the cause they were a part of. This was not a chanting crowd following the dictates of a single renowned leader who they had blindly chosen to admire and follow. Their focus was upon their own progress. Their attention was set on their individual achievement that, when combined into a common purpose, created a cause that transcended any single story of accomplishment.

The applause lasted a full minute, only reluctantly subsiding to give way to a man who would, for the next ninety minutes, serve as the master of ceremonies. D.L. Baker introduced a number of speakers—men alone, women alone, and men and women together—each speaking on their beliefs, sharing their dreams, and urging the group to aspire to even greater individual and collective performance in the months ahead. Awards were given for performance—cars, diamonds and furs. It was an extravaganza of recognition, challenge, and congratulations, and both the words spoken and the applause given were genuine.

At one minute before eight-thirty, D.L. Baker announced that a short break would be in order before the final address by the guest speaker. Mariana York had nearly forgotten her reason for being there, and a wave of nervousness swept over her as her thoughts now came back to the current moment.

Conversations exploded throughout the room. The formality of the evening had been interrupted, but the enthusiasm continued on. Mari sat quietly, observing and listening, and pondering her own feelings. Her thoughts were suddenly interrupted by the woman next to her who, though she had turned fully toward Mari, still looked around the room.

"You people really put on quite a production. I must congratulate you."

"Well, thank you. Yes, they do. I gather you're not a part of American Products either?"

"Oh, no—no, we're not." She looked both confused and relieved. Her eyes moved to the people across the table while her remarks were still directed at Mari. "I assumed that you were a—what do you call them—dealers?"

"Distributors."

"Whatever." Her husband put a match to a pipe and the smoke billowed toward Mari. Her mind flashed a momentary picture of the vanilla-laced eggnog her grandmother used to make when she was a child.

"What are you here for?" Gloria asked.

"I'm a guest of Mr. and Mrs. Freeman," Mariana explained, gesturing across the table to where Becky and Boyd stood conversing with another couple.

"Be careful. They'll try to recruit you before the evening's over," Gloria cautioned as she leaned closer to Mari. "Then again, maybe they already have."

"Tried to recruit me? No, they haven't. Why do you ask?"

"Because that's what these people do. They recruit anything that moves."

"Is that bad?"

"Well, no—but if they keep it up the whole world would be part of their company within six months," she said with a voice of sarcasm.

"By what I've seen so far, that might not be a bad idea," Mari responded pleasantly.

"You're kidding, of course."

Mari smiled, but did not answer. Gloria looked directly at her now for the first time without either her eyes or her attention drifting elsewhere.

"Who would buy their products if everyone in the world were part of their company?"

Mari answered the question with one of her own. "Do you really think it is possible for everyone in the world to be attracted to a cause or a movement? Even one like this?"

"Well, of course. It's like the old pyramid scheme. Someone eventually loses at the end of the chain," she said authoritatively.

Mari studied her comment only briefly before answering her.

"How many distributors do you suppose American Products has?" She asked the question as though she didn't know the answer.

"Somewhere around a half million," Gloria answered, her eyes meeting Mariana's for but an instant before glancing off in another direction. "Imagine what would happen if everyone in this room recruited only one person a piece in the next month . . . they'd have twice as many. What—six thousand? Then if they did it again the next month, the six getting one, I mean . . . do you see what would happen? My God, it would double every month. Twelve, twenty-four, forty-eight . . . by the end of the year—"

"I see what you mean," Mari interrupted, nodding her head twice in agreement.

Gloria gave a smile of one who had just beaten an opponent and was being courteous.

"What do you do, Gloria?"

Her wandering eyes looked back at Mari again, and she tugged lightly at the pearls that encircled her throat. "I'm Director of the Human Liberties Protective League,'" she said proudly.

Mariana's mind flashed an instantaneous picture of the past, and the Gloria Simon who sat beside her now took on a new significance. She remembered seeing her on television, usually speaking out against business and government as being the great enemies of the poor. She was one of those who had become a self-appointed protector of the oppressed in order to enhance her own reputation. She had become a leader in the movement for making individual rights superior to the rights of the majority. She had been directly responsible for several supreme court decisions that led to the freeing of convicted felons on purely technical grounds, had been instrumental in eliminating prayer from schools, and fought vigorously for increased public support against free enterprise organizations like American Products. What would possibly bring her here tonight, Mariana wondered, and she posed the question aloud.

Gloria shrugged arrogantly. "I've always been curious about these people. My office gets lot of complaints from people who've gotten involved in these things, and when I received the invitation last week, I thought I'd sit in on one of their meetings just to find out first-hand exactly what they do."

"You make it sound as though what they're doing is wrong," Mari commented.

"Perhaps wrong is not the right word—*borderline* is better."

"Borderline? In what way?"

"This nonsense of making everyone think they can get rich. It isn't right."

"Do they do that?"

"Of course. You should hear some of the complaints we get."

"Such as?"

"Well—this getting rich nonsense. They make you believe all you have to do is—"

Mariana interrupted. "Gloria, how can you *make* another person believe anything? Is it possible that the people who come to you and complain do so because they participated just long enough to find out that they don't have what it takes to attract the success that they thought would fall into their lap with little or no effort?"

Gloria leaned closer to Mari. "That's my point! They make you think that all you have to do is join and you'll make all this money."

"How do you know that's what they do?"

"They do. I know they do."

Mari smiled. "How could you know? You said this was the first time you've ever been to one of—"

"Hey, the people who come to me tell me what's going on."

"The people who come to you are angry, Gloria, and probably with themselves more than anything else. They were exposed to a dream, and for a while they had some hope. When they discovered that there was work involved, perhaps they gave up. They brought their disappointment to you, coupled with anger, and the anger caused them to distort the facts. From my experience, Gloria, it seems that companies like American Products merely expose people to an opportunity, and finally to themselves. My experience tells me that when you share a dream with someone and later that dream fails to materialize, then those who once dreamed will seek revenge. They'll blame the person who tried to help them rather than blame themselves. All I've been able to see here is an *opportunity*, Gloria . . . an opportunity for little people with hope and limited means to make something of themselves. Isn't that part of the American dream? Isn't it quite possible that in the final analysis it's not the enterprise that fails the people but rather the people that fail the enterprise?"

Before Gloria could answer, Boyd Freeman's voice interrupted.

"Mariana, could I see you for just a moment please?" Gloria's eyes followed Boyd and Mari as they walked away from the table toward a corner of the room. Neither spoke as they walked along except to greet people as they passed by.

When they reached the corner, it was Boyd Freeman who spoke.

"Mari, I wanted to warn you that the woman sitting next to you is Gloria Simon the—"

"Yes, I know—of the Human Liberties Protective League."

"Do you know about her?"

"Not much, but I know a lot about the HLPL. Why do you mention it?"

"Well, she might . . . I mean . . ."

"Say some unkind things about your company?"

"Possibly. She's spoken out several times in the past about us. She's very quick with her opinions, and not always complimentary."

"The HLPL is seldom complimentary about anything, Boyd, and she's already voiced an opinion about a few things. Why is she here? I mean, who—"

"The local leadership thought that if she could sit in on one of our meetings she might not be so quick to misjudge us," he said.

"Don't count on it, Boyd. You shouldn't attempt to explain anything about your company or your personal convictions to anyone—certainly not to someone whose acceptance of your invitation is obviously just to gather distorted facts for future accusations."

"Well, we thought we'd be open with her . . . let her see . . ."

"Boyd, your friends—those who accept and support you—don't require explanations; as for those who are your enemies—they won't believe your explanations."

"You're probably right. What did she say?"

"She thinks you're out to recruit the world, and if I read her correctly, she doesn't think you have the right to offer people an opportunity like this—especially not those downtrodden masses who she feels she must protect from opportunists like you. That's the reason for the existence of the HLPL, Boyd, remember?"

He glanced across the room to where Gloria still sat, whispering now to her pipe-smoking husband.

"You're probably right," he said. "It's just that I don't want to pre-judge anyone. Do you know what I mean?"

"I do know what you mean, Boyd, but her convictions about the need for the downtrodden to be protected by organizations like hers from organizations like yours means that you simply let her exist. There are frogs and there are scorpions, and scorpions sting frogs. You don't have time to change the nature of the scorpion; you merely train yourself to recognize them and then you avoid them."

"But maybe she'll see us differently once—"

"Sorry. Her very existence is dedicated toward the weakening of capitalism, the perpetuation of socialism, and the equal redistribution of wealth from the haves to the have-nots, and you aren't going to change that."

Boyd Freeman shook his head as he looked out across the audience.

"It's just too darn bad that she's so quick to condemn us," he said.

"On the contrary, Boyd. The fact that you'll never convert Gloria or the countless numbers of those like her is an asset."

"You're certainly an optimist, Mariana. Gloria Simon—an asset! How—"

She smiled at him. "An asset, Boyd. By her very refusal to even consider your opportunity, she's giving you proof that you'll never saturate the marketplace with distributors, which is her major argument against your company. The vast majority are skeptical, doubtful, and willing to settle for so very little, while fighting to destroy those who are ambitious."

He laughed. "You're incredible!"

The voice of D.L. Baker rose above the crowd, signaling the end of the short break.

Boyd asked one final question as they walked toward the table.

"Does she know you're the guest speaker?"

"I doubt it. I don't believe she's given any thought to who I might be."

Gloria noticed Mari's return and leaned toward her. "Did he try to get you?"

"No."

"Well, surprise!" she said, raising her eyebrows.

"Gloria, I've thought about what you said . . . about how the whole nation could become a part of this organization within a month."

"Yes?"

"That would definitely be to the disadvantage of those entering last, wouldn't it? I mean, there wouldn't be anyone left to sell to or to recruit."

"Exactly!" Sensing that she had created an advocate of her opinions, Gloria leaned closer to Mariana and spoke again in a conspiratorial voice. "That's exactly why these people need to be stopped. You can't go around the country promising each person that they can build their own organization of hundreds or thousands of distributors. It's an unfair promise. It gets people's hopes up, they get themselves involved, become quickly discouraged, and within a few months are left out in the cold."

As D.L. Baker began his introduction of the final speaker, Gloria winked at Mari and nudged her husband.

"It's going to be the grand finale. The final pitch to recruit anyone who isn't yet in." For the first time, she smiled directly at Mari, for she was even more comfortable now in the belief that she had created an ally.

Knowing she had but a few seconds, Mariana leaned toward Gloria and whispered in return.

"Gloria, just a final thought. I know of one man who started a movement like this with twelve distributors. Their cause has attracted one billion people—a fifth of the world's population. From twelve to a billion, so your theory is possibly correct. In practice, however, I think you're a bit off base. It's taken over two thousand years of constant commitment by the followers of that organization to recruit the billion and they still haven't got everyone, so I wouldn't think that the leaders of this company will be any more successful than the Christians, would you?"

There was no smile on the face of Gloria Simon now. She turned hastily toward the podium where D.L. Baker was concluding his final introductory remarks.

" . . . this woman and her philosophies, as well as her recent accomplishments, symbolizes the very essence of the American dream."

Mari slid her chair slightly away from the table and Gloria turned to look toward the movement behind her. As she watched Mari rise from her chair, a look of shock twisted her face and she swung her body away from Mari in anger.

"Ladies and gentlemen, a true defender of free enterprise, please help me welcome Miss Mariana York!"

As Mari walked toward the stage, the crowd instantly came to its feet with a thunderclap of spontaneous applause. But there was one whose hands remained folded on the table and whose body stayed fixed in her chair. Her lips tightened, the mouth slanting downward in anger and jealousy. Gloria Simon had experienced a defeat that she would not forget. She was accustomed to winning verbal battles—of setting up her victims and enjoying their anguish as she verbally dissected their beliefs. She would endure the humiliation, but she would not soon forget the one who inflicted it.

Worse than what Mariana York had said to her, was who Mariana York had turned out to be.

The view from the stage where she stood was awesome. The theme song of American Products played loudly above the thunderous applause of the six thousand human hands. D.L. Baker stood with her, behind the podium, looking into her tear-filled eyes. Chicago had been memorable—a high point in her climb from obscurity and mediocrity—but this was singly the most moving experience of her life. Here were three thousand people brought together by their pursuit of individual achievement, people of hope and ambition, people of dreams and aspirations, and they had accepted her as one of their own. They had accepted her because of her eloquence, her philosophies that were parallel to their own, and because of her example. In this moment, the words of Culpepper and Gloria Simon, and the silent words of doubt that her mind had once spoken to her, had no place.

The music faded, the applause subsided, and Mari stood silently behind the podium, pausing only to allow the crowd to settle back into their seats.

She began with an expression of gratitude and appreciation. She told of her past—of the hopelessness that had once seized her. She spoke of her lack of ambition and of the helplessness that she had once experienced as she had groped for a new direction.

"But I have not come to Los Angeles to depress you with reminiscences of my unproductive past," she said. "Nor have I come to entertain you with funny anecdotes and witty quotations whose only purpose would be to bring a short-lived smile to your lips. If it is entertainment you are looking for, I would suggest that you have come to the wrong meeting and you have joined the wrong company. In *this* room, and among this gathering, I sense not an air of casualness, but the seriousness of those having made a total commitment. In this room, I detect a hunger for achievement, a desire for independence, and a near obsession for becoming all that you were meant to be. If there is anyone here tonight who wishes to remain as they are, who doesn't mind being broke the day before payday, who would rather watch television than find ways to be productive, or who feels that either the government or those of high ambition should be forced by law to give the fruits of their efforts to those who sit and feel sorry for themselves, then you may be excused from listening to what I am about to say."

She paused and took a drink of water from the glass that had been placed on the podium for her. A few people within the range of her vision smiled, most listened silently and intensely, but not one person moved, not even Gloria Simon.

"Tonight, I would like to share with you what I consider to be the basic steps for becoming independent—for becoming financially independent, emotionally independent, and for becoming occupationally and politically independent. And for those who might consider personal independence to be a selfish desire, I would suggest that the highest form of love and respect for other members of the human race comes only when you have truly attained some reasonable level of independence. Until then, many of our motives will be as the result of greed, of fear, of jealousy, and of envy. It is my opinion that it is not independence that is a dangerous human condition, but rather it is dependence. It is dependence that robs people of dignity and self-esteem and fosters the human desire for obtaining something for nothing. It is dependence that subtly steals away individual ambition. It is dependence that strips our society of much of its potential productivity and causes many to sit idly, letting those who labor and who dream and who risk to provide for them. The pursuit of independence is one of the great human virtues, and you should feel most proud to be a part of an organization that teaches, promotes, and provides a plan for those in search of their own personal and financial independence."

The applause was instantaneous and enthusiastic, for she had spoken a thought that all held to be basic to success.

"First, and before I share with you the basic steps for becoming independent, I shall assume that everyone in this room is actively in search of success . . . in search of achieving more than you currently have and in search of becoming more than you presently are. Is that a fair assumption for me to make?"

She raised her right hand above her head. "How many are serious about becoming more and achieving more?"

There was a mixture of laughter, spoken affirmative responses, and a massive raising of hands. She laughed with them and paused for a moment before speaking.

"Is there anyone here who has everything they want and who has become all that they want to become?"

She paused again, looking facetiously around the room, amid more laughter and the hum of hundreds of voices making their own humorous response to her question, but there were no raised hands.

"Since it is clear that nearly everyone in this room is in search of independence or more independence than you currently have, then I would like to spend my time here with you this evening outlining the necessary steps for achieving that independence.

"The ideas I'm going to share are a product of my own opinion, gathered up through my own life experiences. I do not come here to express an authoritative doctrine, only to share my *views*.

"Here is the first step for becoming independent."

She looked deliberately out across the audience, pausing now as note pads were pulled from pockets and purses, for there was something about her appearance, her confidence and her poise that suggested that what she was about to say was to be of unusual significance. There was an aura about her as she stood before them that was not immediately apparent in environments of lesser significance. There was a charisma, a certain sincerity and a sensitivity that made her words sound more like a conversation than a speech.

"Learn the value of working on yourself with greater intensity than any other part of your life," she said. "*Where* one happens to work is not the reason for one's poor circumstances. *What* a person earns is not the reason for a person's poor circumstances, nor is the lack of education, where we were born, how we were raised, or how old or how young we may be. If we are unhappy with our circumstances, and if we wish to find the real reason for those circumstances, then we need only look within ourselves for the causes of those circumstances. It is to be found within the pages of the Bible that '*As a man thinketh, so he becomes.*' And we can add a line to that admonition—*As a man continues to think, so he shall remain*. I have learned, particularly within the last few years, that for things to change for us—for you—for me—*we've* got to change. Not the government, nor the company policy, nor the tax structure. It is not the leadership or the products produced by the company you represent. It is not the marketing plan or commission structure of that company. If one distributor among you earns five *thousand* dollars a month and another earns five *hundred*, and both retail the same product, with the same commission schedule, within the same company, under the same leadership, attending the same training classes, what, pray tell, could be the real reason why one earns a living and another earns a fortune? The answer is—*YOU*. What you *think* makes the difference between success and being average. How you talk, what you say, and how you say it makes a difference. What you read makes a difference. What you wear makes a difference. What you drive makes a difference. The friends you choose to associate with make a difference. How you shake hands, the way you walk, the look in your eye, the intensity of your efforts, and the discipline you impose upon yourself make a difference. So, if you don't like how *things* are, then *you* must change *yourself*, because *things* aren't going to change. Things are always going to be about like they're always been—hot in the summer, cold in the winter, wet in the spring, colorful in the fall. Opportunity will always be followed by difficulty, heartbreak by joy, and regression by progress. You see, *things* are fairly predictable; they follow patterns that are not likely to change. Only you can change. So, step number one for living the better life is learning to work harder on yourself than anything else."

Her intensity increased as she continued and her thoughts instantly were transformed into words that were spoken with eloquence, with balance, and with style. She continued on the subject of the value of paying attention to one's self as a foundation for improving one's life.

"What we think, we attract, and what we attract, we are. Thoughts of fear attract fear, thoughts of poverty attract the circumstances of poverty . . .

"What you *want* is not as important as what you become. You cannot be more than you are, but you can *become* more. The past has molded each of us into what and how we are. Find someone who has the attributes that you admire and make a conscious daily effort to become more of *that* person, having more of *those* attributes. With the passage of time, your old limitations will give way to new skills, and a new personality will emerge. As surely as the butterfly emerges from the cocoon, so shall you find new wings that will lead you to a new place, with new personal value and a new attitude.

"The value of experience and education is over-rated. It is not what you know, it is what you *are,* and it is how you *feel* about what you are and about what you know that determines the quality of life.

"Changing old and limiting habits for new, constructive, and attractive habits takes patience. Changing ourselves is more than making a *resolution* to do so. Resolutions and affirmations are the beginning, but they must be followed by discipline . . . the discipline to turn off the television and pick up a book, the discipline to believe where once we doubted, the discipline to try where once we were afraid, the discipline to stay until the job is finished, the discipline to commit ourselves to a worthy purpose with all our heart, mind, and strength, even when others around us may be walking away, the discipline to look for opportunities hidden among the risks rather than to spend wasteful hours searching for risks within the opportunities."

As she spoke, heads bowed in waves at frequent intervals to capture her ideas on paper.

"Now, let's look at the second step for becoming independent," she said.

She paused again, took a drink of water from the glass, then continued.

"Learn to find an occupational challenge that gives you great joy as well as great opportunity and great incomes. One of the most important things in life is to discover a worthy endeavor that lets you use your greatest talent. And if, as a result of applying your great talent to a worthy endeavor, fortune becomes one of the possible rewards, then you are indeed among the blessed on the Earth. Let it be known by everyone in this room on this night, whether you have made a full-time or part-time commitment to American Products, whether you are an observer or a participant, whether you are a believer or still a skeptic, let it be known that the opportunity for above-average excitement, with above-average joy of accomplishment, and above-average rewards is equally available to each of you. But let it also be known that opportunity knows no favorites . . . it will rest upon the shoulder of anyone worthy of it but will quickly remove itself from the presence of anyone who finds fault with it, for opportunity is a thing to be pursued, not a subject to be studied.

"I wish for you that you might discover your *own* magnificent obsession . . . your love affair with some worthy enterprise, whether it be here or elsewhere. Remember, the great issue of life is not *where* you finally succeed, it is *whether* you finally succeed.

"An interesting question might be: Are you doing what you currently do to earn an income by choice and design, or are you doing it by necessity? Did you choose it because of the joy and the rewards, or did *it* choose *you* out of economic need? Are you working where you work, and earning what you earn, because you *want* or because you *must*?

"Some of the best advice I have to share on this subject is that if you don't genuinely love what you do to earn an income, if it doesn't drive you out of bed early each morning and keep you up late each night plotting, planning, designing, and putting your genius and creativity to work with a driving intensity to master your craft, if it doesn't do all this and more, then my advice is, QUIT! Find something else! Get serious about using your time, your genius, and your God-given skills, for as it has been said *'What you do not use, you will lose.'*"

The words were not difficult for her to find. It was as though her mind were feeding out flawless ideas with computer-like precision.

Part of her brain scanned through the thousands of individual thought pictures that had been stored there, then selected and arranged the words that would convey the thought with clarity.

It was as though her conscious mind were merely servant to a voice within her, as though she were merely a vehicle . . . an instrument for providing mental food to an audience with an insatiable appetite for hope, guidance, and inspiration. On the podium before her there were no notes; there were only years of carefully and sometimes painfully assimilated experiences stored in a mind possessed of unshakeable confidence, spoken by a being guided by a clearly defined purpose.

All who heard her this night were captivated, not only with what she said, but also with how she said it. Her smooth gestures added a sparkle of emphasis to certain words that she spoke, and the sentences she uttered painted mental pictures within the minds of those who listened. There was a symphonic flow to her verbal rhythm and a certain humility and empathy about her that made her ideas sound suggestive rather than authoritative.

No one thought about disagreeing with her concepts; all sought only to absorb as much as possible from this human fountain of ideas.

"Our time grows short, and I have three other ideas that I must leave with you before we move to our separate worlds," she continued.

"The third fundamental for finding independence is to learn to appreciate the value of family happiness." She paused again to watch the pens and pencils race to capture the idea. There was a momentary look of surprise on their faces as they wrote. Many couples glanced at one another—some with a smile, others with an expression of seriousness.

"Is it possible," she asked them, "for a person's personal life to affect their business life?"

The audience responded with affirmatively nodding heads or spoken responses of agreement. She could not help noticing the ever-present few who neither responded, wrote, nor smiled. They sat motionless, looking around on occasion as if measuring the response of others. She remembered something Jonathan had said as she paused to let them write.

"People are in one of three categories: those who watch things happen, those who make things happen, and finally, those who wonder what happened."

She did not verbalize her thought, for it was not the time. It returned back into the mental reservoir from where it had come, but it would present itself again at a more appropriate moment.

"Can one's family life become so out of control that the negative influence of that personal situation totally offsets any real effort made in the business world?"

She paused only for a moment now, knowing that the answers to her questions were obvious.

"Imagine, for a moment, a scene that often occurs at an early morning hour as a man—a husband and a father—prepares to leave his home for work. His dissatisfaction with his job or his insecure financial situation leaves him constantly with that nagging sensation of instability and uncertainty. His breakfast is not ready on time. His wife talks to him of things he would rather forget—of unpaid bills, of household responsibilities he has neglected. At the same moment, his children begin fighting with one another. His temper wears thin and in anger he leaves his home without goodbyes, slamming the door behind him as he leaves.

"As he drives to his office, he carries his anger and frustration with him, passing other drivers recklessly, growing impatient at traffic signals and blowing his horn at anyone who is unfortunate enough to get in his way. When he arrives at his office, he continues to wear the facial expression of a person who had long ago forgotten the meaning of happiness and serenity.

"As the man enters the door of his office building, he is greeted by some of his co-workers. What do you suppose the man does now? Is it not likely that he would paint on his artificial smile and greet his friends with warm words?

"All of us know of people who have acted out this same scene in their own personal lives. The great tragedy is not only that the man has failed to show love and affection at home to those who most need his love; the tragedy is that the man will now enter the world of business and, for the next eight hours, will attempt to impress people with his leadership skills, with his courtesy, with his patience and understanding, and with his kind words of encouragement. He seeks to become a successful entrepreneur, but he has not yet mastered his family challenge . . . or himself!

"Remember, the disciplines required for success in the world of business are the same disciplines necessary for a successful family life. As my grandmother often remarked, 'If you cannot make your bed in the morning, you cannot become rich.'"

There was laughter and she laughed with them.

"I once wondered about my grandmother . . . the connection between making one's bed and getting rich were not easy for me to see. I now understand. It is now clear to me that by mastering the *small* disciplines, we prepare ourselves for the *large* disciplines. We do not have the liberty of going through life doing only those things that we *want* to do. We also have to do those things that we *must* do. Pain, discomfort, and difficulty are signals of growth toward self-improvement—if you move forward in *spite* of them.

"Listening to the stories of our children may not be something we *want* to do, but it is something we *must* do. Taking the time to share our love for those at home is something we *must* do. Showing patience, love, understanding, gratitude, and thoughtfulness at home is something that is not always convenient or easy, but it is *there* that we *must* do it, for if we cannot master our moods and our habits at home, we cannot master ourselves *anywhere*."

She glanced at her watch, noticing that the time she was to take was nearly used up.

"I'll quickly share with you the final two steps for becoming independent so that you can be on your way. You've had a full evening.

"The fourth requirement is to learn the value of spiritual contentment. I would not be so unfair as to suggest the need for anyone to become more religious than they are—that is an extremely personal matter. But let me leave a special caution with each of you. Regardless of your religion, regardless of your beliefs or how you even feel about the need for religion, my opinion is that whatever your beliefs are, you should *honor* them. If you believe you should pray, then pray. If you believe you should go to church on Sunday, then go. If you believe you should pay a tithe, pay it. *Whatever* you consciously accept as a religion, a belief, or a personal code of conduct, you must honor it, for not to do so will give you a severe case of the 'guilties.' You will move through life feeling that something is missing. It will haunt you and leave you with an unexplainable void that will affect all other areas of your life."

Her final remark contained a message that she had read or heard somewhere years before. She offered it to them as a promise given to them at birth—a promise and a challenge. But only a handful of the three thousand would hear and know its meaning. To the rest, it was vague and beyond their ability to comprehend.

"'*As man is, God once was. And as God is, man can become.*'

"And now, my final step for achieving independence. It is simple. It is basic. And, it is elusive. It is called 'commit yourself to the achievement of financial independence.' Call it economic success, call it getting rich, call it what you wish, but find it, for it is essential to your freedom, to your happiness, and to your self-esteem."

She reflected now into her past, and with obvious emotion she continued.

"I was raised as a young girl to believe that money was the root of all evil. I was taught to memorize scripture that had been taken out of context. I clearly remember something I was taught at age five. '*It is easier for a camel to pass through the eye of a needle than for a rich man to enter heaven.*'

"Is it any wonder that many of us grow into adulthood and have difficulty finding financial security? Here is what this woman," she said, pointing toward herself, "has finally discovered, after three decades on this sphere called Earth."

She paused, the emotion that was in her words now demanding the full and complete attention of nearly all of the three thousand.

"Money is *not* the root of all evil . . . *poverty* is the root of evil. Being consistently broke the day before payday is evil; it leads to lies, to dishonesty, and to the loss of dignity and self-esteem. The lack of enough money to meet our needs is behind theft. It is also behind divorce and family dissent. In fact it is behind *most* of whatever we choose to call 'evil.'

"And the absence of enough money is not a cause. It is an effect. *We* are the cause. With a few exceptions, the attainment of financial independence is a measuring stick of our true human value.

"To attract more—become more. One of the greatest frustrations in life is to want an above-average job with an above-average income without *first* becoming an above-average person.

"I encourage you to read the good books; they provide a wealth of collected experiences written by those who have failed but who have now succeeded, as well as of those who have succeeded and have since failed. Gather up the experiences of others and learn from those experiences. I encourage you to take a second look at your talent, at your personality, at the way you dress. Take a fresh, new, objective look at your effect on people. I encourage you to look again at your opportunity, and commit yourself to either get serious or get out. Do not linger in unproductivity, uncertainty, or mediocrity. I encourage you to share your knowledge and your love, your talent and your experience.

"I encourage you to become all you were meant by your creator to be. I encourage you to continue your search for an occupational endeavor that excites you and challenges you; one that also rewards you in fair proportion to your results . . . not your *potential*—your *results*. I encourage you to spend time with your family, *teaching* them and learning *from* them, for indeed the family should become a source of loving harmony and deep friendship. I encourage you to honor your beliefs if you have them or to find some if you don't, for each of us needs to find *something* to believe in. And finally, I encourage you to begin an all-out pursuit of total financial freedom, so that never again do you have to check menu prices *before* you enter a restaurant, or fear a ringing phone, or the delivery of the mail. I wish for you this day, this moment, the joy that comes from having money out of the way as a source of consideration in the process of life. You have the ability—use it! You have the opportunity—grasp it! You have the freedom—cherish it! You have the access to knowledge—listen to it! You have something that millions want and need—share it! You only need one good *reason* for getting into action—find it!"

The audience had stopped taking notes now. Her emotional challenge was etching itself into the minds and souls of her audience. Words leading to notes lead only to *knowledge*. Words leading to a reborn human emotion and inner intensity lead to *action*.

She paused once more. There was silence. There was a single cough from somewhere in back of the massive room. There was also Gloria Simon tapping her fingers against the table top.

"Tonight, I ask that you commit yourself to three specific things that can help you find your fortune. First, a willingness to try. Try in *spite* of as well as *because* of. I ask that you try in spite of the restrictions placed upon you by government or by those who pose as guardians of the public good when in reality their true objective is the promotion of their personal ambitions."

From the corner of her eye she saw the head of a woman turn as though released by a spring and the eyes of Gloria Simon flashed a look of anger toward her.

"I ask for your willingness to believe in yourself, your willingness to believe in your enterprise, and for your willingness to believe in America again, for in spite of its faults, it remains the last bastion of freedom and individual hope on the face of the globe.

"Second, I ask for your *eagerness*. To try is a good beginning, but to try with *intensity* gives you a far better chance for success. Be eager to learn, eager to earn, and yes, even eager to fail, for it is failure that gives greater substance to the success that will inevitably come if you will continue to try.

"And finally, I ask for your firmness in all your beliefs. Be firm in what you stand for; allow no one to shake your resolute commitment to become more than you are. Be firm when your company is attacked. Be firm when the fairness of your marketing plan is attacked. Be firm against those who would lure you into believing that what you are doing is wrong, or unworkable, or unrewarding. The very nature of your opportunity is built upon the same premise that made America great. Its challenge is fair and its challenge is simple. The premise says, 'Take your talent to the marketplace. If you're as good as you *think* you are, the chances are good that you will succeed. If you are *not* as good as you think you are, the chances are good that you will fail.' Either way, you will *find out*, and believe me, there is nothing like finding out. The process lets you discover yourself and it lets you *learn* from that discovery. That is the essence of America's greatness, and I condemn anyone who would seek to protect us from our right to fail.

"I wish for you willingness, and eagerness, and firmness. Do not let yourself believe—*ever*—that anyone owes you anything, or that someone out there has the responsibility for taking care of you, or even that we should take care of one another. Let no one take *care* of you, lest your caretaker become your jailer. Take care of *no one*, lest you become their *keeper*.

"I want to thank you for allowing me to share your time with you. I am grateful to each of you, for this day, for this opportunity you have given to me, and for your attention. God bless you. Good night."

The audience exploded, coming to their feet in one instantaneous motion as though trained to make three thousand individual movements look like one. The American Products theme blasted again as D.L. Baker jumped onto the stage and ran toward her. The applause continued. The tears of joy welled in her eyes again. As she looked down to unsnap the lavalier microphone that hung around her neck a single tear fell onto the back of her left hand. For a fleeting second, she remembered other tears for other reasons, and she was glad . . . for then *and* for now.

The event ended shortly after her speech. As she stood by the chair where she had been sitting, she found herself surrounded by people, having one short conversation after another, shaking hands and autographing programs.

Gloria Simon stood motionless as she watched these expressions of gratitude. She had purposely lingered behind, not to speak with Mari, but to communicate her response to the speech. As Mari turned toward her, their eyes met for but a moment. There was no mistaking the challenge or the anger in Gloria's eyes. They were two women of diametrically opposed views, but while one would invite the opinions of the other without animosity, the other would not. Mariana had had the last word in the closing of her speech, but Gloria's look clearly communicated that their opposing views would bring them together again on a different field of battle.

Mari smiled at her and waited for a response. There was no response—only an intensification of coldness. Turning abruptly, the slender, black-haired woman stalked away in a cadence of defiance.

Mariana's attention transferred back to the gathering around her—those who felt no animosity, but who hungered only for a few more words and a willing ear. These were the people she chose to associate with—people of fairness, people of honest intent, people whose efforts and attitude contributed something of value toward the vitality of the nation. Surely they would not all succeed, but what set them apart from others was their willingness to try, and their belief that they were the inheritors of opportunity drove them to find their fortune rather than to find fault.

Mariana would always be thankful for both those who admired her as well as those who despised her, for each needed the existence of the other for life to remain interesting and challenging, and she needed the existence of both to give depth to her insights.

CHAPTER TEN:

The Encounter

The pilot pointed out the lights of Washington off in the distance and announced a holding pattern that would delay them for ten more minutes. The excitement of Los Angeles was becoming a memory now, overshadowed by the anticipation she felt about being met by Jonathan Locke at the airport. Since first meeting this man whose philosophies and concepts had taught her so much about life and about herself, their only conversations had been about business, and always in a business or formal social atmosphere. Meeting her at the airport had to be for some special purpose.

Her mind flashed over the time that had passed since she first had walked into his office by mistake. She remembered her circumstances then and she thought of her circumstances now. Her mind flashed pictures in sporadic sequence. She remembered their first conversation over coffee when she returned to thank him for the book he had given her. And there were the many monthly business conferences over which he presided . . . teaching, counseling, and sitting there as he often did, listening to reports and taking notes.

She glanced across the aisle as she pondered her thoughts and her eyes caught the shiny redness of an apple that a young boy was flipping into the air. A picture flashed . . . an envelope hanging on a frame of antiquated gold on the wall of Jonathan's outer office with the words "To Jonathan . . ." What were the words? The sound caught her attention, but her mind clung to the mental picture of the envelope . . . tap-tap-tap. The boy flipped the apple, and the sound of crisp apple colliding briefly against his hand presented a strange collage of incoherent mental pictures. The envelope . . . a gift . . . to be used and . . . shared. But her mind was playing tricks. First, an envelope in a frame, but then . . . the frame was gone, and she saw only an envelope . . . and a ribbon, whose redness matched . . . what did it match? The envelope—the ribbon, and . . . the apple. Her mind relaxed, and she slid into the gray area between sleep and consciousness, that area where both realms of the mind are equally active.

The mental tape recorder played back the sound of a voice within her head.

"How do you tell an apple to grow?"

Where had she heard that? Her mind had just presented her with a clear and distinct voice that she could not identify. She had a unique sensation—a feeling of recall from a childhood experience that flashes instantly into one's mind and then disappears as quickly as it comes. But the voice . . . who . . . where had she heard that voice?

There was no awareness of those around her, only the shrill but distant high-frequency whine of the Rolls-Royce jet engines thrusting the 747 across the continent. In a flicker, the eye of her mind detected the faint silvery glow standing before a turquoise background. The glow moved in an ebb and flow, forming itself into the vague figure of a man. Slowly the silvery pattern condensed into a more distinct white and there before her stood the elegance and reverence that was the man called Noah. He stood still, smiling the warm smile that emitted calmness and confidence.

Only his right arm moved—slowly and in the undulating movement of a gentle ocean swell. It was his right forearm gliding back and forth, his hand holding the apple that he methodically polished against the sleeve of his opposite arm.

"I come to you for only a moment, Miss Mariana. Listen to me closely."

She knew him, accepted the moment and instantly recalled their two previous conversations in vivid detail, almost as though no event, no earthly activity had occurred in the span of time separating then and now.

"You have performed well, Mari, and your progress carries you now into a momentum of unimaginable proportions. Soon you will merge your ideas with the ideas of others, chosen as you have been chosen, for a most worthy and urgent project. Respond without logical thought to your intuitions, Mariana, for in your intuitions you shall find me, and in me you move toward the magnification of your calling. Prepare yourself for a recognition and acceptance by those of great power and influence, for you are part of a plan whose purpose is the preservation of freedom."

The voice of her mind spoke to him even though she knew he was not finished.

"Noah, what is it that—"

His smile remained and he continued speaking as though she had said nothing.

"My presence before you until now was for the purpose of planting the thought seeds of confidence in your mind, and those seeds now provide for you the harvest of a new life. I have, in truth, given to you reassurance, Mariana . . . reassurance that all will be well *for* you and in your life."

He began that strange process of tossing the apple again—twelve inches up and twelve inches down, plopping into the cupped palm of the right hand as though the apple had its own internal guidance system.

"Now, Mariana, the reassurance that has been given to you from *outside* yourself must become *faith* from *within* yourself. Reassurance is at best temporary and provides only initial direction toward a desired end. Faith is *permanent* and serves as an ever-present companion at the very moment in which you require divine counsel and guidance. Through faith, you have immediate access to all that you require, while reassurance is only an infrequent advisor and the poorest of all servants.

"Listen to the still, small voice, Mariana. Listen and respond, and that which you need will be yours."

The whiteness became gray and then silver, and in an instant the vision gave way to a sound . . . the sound of the whining engines and the faint sound of an apple falling into an extended palm.

The thought faded and only a vague curiosity remained. The tapping had stopped as she opened her eyes and turned her head, to see the boy drop the apple into his jacket pocket.

The engines of the plane roared and the wing outside her window swept upward. As she looked into a star-filled sky, the soft bell sounded over the intercom system and the flight attendant announced that they had been cleared for landing. The words made her heart race for a moment at the thought of what might await her. Jonathan Locke was not one to waste time, for it was too valuable to him. He had often talked about life not being a "practice session," and how time was too precious a commodity to be treated casually.

She was letting her mind play tricks again, imagining things and fearing things. The imaginings were healthy, but the fears were not. She would have her answers within minutes. She flicked an imaginary mental switch as she turned loose of the thought, and reached for her lipstick.

The picture of the envelope, the ribbon, and the apple appeared and faded one more time. As she lost the thought, she breathed deeply and closed her eyes, deliberately bringing back the memory of her speech from the night before, even though another thought fought to penetrate her consciousness.

Her mind wandered aimlessly for the next several minutes, and she made no effort to concentrate on anything specific. It was her way of mentally relaxing and preparing herself for an event that had the capacity to make her more apprehensive than she wanted to be. The plane parked at the gate, the bells of the intercom chimed to announce the arrival, and passengers jumped in unison, some reaching for items stored under seats while others reached above them to retrieve articles in overhead compartments.

And then everyone stood, waiting—the inevitable wait—as more than two hundred people prepared to file along two aisleways leading toward the single open door of the 747.

Mariana York waited in her seat until the human movement toward the door was smooth flowing. Moments later, she stepped from the boarding ramp into the terminal building.

"Mariana York—Miss Mariana York . . . Please meet your party at the baggage claim area of TWA."

The PA system repeated itself a second time. She smiled and followed the overhead signs that lead her toward her destination.

The walk took less than five minutes. She was approaching the baggage carousel when a gentle hand squeezed her left arm. "Welcome to Washington, Miss York."

She turned and looked into the smiling blue eyes of Jonathan Locke. The two shook hands, exchanging the normal comments typical of two business people with a few years of friendship and mutual respect between them.

"Did you have dinner on the plane?" he asked later, as he unlocked the passenger door of the brown and beige Seville. "No, only coffee," she answered, as she slid into the beige leather seat.

The Cadillac engine responded instantly to the turning of the ignition key, and soft music and the chimes reminding them to fasten their seat belts filled the interior of the car.

They looked at one another. She waited for him to speak.

"How would you respond to an invitation for dinner?" he asked.

"Sounds wonderful . . . I'm starved."

"You don't have anyone waiting for you?"

"No one."

"Your apartment is in the northwest part of the city, isn't it?"

"Rockville."

"I know a nice place up on Connecticut Avenue. Can you hold your appetite for that long?"

"Sure." The drive along the Parkway toward the Maryland suburbs was filled with conversation about her trip and about the speech she had given. They talked about the quality of people who seemed to be attracted toward American Products and about her book. The drive took nearly forty minutes, and after having the car valet-parked, they sat in a corner booth of a restaurant near the Connecticut Avenue exit of the Beltway—a restaurant she had often seen, but had never had the chance to try. Their talk about the incidentals of business continued throughout the dinner, and none of the subjects they discussed seemed to her to be the reason why this man would want to spend private time with her.

"How did you like California?' he asked as he stirred his coffee.

"What I saw of it was absolutely marvelous," she answered. "I'd always wanted to go there, and to do so under those conditions made it terribly special."

"Is it a place you would ever consider living?"

"I think I'd love it, if the circumstances were right. The very thought of walking a warm beach in January is almost beyond my comprehension . . . especially after this past winter."

Jonathan took a drink from his cup, placing it back onto the saucer in a slow and deliberate way that clearly announced the beginning of a serious subject. He looked straight at her, folding his hands on the table in front of him. The gold chain bracelet on his right wrist showed just below the white shirt cuff with the initials "JLL" monogrammed in black. On his left wrist was the gold watch she had noticed the first day she had met him.

"Mariana, I had a particular reason for wanting to meet you at the airport tonight."

She smiled at him. "I assumed you did . . . and you're about to get into whatever it is that we need to discuss?"

"Yes, but go a little easy, Mari. I need to work into the subject gradually." They both laughed.

"Is it that difficult?" Her mouth smiled, but she felt a slight uneasiness inside her, a feeling like she used to have when her environment and circumstances seemed to always control her moods.

"Perhaps. There are several things I want to cover. Whether I choose to cover everything I'd *like* will depend upon how the conversation goes."

"Jonathan, you're so innocently clever. You know, you really shouldn't give away your battle plan in advance." She laughed again. Two years ago she would have been too insecure to offer to shake his hand, or to say anything to him other than a response to his direct question. Now, she was thinking on his plane, and put her hand across the table to touch his folded hands as an unnecessary gesture of reassurance to a man who needed no reassurance.

"It's all right, Mr. Locke. I can handle it," she said jokingly. He sat back in his seat, pulling his hands from under hers, but not at all in a way that suggested rejection.

"All right," he said with a slight smile. "I'm giving very serious thought to moving my entire operation to California."

She sat back slowly, her eyes not moving from him. "Everything?"

"Everything—the publishing, the production facility, administrative, the entire operation, leaving regional offices to serve our clients here on the east coast. I'll probably lease out the Philadelphia office and keep the Washington office as the East Coast location."

She showed no emotion, but inside her mind a mental computer was working. It contemplated the effect on her and it searched for why he would be discussing a thing like this with her.

"I want to greatly expand our video and film programs, Mari. The schedule is getting too difficult to handle. I'm booked nearly a year in advance, and now you're spending most of your time—or soon will be—giving speeches around the country. What we say and how we say it seems to be more popular than we thought, and for every crowd of a thousand or two that we spend an hour or two with, there are several hundred thousand more we could reach if we only had other methods of sharing the ideas, Mari. Cassette tapes are not the real answer. Videotapes are the future, and California has the type of facilities I want to have access to."

"Have you made a definite decision yet?" she asked.

"A mental decision? Yes. A commitment? No, not yet. We've found a facility in Orange County that would give us everything we need—the printing facility . . . everything . . . and the price is right."

"But you have a reason for delay?"

"Not really. I've learned to run my life and my business on instinct. I once tried to figure everything out—the logic and reasons, the pro and con—but now I listen to that still, small voice that each of us has inside, and on this subject the answer is clear. We're going to make the move."

"May I ask how soon?"

"It may take as long as a year to affect a full and orderly transfer."

The waiter poured fresh coffee into the cups. She watched Jonathan add cream and sugar to his cup before she spoke. "Jonathan, all the good things that are happening to me—the recognition, the success of my own book—these things are to a large degree due to your guidance and influence at a time when I most needed it. But I'm not an officer of your company, or even an employee. I'm—I'm an independent contractor. We associate together, you and I, because . . . well, because of a mutual respect and profitability."

He interrupted her, posing the question that he knew she was leading up to but found somewhat difficult to ask.

"What you're wondering, Mariana, is why I'm telling you something that is not only an executive-level decision but also is something that has already been decided anyway. I want you to move to California when we make the transfer out there."

"In what capacity? Most of my clients are here in the east, Jonathan."

"I want you to become the chief executive officer of Camelot Productions."

"You want—what?"

"Let's not talk about whether you *can* handle it, Mariana. The only issue is really whether you *want* to. At this point, you really don't need Camelot any longer. I don't need Camelot. Between speaking fees, the profits from my books, and the investments I've made, I can do quite well without the burden of administering a company. Anyway, there's another project that's taking more and more of my time, and it's top priority."

"Then why go to all the trouble to move your entire enterprise all the way to California?"

"Because the company is a vehicle that will be invaluable a few years down the road . . . not as a profit center, but as a means for producing the material that is going to be needed as the demand increases."

"The demand for what, Jonathan? If you believe that you—and I—going in separate directions can do well economically, and we both know we can, why not let someone else take over the publication of books, and then you and I . . . separately . . . collectively . . . whatever you have in mind, go about the country conducting occasional seminars and giving speeches?"

"Mari—Mari . . . you have such a talent . . . such a gift, and that talent is going to create a place for you far beyond that which you currently realize. What you're doing is only a fractional part of what you're *going* to do, and the existence of Camelot is going to be essential to us . . . not from a business standpoint, but as a supportive source. Believe me, Mariana, Camelot must continue to grow, and it must be in California, and you must play a major role in that growth—and in California."

There was a certain intensity about him that she had not seen before this moment. It was as though there was something that he wanted to reveal but could not. His eyes searched hers for a response, but she looked past him, as though her thoughts were somewhere else.

"Mariana, is there some personal reason why accepting a move like this and a new position of responsibility would cause you difficulty?"

"Well . . . no . . ."

"I have no right to ask this question, but I must." She looked directly at him now.

"Is there someone in your life—personally, I mean?"

"No." Her answer was quick and it was emphatic, and he smiled.

"Is there someone you're trying to forget?"

Again the answer was no. She looked at him curiously now. "Why are you asking these questions, Jonathan?"

"Partially because I would not allow myself to attempt to persuade you to do something of this magnitude if it were going to disrupt some special relationship you may have with someone else."

"There are no special relationships. I think that you're aware that I've been married before, but that didn't work out, and no, there are no lingering emotions of any kind. Now, you said 'partially.' Why else are you asking these things?"

He smiled, but only slightly, and took a drink of coffee. Her eyes never left his, and for the very first time she detected a hint of discomfort within the man from whom she had learned so much and received so much. Since they had first met, there had always been a certain formality between them, but tonight was different. The distinct aroma from his cologne drifted across the table that separated them. She had asked a simple question, not anticipating any particular answer, but as she sat looking at him in the semi-darkness, pondering his silence and thinking again of the question she had just asked, a strange sensation emerged within her. It was an awareness of what she had asked and of what the answer might turn out to be. The ever-present mental barrier of teacher and student was not there . . . not this moment. Her brain scanned the possibilities . . . the phone call from Washington to Los Angeles . . . his meeting her at the airport. He was looking at her in a way that made one possibility stand out among all the rest, and it was as though she had been shot.

"Jonathan, what is it that you're not saying?" There was a rush of emotion within her that made her anxious to hear him speak, and at the same time she was afraid that he wouldn't.

"Mari, do you really like what you do?"

"What?"

"The business we're in—the writing, the speeches, the sharing of philosophical concepts that are designed to change people's lives—do you really enjoy it, or is it just a temporarily convenient way to earn a living?"

He was drifting from the line of thought that she wanted to pursue. She could see in his eyes that something was there and that he was reluctant to discuss it.

"That's a strange question to ask, isn't it?"

"Strange perhaps, but terribly important to me. There are a lot of people in our business who speak the language well, but they don't live the principles we teach. They do what they do because it makes them look good, or sound good, but it ends there. They're entertainers, Mariana. Their presentation is an act . . . a performance. People come to hear them for assurance and guidance, but these people give them hype . . . they give them—"

"Jonathan, I do what I do because I believe it. Your book pointed me in a new direction. It made me see that my circumstances were the direct results of my thoughts. Then there were other books, other concepts from other people, Jonathan. But the one thing that your books and your counsel, and the ideas I've gotten from others, did for me was that they led me to myself. I've *always* believed in the things we teach, and I think deep down inside we *all* do. You merely revealed *me* to me, Jonathan. That's what you and I and others do for people—we reveal themselves *to* themselves. Of *course* I like what I do. I *believe* in what I do. If there were no Camelot Productions, I would continue to do what I do. Why do you . . ."

She saw him smiling at her and stopped in the middle of her thought.

"Mariana, I think I have a bit of a problem." She didn't answer.

"It's important to me how you feel about our business. I really *know* how you feel, but it was necessary for me to hear it from you directly. Now, are you aware that it has been a policy of mine for some time that there are to be no personal relationships of any kind between the staff members of Camelot . . . or our customers and our staff?"

"I've heard about it, yes, but it's never caused me any difficulty. Why?"

"Because it's become obvious to me that you've aroused the affections of one of our key executives, Mariana, and it's causing a great deal of difficulty at the home office."

"Me? Who—?"

"Do you feel anything special for one of the executives of Camelot?"

"Jonathan, of course not! Who would make such a ridiculous accusation?"

"Then that presents perhaps even a more difficult situation to be dealt with."

"What do you mean?"

He leaned forward again, his forearms across the table. The expression on his face was more serious now, and she felt confused and apprehensive.

"Let me come right to the point, difficult as it may be for me." He paused a moment, looked down at his coffee cup, then back up at her. "For several months now, I've found myself spending time thinking about you. I look for reasons to call you directly, and I know that I can't. I find myself fascinated by some of the material you've developed . . . by your book . . . just by what you are. I remember the first day you came into my office—a hopeless, helpless young woman who had no idea what she wanted. Then there was that almost instant transformation. Within twenty-four hours, you became completely different. And now . . . look at you! You're a warm, radiant, talented, and beautiful young woman who believes in everything I believe in, and whether you're next to me in a conference session or three thousand miles away as you were yesterday, there's something special that I feel for you. I can pretend that it isn't there, which I've done for several months, or I can search your eyes, when there's no one around to notice, to see if perhaps anything is there . . . anything that you feel . . ."

"Jonathan?" She watched him struggle with something that was terribly difficult for him and had decided to give him answers to unasked questions.

He felt a sense of relief at her interruption, and his silence was a signal for her to speak if she chose to do so.

"Jonathan, because of who you are and because of what you are, because of what you teach, and what you make people feel when finally they find themselves, because of these things there are perhaps thousands of people out there—and I'm speaking about women—who have special feelings for you. You're what they wish their husbands were, or what they wish their fathers, or lovers, or their children were. But then, because of what you *are*, they can't tell you what they feel for you. They can express their *gratitude*. They can say a few warm words to you, shake your hand, or ask you to auto-graph a book, but because of the respect you command, it ends there.

"I'm one of those women, Jonathan, but I have even greater complica-tions. I have *greater* reasons why I'm permitted to get only so close to you. You're my employer, Jon. You're my teacher, my mentor, and my greatest source of inspiration. I couldn't allow myself to even entertain thoughts of getting any closer to you than I've been. But that doesn't mean that I've not had moments of wishful thinking. I was attracted to you the very first time I saw you, Jonathan. You were successful, you were articulate . . . you were obviously everything I would want to be and everything I would want to be associated with, but I was Mariana York. I was lost, Jon. I was not someone who you could be attracted to and I accepted that. Even now, Jonathan, I'm still learning. I have no cause to believe that I've become the kind of person that you would be comfortable with, so I've not given a moment of serious thought to how I might feel about you— personally, I mean."

He listened closely, looking at her, then looking down briefly at the spoon he twirled between his thumb and forefinger. She had paused now feeling the need to measure the effect of what she had said and to wait for him to respond to her words.

There was but a short silence before he spoke.

"What I said to you, Mariana, was merely an expression of my feelings that I have inside. I wouldn't be so presumptuous as to suggest that you've been going about your life with the same feelings for me. I felt a need to share with you what I feel. Whether that feeling is love, or a unique friendship, or whatever, I don't know. What I *do* know is that I am a man and you are a woman. Whatever you think me to be, whatever I may or may not teach you, or whatever may exist in the form of corporate policy, I would like, whenever conditions permit, to invite you to dinner, or to a play, or . . . or wherever. I enjoy being with you, Mariana. Wherever that may lead us, or not lead so be it, but I want you to know that I shall want to spend time with you, and whether you choose to accept or reject my invitations will have no bearing whatever upon your future with Camelot."

"None?"

"Only that if you refuse, or even hesitate to give me an emphatic, immediate and affirmative reply, you will be either immediately dismissed or summarily shot, depending upon my mood."

They laughed together. It was an open, relaxed, and genuine laugh. The waiter poured them each a final cup of coffee and presented the check to Jonathan.

"Mariana, have I offended you or disappointed you in any way?"

"Jonathan, don't be silly. Within the deep corners of my mind, I've probably imagined a thousand times or more what it would be like to be noticed by you, and now that I discover that I am—well, I'll have to wait until I've had time for the impact to be . . ."

"Mariana York, the truth is that I may well be in love with you, and possibly have been for some time. Not being an expert on such matters, I, too, will have to watch the future unfold. Once before, I made the mistake of confusing love with infatuation and married a woman for the wrong reasons . . . we were both eighteen at the time. Since correcting that mistake, I've been most careful about my emotions . . . this kind of emotion, I mean."

She did not respond.

"You were once married."

"Yes," she answered.

"And you learned something of value from it?"

"I would hope so. It was good and it was not so good, and I learned from both."

"It's especially valuable when we learn from our mistakes. Someone once said, 'Those who do not learn from past mistakes are condemned to repeat them.'"

There was a brief moment of silence, finally broken by the woman.

"Jonathan . . . about California . . ."

"Yes, what of it?"

"I'd be glad to go—especially if that's where you're going to be."

He smiled and their hands met halfway across the table.

It was nearly midnight before she unlocked the door to her apartment. She looked through the wrought-iron grating on the balcony and saw the Seville turning the corner of the driveway onto Rockville Pike. Jonathan had waited until they had pulled into the parking space in front of her apartment before inviting her to appear with him at a speaking engagement in Boston scheduled for the following Thursday. She had thanked him for what she had called a "special evening" and she leaned across the center armrest to place a quick kiss on his cheek. She smiled, thanked him again and slid gracefully from the front seat of the car, waving back at him as she closed the door, and walked toward the apartment.

Mariana York sat now by the fireplace, recording her recall of the evening's events in her journal. Dvorak's *New World Symphony* played in the background.

This warm spring evening was of monumental importance to her. Within a few short years she had reversed the direction of her life. Where there had once been doubt and fear, there was now an over-whelming confidence. Where once she had sought after the security and the income from a job, she now sought ways to develop newly discovered talents. Rather than running from the past, she now raced toward the future.

The words flowed into the pages of her journal.

> *"Some days I am amazed at how far I have come, and other days I find myself intrigued with the thought of how far I still have to go. Each accomplishment seems to lead to the threshold of yet an even greater opportunity. The ordeal of Philadelphia and the mystery of what to do with my life seems so very long ago. And yet, if I regress, if I fall back into the habits that controlled my life at that time, I will surely find that the nightmare I experienced at that time and place will return in the twinkling of an eye.*
>
> *"Life is indeed like the fertile soil. It will give to us that which we have given to it. Life—and the soil—have no concern for our needs. It will reward us in proportion to our efforts. Relax in the spring, and you must surely beg in the fall.*
>
> *"Tonight I have had the good fortune of yet another discovery. Where once I would wish for the love and friendship of a man of means, of a man of accomplishment willing to take care of my needs, I now find that by becoming more of what I can be, I have attracted the attention of one who, not very long ago, might have pitied me, who would not have sought after my friendship, or my time. A woman of means seems to attract a man of means. A woman without direction, ambition or the willingness to change herself will attract a man of the same fiber."*

She wrote and she remembered long into the night. She remembered her marriage to Aaron—the happiness in the beginning as well as the heartbreak at the end. She remembered the years she had spent trying to preserve and protect that relationship before finally deciding that the value of her life, and the potential of her future, was of greater significance than any relationship. Her thoughts drifted to Jonathan Locke. She could see him standing before her. He was not a tall man, standing only a few inches taller than she. His brown hair was streaked blond from the sun, and his manner of dress was impeccable. His physique accentuated the cut of his well-tailored clothes, and his manner of speech was slow and deliberate, with a slight southern accent. She could see the blueness of his eyes even now and hear his soft voice speaking as though he were there with her this very moment. Jonathan Locke had a brilliant mind. He had personally produced and directed his own videotape series. He had designed the products and the literature used at Camelot. He was singly one of the most creative and articulate men she had ever met. Only two months before did she learn that he was unmarried. She had noticed a gold ring, one of very special design, on his right hand and had thought it to be a wedding ring. She remembered the feeling she had experienced when being told that he was entirely unattached.

Her mind searched her mental archives to assemble for this moment all that she knew about this man who had suddenly and unexpectedly stepped forward to seize her attention. She knew him to be an honest and genuinely caring person. He was a student of government, often quoting men and women of history who had played a role in politics. He strongly believed in the capitalist theory and in the preservation of freedom. She had once heard him express his views of those who would misuse their political power and influence for personal gain—views that revealed to her that the man was an advocate of justice—of deserved and certain punishment for all who would violate the law. She remembered something he once said: "The only equality among men is the equality we have to make something of ourselves."

She filled several pages of her journal and reflected for nearly two hours before sleepiness forced her to leave the warmth of the white sheepskin rug near her fireplace for the bed that would give rest to her tired mind and body.

CHAPTER ELEVEN:

The Seasons

The remaining weeks of the season of spring were a time of discovery for the woman whose name was Mariana York. Her trip to Boston with Jonathan Locke ended with a weekend spent at his summer home fifty miles south of Boston at Horseneck Beach. They stood together on the shoreline looking eastward toward Cuttyhunk Island, and beyond it they saw the faint edges of Martha's Vineyard. Jonathan taught her the history of the area—of colonialists seeking freedom and refuge from an unfair government, and of pirates seeking refuge from the storms of the Atlantic and from their pursuers. It was a time of restoration and change. Old leaves and bare branches gave way to new blossoms and early hints of green. The robins were returning and the storm clouds of winter were giving way to a brilliant blue sky. Where the sky met the sea, the emerald green of the far waters created a contrast of beauty beyond the ability of any artist to capture with brush and palette. The air was still cool, but with a hint of returning warmth. Bees began playing with the emerging blossoms, and the magic of springtime's slipping from the clutches of winter was all around them.

During the first evening, just before sunset, they sat together on a wooden box on the dock along Fall River and watched returning fishermen unload their day's catch of lobster, and Jonathan taught the woman about lobster traps, old ships, and the similarities between the changing seasons and the human drama.

"Life is truly a constant beginning," he said as they watched gulls flocking above them just before sunset. "Life is a constant opportunity . . . a constant springtime. We only need to learn to look at things with the curiosity and fascination of children. How often we get caught up in the routine and forget that there are miracles hidden among the common. It's the unique blending of sun, soil, and seed at the springtime of seasons that will provide predictable and almost miraculous results for anyone who will learn to take advantage of all that surrounds them. Springtime comes, Mariana, with great regularity, and it merely says to us, 'Here I am. What are you going to do with me?' The fertile ground sits waiting, the air and sun grow warmer, the spring rains offer the final catalyst for the creation of all things within our imagination that do not yet exist. The miracle awaits us, Mari. It awaits the human decision to take advantage of this brief opportunity. For you and me, we have our health, our creative minds, a willing audience, and our hunger for changing people's lives, but we must take advantage of our gifts. What we do not use, we will lose."

The moon glow filled the night sky with a brilliant orange at the horizon, and within moments the white sphere emerged slowly, as if from the sea, the waters twinkling streaks of silver that reached toward them as the breaking waves seemed to bring luminescent radiance to their very feet. They walked barefoot through the cooling sand and over the quarter mile of large gray rocks that had washed ashore from the years of winter storms. They watched the faint lights from ships passing in the distance, and exchanged ideas on life and its meaning and purpose, and wondered about the captain at the helm of a distant ship.

Together they drank coffee from a thermos that she had brought . . . sometimes talking, sometimes listening, but always content with both the words *and* the silence. They listened to the clanging bell of a buoy warning of a reef, and watched the white ball grow smaller as it crossed the sky to look down upon them from directly above. For Jonathan, and for Mariana, this was a special springtime with a special opportunity. It was a time for the merging of one mind into two bodies and the intimate embracing of two bodies together.

The showers and warm sun of spring gave way to the heat of summer, and the buds and blossoms were mature. The days and nights alternated between clear and stormy skies as the evolving process of nature moved on. The seeds of springtime had become the green fields of summer, and it was a time to protect the crops from the bugs, weeds, and summer storms that would show no mercy to the sower of springtime seed. As spring is the time to take advantage, summer is the time to nurture and to protect, for indeed all good—all well-intentioned effort, either of man or nature—will be attacked. The hawk will devour the egg of the lazy or inattentive sparrow, and the bugs of summer will destroy the growing crop of corn. The greedy and dishonest will take away the carefully planned opportunity of the businessman whose attention has been diverted to the beach rather than to his task of labor.

Jonathan Locke and Mariana York crisscrossed the continent separately, but on special occasions met together when their individual schedules brought them near to one another. There were a few moments in Denver as each waited for their own plane connection, and there were a few hours in New York as both met with the publishers of their books, and there were the special few days in Toronto where their schedules permitted leisure before each would have to leave again, protecting, through constant daily effort, all that they had labored to produce, both individually and collectively. They spent their time together in the city, soaking in the magnificence of Toronto. They marveled at the glistening gold glass of the Royal Bank of Canada building and rode the subways from end to end, both north and south, east and west. Jonathan insisted that they sit in the head car, and he sat looking forward with the fascination of a small boy as the train rolled through the corridors beneath the bustling city above. Mariana watched the man, whose brilliant mind had served to inspire her, and smiled now, knowing that within him was that spark of curiosity that one must never allow to mature and grow old with the passing of summer.

They walked Bloor Street and Yonge Street, and shopped on Yorkville. They ate at an obscure but warmly inviting restaurant called the Bloor Street Diner, then explored the underground complex of shopping malls beneath the center of the city. They laughed at stuffed rabbits in shop windows, and Mari shed a tear for a small puppy in a cage that needed only to bring joy to a small boy or girl with its wagging tail.

They sat atop the revolving rooftop lounge of the Harbour Castle Hilton, and within forty-five minutes, revolved the three hundred and sixty degrees that revealed the full beauty of light and skyline that was the city, and darkness and star-filled sky that was Lake

Ontario. They dined on steak and lobster, and sipped coffee together, looking into each other's eyes that sparkled blue from the twinkling candle that burned between them. There was conversation on matters of business, on the newly evolving plans for the move of Camelot Productions to California, and on the deteriorating national and world economy. Jonathan spoke softly on times of prosperity followed by times of recession, with the ever-predictable return to prosperity, but at the cost of broken lives and battered souls who had unwittingly failed to provide for the heat of summer. Mariana shared with him her dreams and ambitions for improving the educational and political system, for teaching goal-setting and other worthy subjects to children, and for challenging governmental leaders to lead by example by demanding more of themselves than their constituents could possibly demand of them. And there were the moments of silence and mutual admiration, not for what the other had said or done, but merely for what the other was. It was at the end of one of those moments of silence that Mari quoted something she had read . . . something on the subject of friendship that had grown between the two of them.

"Friendship is the inexpressible comfort of feeling safe with someone else . . . having neither to weigh thoughts nor measure words," she said softly and with a smile that told him more than the words she had quoted.

They stayed long after most had left, to watch a gathering summer storm, as the lounge rotated to look across Lake Ontario for the third time. The lightning flashed twenty miles to the southwest, illuminating the sky long enough to reveal the distant clouds and cast a brief light upon the waters of the lake below them.

Mariana spoke on the greatness of the country in which they were visiting, and upon the greatness of their own America, in spite of the current times of challenge and disappointment.

"Could we lose it all, Jonathan?" She asked about the freedom, the independence they admired and shared, and the system of government that they had been discussing.

"Only if we don't protect it," he said. "Nothing is forever unless human commitment and attention make it so. What we, and those who came before us created, can be lost through neglect . . . by taking for granted."

"Not as long as the writers write and those who speak words of hope and encouragement have a voice, Jonathan. Not unless all of us give up and decide to settle for the lure of the beach.

"And not unless the Gloria Simons of the world speak longer and louder and are more convincing to the masses than people like us," she added.

"You know about Gloria?" he asked.

"I met her in Los Angeles several months ago and we—spoke briefly."

"I can't think of two people—two women—more totally opposite than you and Gloria. How did you get along?"

"We didn't," she said.

"She would move America in one direction, and you would move it in another. If she wins, we lose."

"And if we win?"

"We can't . . . we can only stay ahead. The Glorias are like the bugs and weeds. You can remove those that are after your crops today, but as soon as you stop the battle, as soon as you relax for just a moment, they're back again. There will always be a Gloria who is out to destroy freedom by supposedly trying to protect it. There will always be someone who seeks to protect the minority cause even at the risk of destroying the majority."

There was a half moment of silence as they looked into the black distance together.

"Jonathan . . . let's not let Gloria and what she stands for come to Toronto—not now . . . not tonight. She isn't here, Jon, and let's not bring her here with *our* thoughts. That's her best weapon, you know . . . she can force herself into our thoughts, but we don't seem ever to affect hers."

He smiled and reached across the table to place his hand on hers. They spoke of the coming end of summer and of the completion of Mariana's new book. They compared schedules from memory and planned when they would be together again. Finally they sat in silence, looking at one another with gratitude and feeling joy for the hours that still remained before them this night in Toronto.

The heat of summer remained but the green turned to gold and yellow as nature's cycle ushered in the autumn of the year. The days passed into weeks and with the parading children in costumes of witches and funny animals, the season of Thanksgiving was only a few weeks distant.

The two-day seminar on management and leadership had ended on a cool Sunday evening in the mountains of Western Maryland. The fifty-five couples who had spent the two and a half days with Jonathan and Mari had taken away enough wisdom, knowledge, and inspiration to last a lifetime. Some would perhaps use their new understanding to teach others. They had come from many areas—most from the middle Atlantic states, several from Chicago, a few from Florida, Tennessee, and Kentucky, and one from Bossier City, Louisiana. All had heard of the seminars conducted by Jonathan Locke from friends, relatives or business associates who had previously attended, but this was the first time that Jonathan had permitted anyone other than himself to teach at this special seminar. Mariana had deserved the opportunity, he told himself. She had mastered the skills of selling products and was becoming a master at selling ideas, as well. She had a sincere and persuasive manner that gave an uncommon power to her words. Those words, when blended with the emotion of Mariana York, enabled all who listened to *feel* as well as *hear* her ideas. Each would teach for nearly three hours before yielding the time to the other, and their style and wisdom complemented each other.

The last two members of the executive staff of Camelot Productions had left, and both Jonathan and Mariana sat on the railing of the sun deck that encircled the lodge. They faced westward toward the sun whose only proof of existence was a ruby red sky rising above the hills on the far side of the south branch of the Potomac River.

In the distance, the faint noise of tractors and farm equipment broke the silence as farmers brought in their remaining harvests before the cool breezes turned to winter storms. While the area around them fell into the shadows, the mountains behind them still glistened in yellow, red, and orange from the last rays of the sun that still reached the top of the mountain. The man and woman sat listening to crickets and watched hummingbirds dart with lightning speed as they prepared to nest for the coming night.

Down the valley, to the south of where they sat, they could see what looked to be a man and two young children loading hay into a wagon, rushing to beat the impending darkness. Mariana pointed to a large oak tree at the end of the clearing ahead of them, near the tree line that separated the property from the river where squirrels were gathering acorns and carrying their load into the tree trunk that would serve as their winter home.

All around them were signs, sights, and sounds of life forms scurrying to prepare for the season of short blustery days and long, cold nights. Some were bringing in their crops, yielded by their own efforts from tilling the soil during the previous spring while others merely worked to take advantage of nature's crops.

Both sensed that the seasons of opportunity and harvest were now behind them, and that this was their final attempt to prepare for the uncaring and unfriendly winter.

"It's been a hectic six months, Jon," she said.

"The office staff mentioned that between us we've spoken to over a quarter million people," he answered. "Two hundred and fifty thousand . . . in seven months."

There was a half minute of silence interrupted by the hoot of a nearby owl.

"And there are two interesting questions," she said finally. "What?"

"How well did *we* do and how well will *they* do?"

He zippered his jacket against the cool breeze and put his hands into his pockets.

"We did incredibly well. It was—or will be—our best year ever."

"And *they*?"

"We taught them to fish, Mariana. It's not our calling to feed them. Most will go through their lives attending one seminar after another, looking for someone to feed them one more time. A few will feed themselves and go onto affect others. How many? Who knows . . . a hundred . . . five hundred? To find one who is unique, you must share both ideas and time with many."

"Do you know what one man said to me just before he left tonight?"

Jonathan turned to look at her.

"He said that there were very few things he heard that he hadn't already heard, but very *many* things that he heard that he had long since forgotten."

Jonathan smiled. "They all once knew what they wanted to do— and what they wanted to become, but that's the way life is, Mariana. We know, or knew . . . we neglect . . . we forget . . . we fail. You and I are reminders, I guess, not teachers. You cannot teach what someone already knows. You merely persuade them to rediscover or to use what they've allowed to go to sleep."

"Know what?"

"What?"

"I'm cold. Can we go inside?"

He smiled, stood up and held his hands out to her.

After a feast of clam chowder and corn bread, they sat quietly in front of a warm, crackling fire, sipping coffee. Jonathan made word parallels between human circumstance and the season called autumn. "We reap in the fall what we've sown in the spring," he said. "If we're alone and broke and unhappy, it is simply because we missed a springtime somewhere. We decided to play, or sleep, or linger by a stream when the springtime of life presented us with opportunity. We decided to play until tomorrow, or sleep late, or watch the birds. We wait and delay and procrastinate until springtime passes us by. Then we awaken to find that the season of harvest is upon us and there are no crops—just barren fields and empty storehouses, and a coming winter for which we are totally unprepared. The bank account is empty, the rent is due, the creditors are calling, and our job is gone. That's the current American story, Mari. People are losing their jobs and discovering that when the job disappears, so do their values. They failed to grow while they had their jobs. Now they're losing their homes and what little savings they had, and they're sleeping in tents and in cars. Our country is in trouble—more serious trouble than it's been in for a while, and we've got to change the trend . . . not *they*, Mari, *we!*"

They shared insights long into the night, each writing new ideas not heard or thought of before into their journals. They laughed, they recalled, and they planned. Finally, in one of the periods of silence, sleep came to Jonathan Locke. It had been a long weekend—a weekend of work, of teaching how to learn and learning how to teach.

Mariana York lay next to her now silent Jonathan, a pillow behind her head that made her own sleep easy to find.

CHAPTER TWELVE:

The Nation

The move of Camelot Productions to Southern California began during the eastern snows of January. Washington, D.C., had experienced an uncommonly cold winter, and a white blanket spread from Canada to northern Georgia. People huddled together at bus stops for warmth and stood in doorways, shrinking from the wintry winds. Nature's life cycle had ceased and lay dormant. Only those who had prepared would survive in comfort— all others would regret, or shiver, and some would pray to their God for the strength to survive.

The mood of the nation had become as somber, as lifeless, and as threatening as the winter itself. The leading economic indicators of business suggested that an economic winter was indeed blanketing the nation. Unemployment began a rapid increase, rising beyond ten percent, and the interest rates for borrowed money had broken all records, increasing to twenty percent between Thanksgiving and Christmas.

The escalation of federal and state laws over a period of four decades had made the rewards of capitalism and the challenge of free enterprise an almost unattainable dream. Across America, businesses failed with such frequency that no one bothered to comment any longer. Family-owned small businesses that had come to be landmarks were giving in under the pressure of tight credit controls and rapidly escalating costs.

The cornerstones of the business community, the banking and financial institutions, were not immune from the effects of the recessionary spiral, and mergers among the smaller banks went almost unnoticed as public relations firms sold the mergers as new and positive steps designed to provide better service. Steel companies, feeling the economic pinch from cheaper imports, merged with oil companies who began showing decreased profits from declining sales. Enormous conglomerates were created nearly overnight as the strong swallowed up the weak, and by January of the new year, one government report suggested that eighty-five percent of the gross national product was owned, controlled, or in some way manipulated by less than one-tenth of one percent of the population. The value placed on the power of the people at the ballot box diminished, and few felt that they had any tool within their grasp for changing their own destiny. It was a time for recalling the words of President John F. Kennedy who, in earlier times of national crisis some two decades before, had said, "Those who make peaceful revolution impossible make violent revolution inevitable."

Within the political system, ethics, morality, honesty and integrity were not adjectives used by the populace for describing their elected representatives. Scandals within state and federal government structures became so common that those elected to serve the public were looked upon with suspicion and distrust. Unlike times of earlier national challenge, there seemed to be no clear voice of hope within government. There were no voices of Roosevelt with his soothing words and encouraging promise of a New Deal; nor did there seem to be a Kennedy leading a lost America to the threshold of a new frontier. Crowds gathered on street corners to ask, "What can America do for me?" No messiah arose with rhetorical genius to challenge the lost nation to cry out with the unified voice, "What can *we* do for *America*?" The voices of America were silent, asking in quiet and fearful tones, "What can we do to stay alive . . . to keep our homes . . . to save our jobs?"

To perpetuate the stagnation of business and demoralize the public attitude, there was the ever-present four-, five-, six-, seven-, and eleven o'clock news. The nation was inundated with a daily barrage of statistical data and on-the-scene coverage of any event that seemed to underscore the ultimate collapse of the republic. All good was attacked with only infrequent exceptions, and any suggestions of evil were seized by the ever-present minicams with the voraciousness of a hungry shark.

While nearly every business struggled to survive, a handful found themselves prepared to endure the wintry economic climate. Fewer still experienced unparalleled growth in spite of the business turbulence. One of those was Camelot Productions, whose founder and architect was Jonathan Locke. He had foreseen the impending difficulties, and had introduced a broad selection of products designed to provide hope and encouragement at a price that nearly everyone could afford. Three days before Christmas, he had held a press conference to announce that admission fees to his seminars and retail prices charged for his company's products were being reduced by twenty percent, and that he had given instructions to his management staff nationwide that no one was to be denied admission to the seminars, nor were products to be withheld from anyone who felt they needed them but who could not afford them. Seminar attendance increased fifty-eight percent, product sales jumped forty-three percent, and gross sales of all products and services rose eighty-six percent within five weeks. It was the personal philosophy of Locke that in good economic times people turned to self-development because they *chose* to, and in poor economic times they did so because they *had* to.

Americans needed to hear a voice of hope, and Camelot Productions was providing that voice. As months passed following the emerging friendship between Jonathan and Mariana, which had begun at Horseneck Beach nearly a year before, a slow and nearly undetectable change took place at Camelot. While Jonathan had reduced his personal speaking appearances, there was a simultaneous increase in the appearances of Mariana York. Locke began committing more of his time to new product development and marketing, and to master-minding the move to California. The change in strategy was accelerating the growth, popularity, and effectiveness of the shapely and brilliant woman who began to write profusely as she traveled from city to city. She was becoming a master of both the written and spoken word.

The declining mood of America was the inevitable consequence of years of opulence and excess. Deficit spending by one political administration after another had created the current climate. In the thirties, social and welfare programs were needed, and they were needed at any cost. In the forties, weapons were needed to wage war against nations determined to destroy America and its allies, and they were needed at any cost. In the fifties, government sought to get into business and to fund a multitude of laws designed to control and limit the creativity and ingenuity of the individual. The sixties had brought on the Vietnam conflict, and again, it was spending at any cost. And the seventies . . . the seventies seemed to bring on the final catalyst to a nation ripe for its day of atonement. The accumulated national debt, the meteoric rise of fuel costs that affected every segment of society, and government funding of such controversial issues as abortion and programs of questionable morality seemed to break the will of the nation to believe in itself. Politicians and even presidents were disgraced. Courts were interpreting laws in favor of criminality, always rationalized by claiming that the legal opinions were handed down for the protection of individual human rights. Organizations such as the Human Liberties Protective League became particularly influential, demanding legislation to enforce legislation, all of which multiplied the burden of debt that had to be paid. Every law, every program, every court case—including the protection of human rights—every weapon, investigation, welfare program, and government project had to be paid for, and payment was made with dollars rolling from the presses of the federal government—dollars whose real value diminished with every new program, law, project, or investigation that needed to be funded.

The philosophy of funding programs at any cost finally accumulated to a national debt of over one trillion dollars, and the generation that would one day be called upon to make the painful sacrifice of readjustment and reform had finally been born. The decade of the eighties entered the history books with a wave of economic, moral, and political turbulence. Sacrifice was finally necessary. Libraries, with their books of insight, answers, and inspiration, were closing due to the lack of funds. State and municipal services that had long been taken for granted were being discontinued. Families were breaking up as mothers were becoming working wives, leaving children to develop their minds from the direction provided by television and to feed their bodies with fast food and TV dinners. The only certainty was uncertainty. The only consistency was inconsistency. The only hope seemed to be an ambiguous faith that somehow, somewhere, someone would emerge to push a button that would lower interest rates, reduce unemployment, and increase productivity.

Indeed, a winter had descended upon America. It was a winter of discontent. It was a winter of doubt, of confusion, of recession. And it was a winter of diminishing faith by a nation whose greatest asset had always been its capacity to remain optimistic and to believe in itself. This strange winter saw Democrats blaming Republicans, Republicans refusing to cooperate with Democrats, and a populace losing its patience with both. There had been an election just two months earlier, and the nation had a new president. A new adminis-

tration was offering a new beginning, but the old problems seemed to
overshadow the political rhetoric and well-intentioned promises of the
nation's new leadership. Even before the president's inaugural address,
the vehement and condemning press had found fault with what they
had decided would be unworkable programs. News commentators
gathered to discuss, to dissect, to question, and to speculate. Those
who watched and listened to these self-appointed authorities grew
even more disenchanted, condemning the man and his intended plans
and programs even before they were implemented and given a fair
chance to succeed or fail. America wanted answers. America wanted
change, reform, prosperity; but the country and its people—whose
actions, greed, and apathy over the previous forty years had brought
about the current climate and circumstance—wanted its prosperity
now. It wanted it, even now, without sacrifice and without a commitment to necessary long-range programs. Labor unions wanted more.
Professional sports teams and individuals wanted more. Welfare
recipients wanted more. The poorer states and cities wanted more. And
so did the members of congress in whose hands were entrusted the
change people so desperately hoped for, so they voted themselves new
tax advantages and pay increases.

The new president called men and women to Washington in a
search for new ideas for solving old problems, and the grip of winter
became more intense. The nation needed an early springtime, but
the warming rays of the sun were blotted out by the gray clouds of a
winter that was not yet ready to relinquish its hold on a nation who
had been given its chance to enjoy and take advantage of spring.

Jonathan Locke knew of the challenge before him as well as the
challenge his country faced. He had studied history, government, and
the science of politics as part of his own process of self-education.
He had always been intrigued and fascinated by the potential that he
had seen lying mostly dormant in his country. His decision to move
his flourishing business to California was made at a time when other
businessmen were reducing their expenditures and abandoning their
dreams. But for Jonathan, the winter that now prevailed would one
day yield to a return of spring. The human race had come too far to
allow itself to be crushed by its own accumulative mistakes. What it
had twisted it could unravel, and what it had neglected it could correct.
He remembered the late nineteen fifties and the Russian Sputnik, how
neglect had placed the Soviets in a position of unexpected and shocking
superiority, and how it was feared at that time that with the almost

total absence of comparable technology and resources America would be blackmailed and held hostage by a nation whose new weaponry would peer down from the heavens and threaten free men to yield that freedom to a tyrannical empire whose superior discipline and genius had out-paced its own. In that era, the dark hours had awakened a sleeping spirit. The genius that was America had stood upright and had worked a miracle. The four flights of the Columbia space shuttle were final proof of what capacity America really had for improving the quality of life for itself and for the nations of the world.

And what was it that brought America from the brink of military, technological, and psychological defeat in 1957 to a new commitment for superiority in space just three years later—a commitment fulfilled when an American stepped onto the surface of the moon and looked back toward Earth as if to defy the earlier Soviet superiority? What had worked the miracle? Who had turned the key on the lock that had held human ingenuity in bondage? What had converted threat to fear, fear to action, action to result, result to hope, and hope to achievement? The Columbia space shuttle was the result . . . the effect, but what or who was the cause? Where was the real origin of America's success?

Jonathan Locke, and perhaps a few others, remembered a young senator from Massachusetts who, in the face of the overwhelming Soviet threat to world peace, and in his quest to gain the American presidency and write his name in the annals of history, had announced that it would be the objective of the United States to land a man on the moon by the end of the decade of the sixties. He had made that solemn and seemingly unattainable commitment at a time when the tech-nology for achieving that goal was non-existent. Indeed, his country had been barely able to successfully launch a space vehicle into orbit. The man had a vision and an eloquence of speech in an era when both vision and eloquence were most needed. He had not been among his country's most effective chief executives, but he had been among his country's most inspirational leaders at a time when inspiration was needed. What he failed to do so legislatively because of his brief tenure in office, he had compensated for in his one thousand days of oratorical brilliance and youthful fervor. His words, both spoken and written, had served to inspire Americans who had previously had no collective ambition or dream, and his words had given hope to West Germans who looked upon a Communist wall and Russian tanks with fear and uncertainty. The young man had done more with well-spoken words than most world leaders had ever done with the threat of sword and cannon. He had met the Cuban missile threat with a determination and eloquence that defeated an overwhelming and reckless attempt to invade the Western hemisphere with Eastern weapons and influence. Jonathan Locke knew clearly that what was needed in 1960 was needed again now. The nation did not need jobs and increased welfare. The nation needed a clear voice of reason and hope. The nation needed someone or something it could believe in. America had no challenges that Americans could not solve, but there was one significant difference between then and now. Then, the threat was primarily from a foreign power; now, the threat was from within . . . from apathy, from too many years of too much waste, and from a culture that found more attraction in escape than it did in responding to challenge. In this generation, the effort would require greater tenacity. Americans were now more suspicious of, and impervious to, political leadership than twenty years ago.

But the American spirit was asleep, not dead. It awaited only the proper conjunction of time, fate, circumstance, and a new messiah to return it to its predestined position of leadership amid a world of confusion and turmoil. The messiah, or at least its modern day equivalent, was silently at work—molding and being molded. The plan was in place . . . a plan whose purpose was the preservation of freedom and the rekindling of the American spirit. It was a delicate plan . . . one that must, for now, remain a closely guarded secret.

CHAPTER THIRTEEN:

The Complicity

H e sat with his chair turned away from the desk and toward the window. Outside, another Friday snowstorm had begun, the sixth consecutive weekend that the white blanket would cover the city. Jonathan's thoughts drifted beyond the white snow on the streets below to the white sand on the beaches of Acapulco, the city where his Mariana would be appearing for yet another speech within the hour.

It would be the last day he would spend in this office. Only a few pieces of furniture remained together with six cardboard boxes of notes and records that would be put on the same Los Angeles-bound plane with him the following morning. Within forty-eight hours, Camelot would be conducting business in California.

His thoughts had been drifting for nearly an hour. Eventually his mind turned to the new president who sat somewhere in the historical white building at sixteen hundred Pennsylvania Avenue. He could barely see the building through the falling snow.

His eyes grew heavy now. The last-minute planning and activity had permitted him but two hours sleep the night before. The office was silent and he was totally alone. Even the faint noise from the traffic outside was indiscernible, the low clouds and fog absorbing the sounds and reducing the view. His conscious mind ceased to function and his left hand twitched as his body sank deeper into the brown leather chair.

As if out of nowhere, the figure appeared before him. The man stood for a few moments silently observing the relaxed body resting in the chair.

"Good afternoon, Jonathan," the man said.

Jonathan's eyes snapped open, but his body remained still. "I never seem to know when to expect you," Jonathan responded.

"Which always gives me the advantage." The ever-present smile was there, as was the deep red apple that seemed to be so much a part of the bearded man who polished it against his lapel or his sleeves, or who tossed it like a boy with a baseball, or who sometimes just held it.

"Noah, it's been a while since you've chosen to visit me like this."

"Nearly a full month. Jon . . . a month. I've been quite busy, actually, and the plan is proceeding perfectly. I'm sorry I couldn't visit with you in November to keep you advised, but there were no deviations from the original details. It was picture perfect execution in every respect, as you no doubt observed."

"And the major participant was as you expected?"

"He is now fully informed. He was so convinced that his plan was the final answer that it took a bit longer than normal to prepare him. Only you and he know of the entire sequence and it must remain that way for some time yet."

"I understand. It's been difficult for me not to call him, but . . ."

"I know, but under the circumstances that probably wouldn't work. Anyway, you will be hearing directly from him soon. We must observe protocol, you know . . . this blasted Earthly protocol!" Jonathan smiled.

"Now, as embarrassing as it is for me to admit it, Jon, there is one individual being prepared for inclusion in the plan that I've not told you about. I fully intended to, but the two of you . . ."

Jonathan beamed and he interrupted.

"I think I may know who—well, no . . . go ahead."

"One of your own employees . . ."

Jonathan laughed. "I knew it, Noah. I knew it! Mariana York!"

Noah laughed, and the laugh subsided into a broad smile. "We thought you might need some close assistance, but we had not anticipated the personal involvement that seems to have transpired."

"Does it create a problem?" Jonathan's own smile disappeared because of the possible answer, and he waited the anxious few seconds for Noah's response.

"No, I shouldn't think so. I wouldn't want to interfere in the affairs of the heart, Jon . . . in the affairs of state and the affairs of the mind, but never the heart. However your situation with Miss Mariana may work out, you must say nothing of the plan just yet, you know."

"Of course, Noah. Trust me to keep the two separate."

"She responds and learns so very well, Jon. She has become very dear to me. It's that sparkle in her eyes, and that absolutely uncommon childish excitement."

"I know. She's a treasure, Noah."

"Jonathan, we're going to be calling upon her for a very special role in government. We'll have to wait for a bit, particularly in view of your relationship with her. I do hope it works out for you both."

"The arrangement between her and me or the—special role?"

"Your relationship. She's such a unique creature. And now that she's discovered and is using her special gift so well—well, she's one of our better miracles, and she can be so valuable.

"There are others you need know of, too, Jonathan. I'll keep you advised later on who the principals are, but one you'll need know about is Elliott Brendis. He's most influential, Jon, and since you'll soon be making his acquaintance I should forewarn you that he's quite aggressive. No doubt he'll be seeking you out to join *him*."

"What phase is he in?" Jonathan inquired.

"Phase Two."

"And how soon will Mari be going into Phase Two?"

"Soon, Jonathan—probably within a year . . . maybe sooner, which will certainly simplify *your* life a little more."

"Or make it more interesting."

"To be sure," Noah agreed.

They both laughed as two warm friends.

"I'm so happy that Mariana is included, Noah."

"She deserves it, Jonathan."

"She's more effective than I, Noah, and her books are . . . well, of course, you must know."

"We know, Jon. Anyway, time will dictate what we must do. By the way, one other thing." He began slowly rubbing the apple on his left sleeve again, looking at it as he spoke. "You need to know that this woman—this Gloria Simon—she's of the adversary, Jon."

"I see. I could have guessed it."

"We cannot help you. You must deal with her as best you can. She is to the adversary what Miss Mari is to us . . . an extremely talented and capable young woman."

"The adversary seems to have little trouble converting excellent people."

"Indeed. At the creation, we tilted things in his favor and he's taken full advantage of the human inclination for leaning toward negativity. He has taken some of our choicest souls and we just cannot allow ourselves to intervene. The principles of free choice must remain intact—even for you, Jon—even for those selected for involvement in the plan."

Jonathan was silent. In Noah's presence he would forever remain the student.

Noah continued. "We shall restore the proper direction of humanity, Jon, but we will not interfere with the right of the individual to choose between good and evil. We will give a gentle nudge occasionally, we will *point* people toward the use of their own individual gifts, but we will not *push* them. They shall use it and become *masters* of themselves or they shall lose it and forever remain the *slave* of themselves and of the adversary. Even you, Jonathan, even you . . ."

"I understand, Noah."

"Goodbye, Jon, and good luck with Miss Mariana. Treat her, if you can, with the delicacy and respect she deserves."

"If I can, or if I choose?"

"If you choose, Jon." He smiled and with the smile he vanished.

Jonathan sat quietly, pondering the words of his friend. Mariana York had not yet been given the power to recall with her conscious mind the visits with the strange and stately man in the white suit. *Her* growth was her *own* choosing, fed by the seed placed in her subconscious. She had not chosen to neglect the seed of wisdom and understanding. She had watered it with her own interest and fertilized it with her own hunger for personal growth. She was using her gift without the knowledge and recall of Noah, and therefore would not lose it. Her gift, like Jonathan's, was indeed special, and so would be her reward.

Jonathan Locke stood up and walked toward the door of his office. He looked back at his desk, smiled to himself, and closed the door behind him for the final time.

Noah would know where to find him, and someday he would know how to find Noah.

CHAPTER FOURTEEN:
The Request

The passing of four more seasons had occurred since Camelot Productions had moved its operations to California. It was winter again, but winter in California was different than winter in Washington. Outside the temperatures would reach the low seventies this day, while along the eastern seaboard the wind chill factor had dropped temperatures to single digit levels. Only the national unemployment rate, interest rates and inflation rates had moved into double digits.

It was a brilliantly clear Saturday morning in Orange County. Jonathan Locke looked out the window of his library to the snow-capped peaks of the Saddleback Mountains fifteen miles away and eight thousand feet above him. Camelot had celebrated its tenth anniversary the previous week and its first in California. The executive staff and their families had spent the January day on the beach. Today, while the sky was clear, the morning temperatures were crisp and the breeze from the ocean stronger than usual.

Jonathan had been forced inside for his morning cup of coffee and chose to settle in front of the warmth of the fireplace instead of walking the grounds of the Hill House. He had been up for nearly four hours, writing and researching. In another fifteen minutes, he expected a visit from Senator Elliott Brendis and his wife. The visit was somewhat mysterious and he had been told it would be short. The two had met several months before at a luncheon where both had been invited as guest speakers. They had developed a quick friendship that was now in its sixth month. The senator and his wife were driving north from a brief vacation in San Diego, and when he had called Jonathan two days before, the Hill House seemed to be the most convenient location for the meeting.

"Good morning, Jon." The voice of his wife brought a smile to his face and he turned and held his arms out to the woman who was walking across the room toward him.

"I heard the shower running and started a fresh pot of coffee. Want some?"

"Silly question," she said, their arms encircling one another in a good morning squeeze.

They sat in the breakfast room, sipping coffee and looking out through the sliding glass doors at the ocean less than a mile away.

"The senator and his wife should be here any minute," he said.

"Did he give you any indication of what he wanted?"

"None. From what I hear, Elliott is gaining a great deal of influence these days. For a freshman senator, he's really doing quite well."

He looked to his left and out the window of the family room to see the car entering the long driveway that led to the house from the cul-de-sac.

"They're already here," he said, drinking down the last bit of coffee in his cup.

She moved off quickly to the master bedroom while he ran water into the two cups before placing them into the dishwasher. Glancing out the window of the kitchen as he closed the door, he noticed the hawk circling above the brick barbeque pit near the slope just at the end of the large yard.

His wife came down the hallway from the bedroom and Jonathan walked forward to meet her in the mirrored entryway. They held each other close for just a moment, knowing that for the next little while they must restrain themselves ever so slightly in view of the company they would be in. She pulled her head back slightly to look into his eyes.

"Is there anything I should know . . . what to say, or not say, I mean?"

"Absolutely nothing. Just be yourself, Mari," he said smiling and kissing her lightly on the lips, taking care not to smudge the freshly applied lipstick.

The kiss was interrupted by the ringing doorbell. Through the glass panel on the left side of the large door, he could see the silhouette of his friend.

"Elliott—Nancy, how good to see you. Come in." He shook his friend's hand warmly as they entered, and Mari greeted the senator's wife.

Jonathan took his guests on a tour of the house while his wife went to the kitchen to make a fresh pot of coffee. It took nearly five minutes to go through the three thousand square feet of the single story home, and both the senator and his wife were as fascinated by the home and the majestic three hundred degree view as were all the guests who had visited in the eleven months they had been living there.

"Why don't we sit in the breakfast room. It's bright and maybe we'll see the animals wandering by," Mrs. Locke suggested. She explained the frequent appearances by deer, possum, rabbits, roadrunners, and other visitors from the surrounding countryside.

The four reminisced and updated one another on their respective careers for twenty minutes before the senator's wife interrupted.

"Hey, you only have thirty minutes, Senator. Whatever you need to discuss with Jonathan . . ."

"Thanks, Nancy. Can we have a few moments, Jon?"

The conversation broke into two groups. The women moved into the living room while the senator and Jonathan went into the library. Jonathan seated himself in the deep leather chair leaving the couch for Elliott Brendis.

"Jonathan, I want to come right to the point." He crossed his legs and spread his arms across the back of the couch. "I would like you to consider running against Tom O'Reilly for the senate next year."

Jonathan Locke did not change his expression, nor did he move his eyes from his friend.

"You'd make a fine senator, Jon," Brendis continued. "Your books and your reputation have already created for you a national following. You'd be a natural and a splendid asset to the party."

Jonathan glanced for a second at the green carpet and then back to his guest who waited for a response.

"Well, Elliott—I'm flattered, of course, that you would come to me with such a suggestion. I suppose I've thought about the possibilities of public office a thousand times in the past ten years. But . . . well, I really don't think it would be right for me even to consider it."

"Jon, we've known one another—what, less than a year? Listen for a minute. Have you looked around the country lately at our congressional leadership? In all truth, there isn't a voice out there anywhere that commands the respect of the party, or of the people."

"I don't know if that's a condemnation of the quality of those in congress or a condemnation of those who elected them, Elliott."

"Well, either way, Jon, I'm being very serious. I didn't come here this morning to stroke your ego. I came here to make a serious proposal on something to which I have given considerable thought. Believe me, it wouldn't be easy, but you're highly electable. All you need do is to think about it and then make the commitment to go for it. I've already discussed the matter with some of the key people in Washington—you could count on some influential support, Jon."

Jonathan leaned forward now on the edge of his chair. "Elliott, I'm not treating your proposal lightly. It's obvious that you're quite serious, but—"

"Deadly serious, Jonathan. This country is in trouble and it needs someone who brings a new look and a new voice—someone who speaks the language of the people, Jon, someone who can give the nation a reason for believing again."

"There are a few things wrong with that, Elliott."

"Oh?"

"First, a senator has a primary responsibility to his constituents—in this case, the twenty-three million people of the state of California. *That* should be his primary area of concern—not using the office of U.S. senator for some national purpose that is intended to lead to an even *higher* office. That may be one of the reasons why congress is not as effective as it could be, Elliott. We may have *too many* who are personally ambitious and *not enough* who are satisfied with serving the people and the nation.

"Second, you say we need someone who can give us a reason for believing again. My question might be, 'What's wrong with the man we just elected as our president, Elliott?' He's an honest and capable man, with experience in government. Why not give our support to him and stop looking for some undiscovered messiah to come along and cure us of our problems?"

"Jonathan, of course he's capable . . . and honest, but surely you of all people know that there's an intangible factor involved in successful political leadership. Not very many men and women have had it, Jon, but you do, and America needs it. Call it poise, charisma, charm . . . whatever. With it, you're providing political leadership; without it, you're a politician."

Jonathan smiled and sat back in his chair again. "What are you, in your judgment, Elliott . . . a political leader or a politician?"

The senator gave a single burst of laughter. "I, Jon Locke, am a man wise enough to spot talented people and clever enough to know of my own limitations."

"Well, Elliott, I don't know. I have my own plans for meeting some of what I identify as the needs of our country. Government fascinates me, and I must admit that I'm attracted toward it, but my initial response to your proposal would be that I think I can be of greater benefit from *outside* of government. So many times I've watched talented and well-intentioned people run for office, but the journey seems to have a tremendous price. By the time they achieve the office, they've made too many commitments and promises to too many people and they must back their debts to their supporters by voting for their *obligations* rather than voting with their conscience.

"Jonathan, I know what you're saying." Brendis was on his feet now, pacing excitedly across the carpet. "But imagine what government *could* be like. Imagine if somehow people with vision and ability, people whose only ambitions were the creation of a better America, were to capture the majority of the house or the senate. We could turn it all around, Jon. But we must begin somewhere. To have many, you must begin with one." Brendis had no idea of how prophetic his words were, Jonathan thought.

"Elliott, I've spent more time pondering the possibility than you might imagine. I have a very good friend that I spend time with on occasion, and that subject always seems to work its way into the conversation."

"Anyone I might know?"

Jonathan looked serious for a moment, then smiled. "Possibly, Elliott. If not, then I'm sure you'll be meeting him one day. But back to your proposal. My initial response is to offer my gratitude for the suggestion, but to pass on the idea for now. However, I'll let it settle for a while and we'll discuss it some more later, if that's okay with you."

Two rooms away, Mariana and Nancy had been discussing matters of a different nature. Mari had shown Nancy Brendis the photographs of her honeymoon trip with Jonathan. Nancy had inquired about how she had managed to meet and eventually marry a man with such a busy schedule and with so many ambitions and commitments. Mari told her about Philadelphia and how she had walked into a wrong office on a cold winter morning over three years ago. She spoke of the admiration and respect she had always felt for this unique man who had introduced her to herself and who had guided her into the difficult disciplines for becoming a person of value. She showed Nancy her worn copy of the book Jonathan had given her when they had first met, telling the story with the intensity and zeal of a child who had just made a wonderful discovery. Nancy Brendis found herself as impressed with how the story was told as she was with the story itself.

The door of the library clicked open and the muffled male voices became clear.

" . . . give it some serious thought, Jon," the senator was saying.

"Indeed, I will. Call me on Friday while I'm in New York, Elliott. I'll give you my answer then."

"Where will you be staying?"

"The Waldorf-Astoria."

The phone rang. Mariana started to excuse herself, but Jonathan moved to the extension in the master bedroom and answered before the third ring. He spoke only briefly before calling to his wife.

"Mari, it's for you."

"Is it someone I can call back in a few moment, Jon?"

"Not this call, my love. I suggest you take it."

"Who is it?"

"The White House."

"Jonathan, who is it?" She walked to the extension phone in the family room. The Brendis' had been moving toward the front door but had stopped now because of the expression on Jonathan's face. Mari's voice was clear.

"Hello—this is Mariana Locke speaking." There were several seconds of silence. "Yes . . . Yes, it is . . . of course."

At the subtle urging of Jonathan, his guests followed him into the family room. Mari looked toward them, cupping the mouthpiece with her right hand. "It is the White House, Jon," she said. Nancy Brendis forgot about the plane her husband was to catch and slowly sat down on the edge of the couch. Jon and Elliott exchanged short glances. Mari started to speak to them, but quickly removed her hand from the phone to respond to something that had obviously been said to her.

"Yes? Yes, sir . . . Yes it is . . . Fine . . . Fine, Mr. President." Nancy Brendis spoke softly to her husband after their eyes met. "Could it be for you? Did you give anyone the number here, or . . ."

"Yes, sir." There was another short period of silence as Mari listened intently, momentarily unaware of the existence of anyone else in the room with her.

"I don't have my calendar here in front of me, Mr. President, but I'm certain I can manage it."

She now reached for the pen that lay next to the phone and began making a note while listening.

"Yes, sir . . . I will . . . I'm sure he can, Mr. President . . . Yes . . . Yes. Thank you for calling. Yes, I will, sir . . . Yes, sir. Goodbye."

She placed the phone back in its cradle, stood frozen for a moment, then turned to look at her husband. "It was the White House, Jon . . .

it was President Reardon. He wants us to come to the White House on Monday." There was an expression of confusion on her face—confusion mixed with shock and a hint of disbelief.

She looked at her husband closely.

"Jonathan, you wouldn't trick me, would . . . Of course you wouldn't. That was the president," she said, pointing to the phone and staring, both recalling and recognizing the distinct voice.

Jonathan Locke's mind scanned the possibilities. Remembering the subject of the conversation with his friend in the library only moments before, he looked toward the senator. Brendis, suspecting the thoughts that were weaving their way through Jonathan's probing and imaginative mind, answered the unspoken question.

"No, Jon, it had nothing to do with that. It's entirely coincidental. I've never mentioned it to the president."

"Mentioned what?" Mari looked back and forth between the two men—one with a quizzical smile on his face, the other looking slightly embarrassed.

"Nothing," Jonathan said. "What was it all about?"

She looked again at the phone then back at her husband. "He wants me—he wants us to come to Washington the day after tomorrow—to the White House."

Jonathan looked again at his friend, who obviously felt uncomfortable. "Are you certain, Elliott?"

"Jon, I swear to you . . . I had no idea—honestly!"

"What did he say, Mari?"

"Nothing—I mean . . . let me see . . . Someone will call this afternoon to make the final arrangements, but we're to visit him Monday morning."

Her husband shrugged his shoulders slightly and raised his hands upward slightly. "That's all?"

"Well, no. He asked how I was and . . . and he said that he hated to ask us to leave the sun of California for the snows of Washington, and—that's all."

She looked at Nancy, then at the senator, her mind returning now to the Hill House. "Oh my!" she said, looking at Elliott Brendis. "I forgot to tell him you were here."

"Well," Nancy Brendis said with a sigh that turned to a bright smile, "surely some kind of congratulations must be in order, Mari . . . Congratulations!" she exclaimed heartily, standing up and extending her hand to Mariana.

"Indeed," Elliott said. "I haven't seen the president in nearly two months. Perhaps you can get me an appointment while you're there."

The four laughed and, after several dozen sensible and nonsensible explanations and speculations, the senator and his wife departed. Jonathan and Mariana Locke waved a final farewell from the driveway before turning to look at each other, pondering both the mystery and the possibilities. They slowly walked back toward their house on the hill where they would await the ringing phone that might shed some light on the short and certainly unexpected call. They were teachers, among other things, on the subject of patience and concentration, but the hours ahead would surely test their ability to apply that which they so often taught to others.

CHAPTER FIFTEEN:

The Journey

The limousine pulled onto the highway leading from Dulles International Airport to the nation's capital. It would be a forty-five minute drive, one that both Mariana and Jonathan Locke had made many times before, but always separately and always after a speaking tour or business trip for Camelot Productions. They rolled eastward now for an appointment with the president of the United States, the purpose of the meeting still unknown to either of them. The staff driver had been courteous and friendly, but offered nothing during the brief conversation at the airport that would shed any light on what might lay ahead.

The outlying suburbs of the Virginia side of Washington had a countryside atmosphere. The trees had lost their leaves months before, and the gray and black branches blended into the barren acres of farmland and the grayness of the January sky. There had been an unusually warm day since the Saturday storm and the barren ground was moist as if from an early spring rain.

Five hours had passed since the well-tanned couple had left Los Angeles International Airport. They had spent most of the day before and the five-hour plane trip reading articles written about the man they would soon meet. Mari had been surprised to discover that her husband seemed to know so much about the man who was now president. He had been more informative than her own hurried research, pointing out

Reardon's views, his relationship with congress, his past policies and record as Governor of California, and the philosophy of his economic, national, and international programs. He had become an extremely controversial president, largely because he was an extremely opinionated and determined man who would not permit even political expediency to move him from the course he had set out to pursue.

Jonathan Locke continued to speak to his wife about the president's programs even now, as the car rolled along Route 50 toward Washington, D.C.

"He believes that a competitive society, such as ours, will always cause those who are successful to be looked upon with envy and anger by those who are not," he explained. "He also believes that difficult economic times like these require that incentives be given primarily to those who sit at the top of the economic ladder—the corporations, and those who run and control them—so that those businesses can grow in spite of a receding economy and offer jobs to those who would otherwise be unemployed."

Mariana Locke looked at her husband. "That's what 'supply side' or 'trickle-down' economics is all about, isn't it?"

"That's the basics of it," Jonathan answered.

"I can easily see why those who are struggling or those who are unemployed or on fixed incomes are becoming so angry and impatient . . . it looks as though government is taking from those who need it most and giving to those who need it least."

She had said it in a way that suggested her sympathy was with those who spoke out against the policies of the man they were discussing.

Jonathan looked at her and smiled slightly. "It's controversial, no doubt about that," he agreed. "It's sometimes been hard for those who support his programs to defend them with vigor, and those who do openly defend them are becoming more and more unpopular."

"Things that are necessary are seldom popular," Mariana said after a pause for silence. "I can easily sympathize with people who think that those who are doing well are doing so at their expense." She looked straight ahead through the closed compartment window that gave privacy between them and the driver.

"I once thought it would be a good idea to take the wealth of America and divide it up evenly among everyone so that each person would have a more equal chance." she commented, still looking straight ahead.

" Oh?" Jonathan sounded interested but not shocked that his wife might have once believed in the efficacy of such an idea. "Of course," she answered, "if you're behind on your electricity bill, dodging creditors, and always lying to your friends about why you can't do this or that, it sometimes seems unfair that so few should have so much."

There was silence for a moment before she spoke again. "Jon, I've heard a lot of reporters commenting that President Reardon is a 'rich man's president,' that he gets most of his advice from the wealthy. Is that true?"

"Probably, but *who* should he get advice from? If you wanted the best advice on how to turn the economy around, who would you go to?"

"Good point. I agree."

She turned to look out the window to her left as the car stopped at a traffic signal. In the adjacent lane she saw a well-aged station wagon, looking the worse for its years. As she gazed at the occupants of the car, her eyes met those of a young woman sitting next to the car window. Her youthful features were overshadowed by eyes reflecting a hopelessness and confusion that Mari well remembered. She held an infant over her left shoulder, patting its tiny back with her right hand. Behind her were three children playing in the back seat, and next to her the stoop-shouldered man who Mari assumed to be her husband. Blue smoke fumed from beneath the engine of the car and a coat hanger had been inserted in the dented fender, serving as a substitute antenna for a radio that probably didn't work anyway.

The woman stared at her, then looked away to study the trim lines of the Cadillac limousine. For a brief second she looked back at Mariana, whose fur collar lay smoothly across her shoulders and whose glistening blond hair seemed like smooth silk. The eyes spoke of envy, anger, and jealousy, but the lips gave a faint smile of courtesy for this woman of beauty and apparent opulence. Mariana smiled back and raised the fingers of her left hand slightly in a gesture of almost embarrassed greeting. The small boy in the back seat held up a stuffed Snoopy whose original whiteness had long ago become dulled, and he flapped the black ear of the dog at Mari who smiled in turn. In his young eyes was an obvious sparkle that would diminish with the passing years of living in the paths worn by his parents, and their parents before them.

The light turned green and the Cadillac pulled smoothly and easily away from the tired and reluctant green station wagon whose worn clutch had caused it to stall. Mari did not look back. Behind her was a picture that had, for a fleeting moment, revived painful memories of a life she was racing to outdistance.

Her husband's question brought her mind immediately back to the conversation.

"Do you remember *The Parable of the Talents*?" he asked. "The Bible story?"

"Yes. Only vaguely. I remember it from Sunday School when I was a young girl. Why do you ask?"

"Well, you mentioned the concept of dividing up the money in America equally among everyone so as to give each person a fairer chance."

She interrupted her husband. "Let me guess. Within a short time, the money would all end up right back where it was . . . the rich being rich and the poor being poor all over again?"

"That is true, but it isn't what I was going to . . . it's not quite the same as the economic message in *The Parable of the Talents*." She continued to look at her husband with obvious interest in the point he wanted to make and he glanced at her, crossing his legs in the spacious passenger compartment and continuing. "The story tells of a master who had three laborers. He was about to leave on a trip for several months, so he called the three laborers together and advised them that he wanted to give them the opportunity to become a little more independent—to test their ability to practice the things he had been teaching them about life and business over the years.

"To the first man, the master gave five talents . . . a talent being a piece of money in those days. To the second man, he gave two talents. And finally, to the third man, one talent. The master advised each to find some way to take the money, put it to work and see what they could make it do for them . . . as an investment, or whatever.

"The story says that later on, the master came back from his trip, called the three men together and said, 'Okay, tell me what you've done with the talents—the investment capital I gave to you.'

"The first man, the one with the five talents, said, 'Well, I invested it, watched over it, did some of the things you taught me, and instead of five talents, I now have ten.' He reached into his pocket and showed the money that he had doubled. All of this, of course, made the master quite happy.

"Then he asked the second man what he had done with his two talents, and was told much the same story: it had been invested and, with the passing of time, the talents had doubled from two to four. The master, of course, was happy that this second man had had such great success with a fairly modest amount of talents. He, like the first man, had doubled it.

"The master then turned to the last man, the one to whom he had given the single talent. To this laborer he asked the same question—the result that had been obtained from his use of the one talent. To the master he reported this story. Because of his interest in security, he had taken the talent, wrapped it in a cloth and buried it in the ground so that it would remain safe. Upon hearing of the master's return, he had gone to the place, removed it from the ground and put it into his pocket to return to the master. After telling of his use of the talent, he removed the cloth from his pocket, extracted the talent from its folds, and held it up for his master to see, a gleam of pride showing from his eye.

"The master looked at him for but a moment and then said, 'Take the talent from this man and give it to the man who now has ten.'"

Jonathan glanced at his wife and found her looking at him and listening intently. "You see, my love, most people would think that his act of taking the talent from the man who had only one talent and giving it to the man who now had ten was an unfair and inconsiderate deed by the master, right?"

She nodded affirmatively. He was discussing something in a way she had not before considered and knew it was not a time to interrupt, but a time to listen.

"Mari, those who *have*, must—if history and the teachings are true—those who *have*, must receive even *more*. For whatever the reason, the system seems to be set up that way. What happened to the man back there in the Bible story seems terribly unfair, I know, but it's almost as though those who *have* much will *receive* much. It's just that those who *aren't* doing well are of the opinion that it's at *their* expense."

Mari chose to speak now. "And it *isn't* at their expense, Jon. It isn't. It seems that way, I know, but it isn't. Before I met . . . no—when I met you, I was of that very opinion . . . the opinion that somehow the system owed me an opportunity. I know better now, but back then, I never would have understood this conversation. I would have thought you to be an arrogant, self-centered and greedy person for suggesting that my poverty, my poor circumstances, were my fault."

"Did I suggest that just now?"

"No, not just now, but everything we teach and write reinforces that. Your—your *Parable of the Talents* . . . of taking from the man with little and giving it to the man with a lot . . . it's not the system that's wrong, it's what we *are*, Jonathan."

She looked out the window and pondered what she had just said and what she wanted to add.

"Do you know . . . once, when things were going particularly bad for me, I went to one of the counselors at school, a friend of mine, and we spent hours talking about my dilemma and all the things that had been happening to me. I asked her if she could give me some answers on *why*. Do you know what she said?"

"What?"

"Things like that seem to happen to people like you." Jonathan burst into laughter and Mari laughed along with him. She could laugh about it now. When it was first said to her, however, she took it as an insult and she told Jonathan that.

"Of course you would . . . take it as an insult, I mean."

"We're so often hurt by the truth, Jon. If only we could all accept truth and then place it under the microscope . . . to look for *why* it's true, not *whether* it's true."

There was silence for several minutes as the limousine entered the western suburbs of the city. Both Jon and Mariana pointed out things they had seen when their lives followed separate but parallel paths. Then there was another short period of silence.

"Jonathan, the poor person will never accept the fact that their circumstance is *their* fault. I'm beginning to believe that our seminars and books, the things we do, will most benefit those who need it least and will least benefit those who need it most."

"There are exceptions, Mari."

She thought for a moment, then smiled. "Anyone in particular that you're thinking of?"

She lifted the burgundy-colored leather briefcase from the jump seat in front of her, placed it on her lap and removed several papers from inside. She glanced through the pages briefly, then handed them to her husband.

"You'll need to know that I sent this to the president a few months ago." She watched as her husband looked through the pages. Knowing it would take several minutes for him to read them, she turned slightly to her left toward the window, as if to signal Jonathan that she would not interrupt him until he had finished.

Jonathan began with the first page. It had been written on Thanksgiving Day—their first Thanksgiving together.

"I write to you, Mr. President, being fully aware that your eyes shall not, in all probability, read these words. While that fact causes me to consider that my efforts are yet another exercise in incentives so that business may again expand, thus employing those who are now unemployed.

"It is right, sir, to reduce significantly the expenditure of tax funds on ill-conceived welfare and assistance programs whose only benefit is to take away the dignity and independence of those who accept those charities.

"It is right that busing to achieve racial equality should be abolished, and it is right that those who choose to pray in our schools should be extended that privilege and that those who wish to refrain should be given that freedom as well.

"But while these and other issues you stand for are right, they are also unpopular, for they call for sacrifice and they call for the passage of sufficient time before results can be obtained. And therein lies your great dilemma, Mr. President. Americans—and indeed all mankind—are driven by both impatience and greed. We want the benefits that your programs will produce, but we do not want to be among the multitude who must sacrifice. We want the rewards of low interest rates, reduced taxes and decreased inflation—we want it all but we want it now. We are like the man who turned to his god that he might learn the value of patience and in praying said, 'God, grant me the gift of patience, but give it to me now.'

"As a nation, we seem to be unable to understand that the errors and consequences of nearly five decades of excesses and inequities cannot be eliminated within two years. It has been said that a fleeting moment of neglect can cause a lifetime of repair. Our extravagances and excesses have made it necessary for us to commit ourselves to a sustained program of many years involving many sacrifices to bring about a return of normalcy. For this generation, normalcy must be interpreted as our continued efforts directed toward permanent change.

"This generation must work as never before, not seek a thirty-five hour work week.

"This generation must commit itself to exploration, not the temporary remedy of conservation.

"This generation must rediscover pride in the American system, not turn to another that offers a quick solution to difficult affairs.

"This generation must pay the price of providing an adequate defense against men and nations committed to our destruction.

"This generation must rediscover the magic of dreams, the value of commitment, the rewards of effort and the invigorating spirit of patriotism.

"This, and all future generations of Americans, must embrace an individual and collective philosophy of self-development, that we might tap the depth of intellectual and philosophical genius that resides within us, collectively and individually. We must seek to become obsessed with the pursuit of our own talents. We must read more, try more, cooperate more and commit ourselves more to worthy objectives than at any other time.

"Mr. President, the clock is ticking for us all, and for the very nation that brings us together in a common bond. Being American by itself gives no assurance of success and achievement. Being a free and democratic nation gives no assurance of the continuation of freedom. We stand at the crossroad of progress and decline, and only our thoughts and our beliefs will, in the final analysis, dictate the course we shall choose to follow. We need to discover the truth that thoughts attract circumstance and that we alone must select between commitment and compromise, between the encouragement or the condemnation of one another, and between the belief in ourselves and our nation or the doubt that we will successfully prevail.

"The clock ticks, Mr. President, and neither God nor nature, nor our critics can or will intervene to correct our errors. We alone hold our future in our own hands and time is now against us. If we are not willing to stand up for ourselves, then who will do it for us?

"Your decisions to correct the failures of the past are a race against time, Mr. President, but your moments of despair and disillusionment must not permit you to lose perspective of your original dreams for 'a new beginning' for America. You must cling to the words of the man who appropriately wrote, 'Those who do not learn from the mistakes of the past are condemned to repeat them.'

"I offer you, sir, a single thought of encouragement . . . If not us, who; if not now, when?

"God bless you, Mr. President, and God bless our great republic!"

—Mariana York

Jonathan finished the letter, uncrossed his legs, and reshifted his weight on the seat. She knew it was a signal that he had finished and turned again to look at him.

"What do you think?"' she asked.

"I think I now know why we're sitting in this limo headed toward the White House to see the man," he answered.

"But what's in the letter that would make him invite us? I mean, it's only a letter of opinion and encouragement . . . at least that's all I meant it to be."

"Well, who knows," he said. "Maybe he's decided something special. Maybe you planted the seed of a new thought. Maybe . . . maybe he thinks it's time to look at something new. Well, let's put it this way, little one. I think that perhaps this day was pretty much destined, part of some plan that you're part of but just don't know about yet."

"What do you mean? A plan for what?"

"Nothing specific. Life is full of plans and directions. It's just that we aren't aware of the patterns and plans; we can only respond to them—that is, if we're *smart*, we respond to them."

"Jon . . . why . . . what made you call me *little one*?"

"No reason. Why, don't you like it?"

"No, that's not . . . I don't know that I've ever been called that by anyone before, and yet it somehow sounded so familiar, like . . . like I've heard it . . . somewhere before."

He didn't answer.

The Washington Monument stood high above the Lincoln Memorial three miles ahead of them and a few miles to the south. Mari remembered the cherry blossoms that in years before had signified the end of winter and the beginning of spring. Indeed, springtime seemed now to be so long ago and winter so never ending—especially to those who lived here, who endured the cold and grayness. To others, like Mariana and Jonathan, winter—whether the winter of climate or the winter of adversity—was a condition that could be escaped from. What made them unique individuals was their awareness that winter was a time to study, to prepare, to ponder and reflect in preparation for the spring. And here, in this season, in this city, springtime was not far away. The blossoms indeed would return as they had each year since even before there had been a Lincoln Memorial or Washington Monument and, similarly, the era of prosperity and optimism would one day return as well.

Within another five minutes, instead of passing by the White House, Mariana and Jonathan Locke found themselves the passengers in an automobile that turned into a driveway, drove past the guard house and rolled slowly toward the south side of the building that served as the private residence of the Chief Executive of the United States of America. Mariana looked through the tinted window of the limousine across the south lawn. She toyed lightly with the gold chain around her throat with one hand, unconsciously reaching out for reassurance from Jonathan with the other.

CHAPTER SIXTEEN:

The Invitation

"Good afternoon. I'm Fletcher Kennedy, special assistant to the president. President Reardon will be just a moment," he explained with a smile that was both assuring and genuine. "He's with the Egyptian Ambassador and they were just finishing their business when I stepped out to meet you. He—"

The door opened to the left of where Mari and Jonathan sat. Fletcher Kennedy turned now and stepped aside as though his interrupted comment no longer had any significance. He looked back at the Lockes, smiled and excused himself, knowing that his presence was now dwarfed and made unnecessary by the entry of a man whose physical size seemed consistent with the office he held.

The man nodded briefly to Kennedy, then walked the few remaining steps toward the couple, his two arms outstretched in a gesture of welcome. The Lockes stood immediately in an unconscious gesture of respect.

"Mariana—Jonathan, welcome to Washington!" He shook hands with them and then moved behind the large desk. He waited for them to sit down before lowering himself into the high-backed leather chair.

"You'll forgive us for asking you to leave the sunshine of Southern California—and on such short notice." His smile was so warm and sincere that it was impossible not to smile in return and grant the forgiveness he so courteously asked for.

"Somehow, Mr. President, being asked here, to this room, makes everything—even the short notice and the mystery of it all—rather insignificant," Mariana said.

The president's eyes shifted to Jonathan. "And Jonathan—your presence here is appreciated as well, particularly in view of your schedule and responsibilities."

"It worked out well, sir. I had arranged for a few days off. There was no inconvenience."

"Wonderful! Not that I will ignore your feelings, Jonathan, but for the moment my comments will be directed toward Mrs. Locke."

"Of course," Jonathan answered, glancing momentarily at his wife.

President Reardon opened a folder lying on top of his desk and removed the contents. Mariana immediately recognized the document, though it took Jonathan a moment longer. The couple exchanged a knowing smile.

"I'll admit, Mariana that most correspondence directed to me gets read by someone on my staff because . . . well, it just wouldn't be possible for me to read it all. But once in a while, contrary to public opinion, I do read some of the mail coming in. This letter of yours, dated . . . uh—November 24, being one that I've read. I don't mind admitting, my wife has read your books—and yours, Jonathan—and recommended them to me when I told her about your letter. You might say we've become fans of yours since coming to Washington."

He moved his chair closer toward the desk and laid the document down on the desk top. Placing his forearms on the edge of the desk, he leaned forward slightly and studied Mari's letter for several seconds. The fingers of his right hand unfolded now, and he used them to scan vertically down the page. As the search continued, they moved in slight jerks, his lips moving ever so slightly as his mind verbalized the words.

Mariana Locke watched the process and studied the man. The deep lines in his forehead had not been evident in the pictures she had seen of him, nor was the slightly detectable birthmark just above his right eyebrow. It was darker than the well-tanned skin surrounding it—almost purplish. It seemed odd that the president should have a birthmark, she thought to herself, but then this was the first time that she had consciously thought of a president as being a person. He removed a Cross pen from his jacket pocket and drew a line under something she had written on the page. She had never thought that the president might also use the same gold Cross pen that she carried.

"Did either of you have the chance to hear my television speech outlining my proposals for the budget?" He looked first at Mari then at Jonathan. The thick dark eyebrows raised, making the lines in his forehead deepen.

"Yes, I did," Mari answered. She looked toward her husband who nodded affirmatively and responded with a simple, "Yes."

"The last line of my speech, Mariana. Did it mean anything to you in particular?"

"Well—yes it did . . . but . . ."

"It should have," he said, tapping the gold pen on the page of her letter. This line of yours was in there. Now, I know this line has been used . . . written by somebody else, but your use of it in your letter was most appropriate, and I decided to end my speech with it. It's a darn good line, this . . . this . . . 'If not us, who; if not now, when' . . . a good line. And your letter, Mariana, was a darn good letter. In fact, I started reading your book the evening after my speech on the economy. It was the book that got me thinking about you, Mari, and about your views and how those views apply in our current world."

He looked closely at her now and his face became more serious. But even with the serious expression and the wrinkles that seventy years had placed there, the boyishness remained on his face. The head tilted to the left, and with a slightly sheepish look, he spoke.

"I'm going to probably scare the devil out of you, Mrs. Locke, but I have an extremely serious proposal to make to you in a few moments. For some time now, I've been concerned about the ability of our government to effectively govern. I had some major programs in mind when I first took this office, but at best—and I hate to admit this—the most we've been able to do is pass some legislation which has replaced the hold that government has had on people. I frankly don't believe that our people need or want someone sitting here in Washington telling them what's good for them—what they can and cannot do. In the final analysis, the people themselves are the best judge of what they should or could do. I believe that if you give people the freedom to act and to bear responsibility for those acts, then the results will be far more beneficial for everyone than if government tried to control the lives of its people. How do you feel about that?"

She hadn't expected to be asked a question and felt a sudden surge of discomfort as her mind raced to formulate a response.

She shifted her weight slightly in the soft chair and her left hand moved unconsciously to tug at the gold chain around her neck.

"I couldn't agree more, Mr. President," she said finally. "It is individual creativity and talent combined with the magic of the free enterprise system that gave America its position of influence in the world. We once gave rewards to people in proportion to their willingness to take risks, assume responsibility for their actions, and produce worthy results. To be very candid, sir, we've gotten off track somehow. We provide incentives for those who do *not* produce, we've gotten overcautious about taking risks and, for the most part, we've become an irresponsible society."

"Irresponsible?"

"Yes, Mr. President—irresponsible and undisciplined. But it isn't really the total fault of our people. Over the years, government has assumed, or perhaps I should say, seized, so much responsibility that people feel out of control of their own destiny. And when things go bad for them, they blame others for it—including, of course, the government."

"Are they justified in blaming others, do you think?"

"Of course not!" Her response was immediate and emphatic. Since the discovery of herself, she had developed an intolerance for those who tended toward rationalization of their pitiful circumstances.

"Government is no more responsible for poverty or inequality than the sunrise is for the six a.m. news. The fact that both exist within the same frame of time is irrelevant. There's a Latin phrase, sir, *Post hoc ergo, propter hoc*, which means essentially that event A happened simultaneously with event B; therefore event A *caused* event B. You see, if a recession comes along and I lose my job, then I can blame government for my circumstances . . . which is fine *if* I'm more interested in finding someone to blame than I am in finding a job. I believe, sir, that our challenge is to *do* something with ourselves, our talent and our opportunity in *spite* of the circumstances, not sit back and feel sorry for ourselves *because* of the circumstances."

She caught herself and reached toward the gold chain again. A slightly flushed face signaled her embarrassment.

"I'm sorry, sir. I seem to have the knack for taking five minutes to answer a five-second question."

"I understand," he chuckled. "We politicians have mastered that tendency. Anyway, don't apologize. I'm interested in hearing about how you feel, Mariana." He folded his hands and she noticed how unusually long his fingers were in proportion to the relatively small hands.

"Sir, you are the president. I am capable of voicing only my opinions, but—"

"Which is precisely what I want—*your* view of where we're headed as a nation . . . *your* opinion."

She glanced downward for a second, not at anything in particular, but as an unconscious gesture that signaled the beginning of an answer that he may not want to hear, but one that she would have to give.

"My opinion, sir, is that for the first time we have a future that we would be well advised not to experience. Given our current direction, system of values and national attitudes, this future will inevitably be an era of turbulence unlike anything we've experienced before. I believe, sir, in the law of Sowing and Reaping, and I do not like what we've sown. However, I also believe that there is cause for great hope. The pessimism, the immobility, the disinterest in government, and the lack of trust and respect for our elected leaders, the things that have people concerned and angry, are not as widespread and uncontrollable as the media would have you believe. The people are anxious to improve their circumstances, but as James Allen once wrote, 'They are *unwilling* to improve themselves.' And it's not that they're unwilling, it's that they've not been . . . well, they've not been *encouraged* to improve themselves. And that's where I believe government can and should play a far more active role."

The president stood slowly and walked from behind his desk toward the same window where another president had stood in the photograph she remembered. Mari and Jonathan watched the man stop at the window. He put his hands behind his back, locking his right index finger into his clutched left hand. His body remained straight and poised, unbent by neither age nor the massive responsibility he carried.

He remained at the window for a moment and there was silence in the room. Finally, he turned slowly and folded his arms across his chest.

"What role do you have in mind, Mariana?"

"Pardon?"

"Specifically, what role would you suggest the government play in helping . . . I mean *encouraging* people to improve themselves?"

"Well, first of all, people are too used to hearing about what government is going to do for them . . . *for* them seems to be *to* them. Right now, they're talking about what's *wrong* with their country. In a thousand different ways, both the people and the politicians around the nation are concentrating on changing our direction by changing or creating legislation. You don't change a *nation*, Mr. President. A nation is merely reflective of the combination of the thinking, the attitudes, and the ambition of its *people*. A nation is, by itself, incapable of feelings, or pride, or worthy objectives—*people* provide that. New legislation or ambitious programs won't inspire the people—it never has. Give the people *reasons* to create, *reasons* to dream and produce, and the nation will regain its health."

"Mariana, listen. I've read your books. Believe me, I accept what you've just said. The people out there are going to *wait* for direction. They're waiting right now for someone, somewhere, to start the ball rolling, and I'm convinced we're running out of time. A man that I happen to know you admire, a man who once sat in this room and held the office I now hold, said that 'those who make peaceful revolution impossible make violent revolution inevitable.'"

Mariana remembered for a moment that she, too, often used the same phrase.

The president paused, though something about him said that he was not yet finished with his thought, and Mari remained silent. He moved with deliberate steps toward the corner of his desk, speaking slowly as he moved.

"I suppose I want to initiate a peaceful revolution from this level of government before the people resort to a violent revolution of their own."

Mariana Locke suddenly realized her mistake. He had asked for specifics and she had given him philosophy—a philosophy that he had already accepted.

Reardon eased himself back into his chair. "What would you do if *you* were in this chair?"

"I'd start a revolution of the spirit."

"Specifics, Mariana, specifics." He smiled, but she knew he was quite serious. His responsibilities gave him little time for mental wandering.

"All right, I'd begin by making our government consistent. Number one—you cannot print 'In God We Trust' on our currency and then make prayer in schools unconstitutional.

"Number two—if you have laws on the books to prevent people from taking advantage of one another, then when one of those laws is violated, the violator must be punished in accordance with that law and the punishment must befit the crime.

"Number three—you cannot have agencies of government, agencies such as the FBI, purposely do things to entrap public officials. These actions slowly erode whatever respect remains for public officials.

"Fourth—it is a gross mistake for monies paid out by government for welfare and unemployment to provide a greater incentive than the rewards for honest work and individual productivity. It destroys personal pride and dignity, and the joy that comes from contributing something to society.

"Then, Mr. President, you must begin insisting that our schools return to a program of consistent and quality education. It's time for teachers and school officials to control and teach students, rather than permit students to determine what they should be taught and how they should behave.

"Now, these are but a few of the issues that must be corrected to start regaining the respect that people once felt for elected officials. In the meantime, and of even greater importance, is to deliberately and methodically appoint people to positions in government who take seriously the value of attitudes in determining the quality of life—people who understand the value of setting and pursuing worthy goals, people who will teach these things to others so that a domino effect is felt from the top echelons of government down into every state, every county and city of the nation, so that every family hears the message of personal development. *You can have more than you've got because you can become more than you are.* That's the message Americans need to hear and understand. Another tax cut won't do it."

She told him of companies like American Products who attract and train men and women of all ages and from all backgrounds, and encourage those individuals to raise their income up to the level of a whole new lifestyle rather than reduce their lifestyle down to the level of their income. Reardon listened to her without interrupting. Her enthusiasm and her insights made the forty minutes seem like ten. Only when she noticed the president glance briefly at his watch did she become aware of how long she had been talking.

"Mr. President, you must not give me the liberty to be specific. And I hope you've learned not to ask someone like me what they would do if they were in your chair."

He moved his chair forward toward the desk again and laughed. It was the laugh of a shy but confident man, looking downward and shaking his head slightly from side to side.

"Mariana . . . Mariana . . . I needed to hear exactly what you've said. I need your opinions and your criticisms. Actually, our appointment together still has ten minutes to go, but there's now a matter of great urgency that I must discuss with you. You see, everything you've said is precisely what I believe must be done. However, *doing* some of those things is easier said than done. I'm sure you know that it takes the support of Congress to rectify some of the things you've discussed. Unfortunately, some of those folks up there on the hill . . . some in rather key positions . . . wouldn't know what you're talking about.

"When we started this conversation nearly an hour ago, I told you that I was going to scare the devil out of you. Now, let me tell you why. I'm going to put the government in the business of working on people's attitudes rather than on their problems. I'm going to begin a program that promotes and rewards productivity rather than tries to continue to support people who are able to support themselves. To come to the point, I'm creating a new cabinet position—a new agency of government. Now, before you comment on how *others* have promised to *limit* government only to create more bureaucracies and how this sounds like exactly what *I'm* doing, let me tell you what I have in mind."

The longer she was in the presence of this man, the more she found him to be uncommonly sincere and uniquely persuasive. There was nothing pretentious about him, and she listened with both interest in what he was saying and with fascination at his candor.

"I've decided to create a Department of Human Development. Jonathan, you're an avid student of government, so you'll understand that creating an organization with full cabinet authority is not just a token gesture."

"It certainly isn't, Mr. President, and it sounds absolutely intriguing." It was the first time he had contributed to the conversation, but his response was an emphatic and enthusiastic confirmation of the president's remark.

The president sat back in his chair. "Now, did that scare the devil out of you, Mrs. Locke?"

"I'm excited about the possibilities that I think you have in mind, but I . . . well, I wouldn't say that I'm frightened by it."

"Then let me frighten you. I'm asking you to be the first Secretary of Human Development. I want you to head up the program, Mariana."

There was only stunned silence. Her mouth was open and her eyes moved back and forth rapidly between her husband and the man who had asked her the question.

"I'm . . . I'm not . . . Mr. President . . . I mean, well . . . I'm not sure . . . what . . . it would . . . involve . . ."

"Well, first you might consider thanking me for cleansing your soul," he said with a broad smile.

"My—my soul?"

"Yes, for scaring the devil out of you, Mariana Locke. You should see yourself! Jonathan, I'll bet it's the first time she's been at a loss for words in years." He laughed and Jonathan sat looking at his astonished wife, a smile on his own face, but one that was mixed with apparent surprise.

The president stood up again, leaning forward slightly with his fingertips resting on his desk top.

"You'll have to move back to Washington, and the pay won't be all that great, but it will be one heckuva chance for you to have a major effect with your ideas."

"When—when must you have an answer?"

"Not this second. I'm due to step out and sign the new tax bill in the East Room. It will be perhaps twenty minutes before I'll get back here."

"Twenty minutes to decide?"

"I know it's unfair, but then—well, we've waited long enough as it is. Besides, you in particular must know about the value of decisions versus the danger of delay and overcaution.

"You'll want to talk it over in private before deciding, of course, so I'll leave orders that you're not to be disturbed. Oh . . . and there are no tape recorders running." His beaming smile made his cheeks raise into little balls just under his eyes. A moment later, he was gone.

Jonathan looked at his wife who seemed more bewildered than he had ever seen her—with the exception of the very first day he had met her in his office.

"Mari?" She turned directly toward him, but her eyes seemed to look past him.

"It's something you've wanted for a long time, Mari. It's a chance for your influence to really be felt—and with the influence of the government behind it." He stood up and walked around behind her, kneeling down now at her left side. Her right hand was moving toward her neck and the gold chain. He felt so very proud of her, but knew that at this moment she felt only confusion.

"I don't know what to say, Jon. I—I feel happiness . . . great happiness . . . but . . ."

"At the same time, you feel just the opposite?"

"Yes," she said. "But the opposite may not be what you think. I'm—I'm overwhelmed at the invitation, Jonathan . . . absolutely overwhelmed just in being in this office, and being asked to do something very important, but—"

"What else?" Jonathan knew there was something he had not detected—something more than just the shock of what she was being invited to do.

"It's the *journey*, Jon . . . the journey from where I was not so very long ago . . . to here. This is the destination, Jonathan—the arrival. Why, when we reach the top of the mountain do we only then realize that the true excitement was in the journey . . . the journey, Jon, not the achievement. What scares me more than the responsibility is the thought that I've missed so much."

"Nonsense. Surely you don't think that someone like you will let this be the ultimate achievement?"

"Of course not, Jon, but there's also the question of whether I'm ready for something like this. I've so much more to learn. The memories of cold apartments in Philadelphia are still there, and . . . and . . . well, you know what it was like."

"I know."

Images of the past and mental projections of the future were flashing simultaneously in a collage of disconnected and confusing thoughts. Mariana York, now Mariana Locke, was sitting in the Oval Office of the White House conversing with the president of the United States. That, in itself, was awesome.

She remembered job interviews that had left her with feelings of inadequacy because someone had prejudged her, overlooked her, or ignored her. Her mind recollected people in little bursts of recall—not the pictures of the event so much as the feelings *during* the event. She remembered Mr. Culpepper, the man at the real estate office when she was beginning her career with Camelot Productions. She remembered the woman she had met that same day who had been climbing her own mountain when Culpepper had cut the rope and let her fall. Whatever might have happened to her?

"What are you going to do, Mari?" Jonathan's words brought her back.

"Jon, I've grown, I know, but have I grown *enough*?"

His blue eyes looked into hers. He saw uncertainty and confusion. She saw reassurance and confidence.

"Oh, Jonathan, so much of me still seems . . . back there." Her thumb pointed over her shoulder, but her remark was in reference to the past, not a direction.

"Mari, my dear little Mari, 'back there,' as you call it, was merely a place that you started from to get to where you are. Back there no longer exists. The Mariana Locke sitting here next to me is not the Mari York who walked into my office a few years ago. That was a Mari who was searching, who was dreaming of becoming what Mariana Locke is today. You've done it on your own, my love. You took advice, counsel and criticism, and you blended it with your own ambition and hard work. You sit here today being offered what you deserve—*and* what you are prepared to handle."

He took her left hand in his and put his right hand gently on the back of her neck, stroking her lovingly as he spoke.

"Mari, anyone else would be absolutely ecstatic to be where you are at this moment. Most people would let their ego run out of control and wouldn't hesitate for a moment to accept the cabinet post you've just been offered. While most would eagerly accept the immediate rewards of the prestige and power, you're one of the very few who would pause to wonder if you're ready for the position."

His eyes stayed on hers. He smiled proudly and gently squeezed her neck.

"What about Camelot, Jon? What about our projects and books—our speaking schedule?"

"All those things were intended to let you grow, Mari, to prepare you for *here*. We'll work out the commitments we've made, believe me."

She shifted her body toward him and placed her hands on his shoulders.

"Jon, I must tell you what is *really* bothering me."

"What?"

"You won't think I'm silly or give me an answer that isn't what you really feel in your heart?"

The tilt of his head and the look in his eyes gave her the answer—an answer she already knew.

"The position they're offering *me*, Jon, is something you've always wanted, and—"

"Mari—"

"It *is*, Jon. You've talked and dreamed of something like this since before I met you. You're made for it and could do it much better than me."

Jonathan didn't answer, but stood up slowly. As her hands slid from his shoulders down onto his chest, he took the soft hands and gently pulled her to stand with him.

"Mari, you must believe me. I will feel no loss, anger or disappointment. It is true that something like this is part of what I've imagined I would like to do, but—well, to a far greater degree than you can imagine at the moment, I am involved."

"What do you mean?"

"It isn't important at the moment. Believe me, my love, had I been offered the position I would not have been able to accept it. But the position was meant for *you*, Mari . . . more than that, the position *is* you."

She stepped away from him slowly and walked toward the window where she stood motionless, looking out across the lawn below. Jonathan did not speak or interfere, knowing she needed to be alone for a few minutes. She placed her hands on the waist-high window ledge and leaned slightly forward. She stood where once before another had stood, pondering his own dilemma. Her eyes were closed and she saw the photograph again. Suddenly, as if absorbing the strength and courage of the young president she so much admired, she saw the relative insignificance of the decision she faced. She was standing exactly where once he had stood and would act exactly as he would have acted. She would let the insignificant remain insignificant and would reach a decision based on her own confidence and insights. She had been presented with an opportunity by the most powerful leader in the world, and had received encouragement and advice from the man she most loved and respected in the world. Now she must decide using her own judgment and responding to the most trusted and dependable servant in the world—her own instinct and intuition.

Mari Locke turned to face her husband. "Do you believe that I am ready?"

"I do."

"And you will support me and harbor no emotion of regret or hostility?"

"None."

"Are you prepared to accept the separation, the time we'll undoubtedly have to spend apart—even more time apart than we currently experience?"

"I am."

"And you'll be willing, if necessary, to move back to Washington?"

"I doubt that it will be necessary, but if it were—yes!"

She turned back toward the window again. She remembered the couple from American Products who chose to walk away from a career that was affecting their marriage, in spite of the earnings, prestige and lifestyle. A line she had once read flashed into her mind. *"Be careful of what you become in the pursuit of what you want."*

She pondered consequences—both of action and inaction. Across the south lawn she could see the long line of people standing off in the distance, slowly filing toward the White House, waiting to see and sense the center of power of the very nation she was being called upon to serve. She thought of the hope and the hopelessness in the lives of the people standing in the line, and in the lives of the many who would never be able to afford to come to Washington to stand in that line . . . or who might not want to even if they could because of their anger or, still worse, their apathy.

She felt her husband's hands slip around her waist and she turned slowly to look at him.

"We must be careful not to lose what we have, Jon," she said.

"Mari, the only way we could lose is by not taking risks. Think about it . . ."

"I know, every risk has taken me to a new plateau, but that doesn't mean we can't slide backward from taking one of those risks."

There was a moment of silence before Jonathan finally spoke. "The decision must be yours, Mariana. I'll support you in whatever you choose. Just consider the value of doing it and the risks *of not doing it* before you decide. But remember, if you think the risks of *accepting* the challenge are heavy, you might ponder the risks of *not* accepting it." He placed a gentle kiss on her lips, and she tilted her head back and smiled at him.

"I've never kissed a man in the Oval Office of the White House before. Do you think that makes me special?"

"A lot of things make you special, Mari. Now, what are you going to do about the president's offer?"

She stepped back from him slightly. Only their hands and their eyes touched now.

"What does your logical mind tell you to do?" he asked.

"You should know me well enough by now to know that on issues of major importance, I never listen to logic; it tends to obscure intuition, and intuition is probably the voice of God."

"Clever line, Mari Locke."

"I had a clever teacher."

"We both did." There was a meaning to his words that went beyond her ability to comprehend for the moment.

The side door of the office opened and the tall, ruby-faced president stepped inside, closing the door behind him.

"Well, I've seen to one set of responsibilities, now it's time to return to another." He walked behind his desk seating himself once again in the leather chair.

"Now, before you give me your answer, Mari, there are just a few comments I want to make. First—to you, Jonathan. Your accomplishments and abilities could well have qualified you for the position I'm offering to your wife. A number of my staff did, in fact, strongly urge me to consider that very move. But I decided that because of your—uh . . . already heavy responsibilities and certain *impending commitments,* that to offer you the position would be unwise. Also, I'm smart enough to know that by acquiring Mrs. Locke's skills and rare charm I'll automatically have *your* interest and involvement also, although to a lesser degree.

"Next, I have a major reason for creating this office, Mari. I think that while the world economy is certainly in a turmoil right now, much of the reason for it is our attitude about things. People are losing confidence in themselves, in their employers, and in their leaders in government, and I can understand that. What we need is a new brand of leadership in this country. We need some of the experienced elder statesmen that we have at all levels of government, but we also need something new. We need leadership that can not only bring the knowledge and logic of good business to government, but we need leadership that can, by the strength of their words and of their personal persuasiveness, give hope to America. I want your department of government to promote and make available the seminars and programs you've been teaching. If the things the two of you have been creating and promoting can work so well for the companies who hire you, then it can work for anyone.

"I've watched companies like American Products expand their business across America using the ideas that you began teaching years ago, Jon. Your philosophies have become the nucleus of their business and I want all of America to listen to that same message. Now, we'll have a lot of work to do, but by gosh, we're going to do it! There are going to be a lot of skeptics, particularly in the media, but we'll do whatever we must to give America back its dream. Now, Mrs. Locke, what do you say?"

Mari looked briefly at her husband, then at him. "I accept the challenge, Mr. President."

The president sat back in his chair and smiled. "Wonderful!" he exclaimed, reaching toward a brown box on his desk.

A voice responded instantly.

"Yes, Mr. President?"

"Fletcher, we're affirmative in here. Start the wheels in motion."

"Yes, sir."

There was a slight pause. "Oh—and Fletcher?"

"Sir?"

"Arrange the press conference for tomorrow morning at ten."

"Yes, sir."

He sat back now, a broad smile on his face. "You're going to be presented to the nation tomorrow morning."

There was another five minutes of advice and instruction, and with warm handshakes, the three parted, although Jonathan was asked to step back inside with the president momentarily while Fletcher Kennedy advised Mariana of the arrangements for transportation and accommodations.

A new life of great influence was beginning—and a life of new challenge and opportunity.

CHAPTER SEVENTEEN:

The Reunion

Mariana and Jonathan Locke found themselves being checked into a suite at the Marriott Twin Bridges Hotel. Unlike other times, there was no registration, showing of major credit cards, or even waiting in line. The limousine took them directly to a side entrance and within minutes their luggage had been moved in, instructions given, and keys left behind. They were now alone to absorb the day's events.

Coffee had been delivered to the room without request as though someone knew the habits of Mariana Locke. She had just stirred her first cup of coffee when the phone rang. It was the White House calling to advise Mrs. Locke that a limousine would be picking them up at eight-twenty in the morning . . . not eight-thirty, eight-*twenty*.

The two discussed the unbelievable three days since first receiving the call from Washington. To Mari, it seemed that suddenly their entire lives had taken on an unexpected direction. To Jonathan, however, it was merely the routine unfolding of events that had been strategically and methodically planned long before.

Mari was vibrant and talkative; Jonathan was quietly content to listen to his wife's excited monologue as she unpacked her clothes and laid out her journal and Day-timer appointment book on the writing table. On impulse, the moment she lay the Day-timer on the table and started to walk away, she turned and plucked it back off

the table, thumbing through the pages as though in search of something specific and important. She soon found the page. Repeating the
numbers to herself, she walked to the phone, placed a call, then sat on
the edge of the bed.

"Who are you calling?" Jonathan was surprised by the spontaneity of
the event.

There was no response to his question—only a moment of silence
before she began speaking, although not to her husband.

"Hello, this is Mariana Locke speaking. May I please speak to . . .
What? You silly thing—you don't sound like yourself." There was a
laugh—silence—another laugh.

"Yes, we just arrived a few hours ago. The whole trip was so unexpected we didn't have time to think."

Silence. "No, we're here for . . . Well, I don't really know how
long, Mikki."

Silence. Jonathan smiled to himself as he placed his cologne and
shaving cream on the counter top of the bathroom, knowing his wife had
made contact with an old friend of hers and a former employee of his.

"When are you leaving?" Short silence.

"You're kidding! That's where we're staying. Are you tied up
this evening?"

Silence. "What's the meeting all about?"

Silence. Mari broke into a burst of excited laughter. "Are you serious?"
Short silence.

"Mikki, you wouldn't believe how many times I've been invited as a
guest speaker for American Products."

Silence. "It's probably the tape from the Los Angeles Convention I
did for Boyd and Becky Freeman. How did they get it to you?"

Silence interrupted with a laugh and an "uh-huh."

"Hang on just a moment." Covering the receiver, she called out to
her husband. "Jon, how do you feel about a late dinner—say about ten
or ten-thirty?"

The muffled answer was in the affirmative. "Mikki, it's okay. Ring the
room when you're . . ." Silence.

"Okay. I'll come down at seven-fifteen and meet a few folks, say
hello, and come back here to the room 'til you're finished." Silence.

"Wonderful. See ya . . . Bye!"

Jonathan emerged from the master bath at the same moment she
seated herself at the table by the window.

"How's Mikki?"

"Jonathan, you won't believe it." She put her feet up onto the chair cushion and wrapped her arms around her knees. As often happened whenever she was excited, the little girl side of Mariana Locke was surfacing. The sophistication that had become a permanent part of her, and the brilliant natural beauty were all there, combining with the childish excitement to create a unique picture.

"Guess what Mikki and Charlie Livingston are involved with?"

"American Products."

"You heard. Isn't it terrific, Jon? She said they're doing very well and—you won't believe this—they're having a regional convention here tonight and tomorrow, which is why—"

"—we're having a late dinner tonight with Mikki and Charlie," Jon added.

"Smarty! Do you mind?"

"Not at all. Is she still with the TV station or are they full-time with American Products?"

"She didn't say. She *did* say that they know Boyd and Becky Freeman. Have you ever met them?"

"Just once. Nice couple. Are they going to be here?"

"I forgot to ask. But what I was going to say was . . . oh, yes . . . they—the Freemans—gave Mikki a tape from the speech I made in Los Angeles a few years ago. She says it's almost worn out. She says it's hard to believe that the lazy, wandering, poor soul she once knew could have finally made something of herself. That crazy redhead!"

Jonathan laughed. "Wait until she finds out how far you've *really* come."

"What do you mean? Oh my gosh!" Her right hand came up to cover her mouth and she opened her eyes wide.

Jonathan's eyes sympathetically opened wide with hers. "What's wrong?" he asked.

"I wonder if I'm permitted to tell anyone?"

Jonathan shrugged his shoulders and took a drink from the cup of coffee. "I suppose we should have asked," he said. He glanced out the window just as a silvery American Airlines jet lumbered slowly above the Potomac River on its approach to Washington National Airport. Jonathan saw it, but his mind flipped elsewhere. He glanced at his watch, the expression on his face signaling her that he had had a flash of an idea. He jumped from the chair and went across the room to the television. It was exactly six o'clock.

The audio preceded the video by just a second.

" . . . and White House insiders report the news conference will confirm that the nominee to the new cabinet level position will in fact be

Mariana Locke, noted author and lecturer who along with her husband, Jonathan Locke, are the principals of a California based firm, Camelot Productions. The news conference for the formal announcement is scheduled for tomorrow morning at ten."

And then, that now famous sign-off line, "Irving R. Levine, NBC News, the White House."

"Well, there's your answer, love," Jon remarked, as he stepped back from the television and returned to his chair. He hadn't noticed the beaming smile on his wife's face.

"I wish I had a picture of that. It's worth—"

He jumped from his chair, went into the next room and returned within twenty seconds. Mari had left her chair, switched to another channel and was watching another network account of the story that was breaking, the smile still there.

"Mari!" She turned to face him and the flash of the camera caught the moment.

"Jon!"

"I wouldn't miss that expression for the world. You should see yourself."

"I must work on not becoming too smug," she said.

"Savor the experience, little one. Remember, this is the beginning of a *new* journey. Every second ought to be caught up and enjoyed. There will be plenty of times when it will be terribly serious and you'll always refer back to your mental tapes of this day. Give yourself license to soak it all up."

She smiled at him. It was a smile of love, of pride, and of the joy of a major triumph.

Inside, Jonathan Locke knew that she had reason to feel far more triumphant than even she imagined.

"I love you, Jonathan," she said.

"And I love you, Madame Secretary."

"Hey!" Mari exclaimed, glancing at the watch on her left wrist. "I'm supposed to meet Mikki and Charlie downstairs in less than an hour before their meeting starts. She wants me to meet a few people. Can you come with me?" She asked the question as she started removing an earring from her left ear.

"Sure, you shower first and I'll go into the other bath and shave," he said.

The phone rang twice while she showered, and both times Jonathan took the call as he shaved. The first was *The Washington Post*. A clever reporter had tracked them down looking for an advance interview. The second was the executive vice president of Camelot Productions calling to congratulate Mariana—and to apologize for giving out their location to the inquiring reporter. The vice president himself being a clever individual had called the White House switchboard and had somehow managed to find out in which hotel the two were staying.

At seven-fifteen the well-dressed couple were following the movement of people along the corridor as they headed toward the meeting room. Groups of five or six walked along together, talking, gesturing and laughing. Everywhere they looked there were couples—most of the men wearing suits, the women tastefully dressed for the occasion.

Just before passing the registration table, the high-pitched voice rang out . . . "MAR-EE-AN-NA," and the two friends who had not seen one another for over two years were clinging to one another, the happy tears flowing as each patted the other like mothers trying to soothe a tearful child. Jonathan took his turn at giving Mikki a squeeze while Charlie Livingston lifted the much shorter Mari Locke into the air, her feet dangling for support that was eight inches beneath her. Then, for the first time, Jonathan and Charlie formalized a relationship that had only previously existed by what each had heard about the other, and the handshake between them was warm and respectful. As was most often the case, Jonathan and Mariana were separated now, with Mari on one side of the corridor and Mikki, and Charlie, Jonathan and a gathering of autograph seekers on the other, shaking hands, accepting compliments, and answering questions he had answered a thousand times before . . . questions posed by those still believing that success is to be found in a phrase.

From the corner of his eye, Jonathan noticed a man moving through the crowd toward Mariana. His style and his appearance spoke of authority won graciously by achievement. He was the kind of man who simply acted in response to his wants. Jonathan heard the words he spoke from across the hall—words that conveyed the same authority as his appearance.

"'Scuse me . . . 'Scuse me folks . . . Mrs. Locke? I hate to introduce myself by breaking in on such a first class gatherin' of people, but I need to have a word with you. Do y' all mind if I steal this pretty young thing away for just a minute?"

He took Mari by the hand and the crowd separated to let the man do precisely what he wanted, giving immediate confirmation that he wasn't seeking permission at all but merely making a statement of what he was going to do. He was the kind of man the country needed more of, Jonathan thought as he glanced at the event.

With Mari Locke's hand still in his, the smiling, middle-aged man with the silver hair and silver-framed glasses moved in one quick motion away from the crowd and toward the group that had surrounded Jonathan. He caught the man's eyes locking in on his and he now made the same authoritative move toward Jonathan who stopped in the middle of his sentence with an "Excuse me. I think someone needs me."

"Mr. Locke, I have this pretty little wife of yours by the hand and would greatly appreciate it, sir, if you would break yourself free from these fine folks. I promise you I'm not always so discourteous and that I'll only need you for one minute."

Jonathan separated himself from the group who were stepping aside as if in response to an order from a commanding officer. The man took Jonathan's upper arm in his hand and the three walked away from the area toward the end of the corridor where only a grand piano and a few wandering people existed to break up the spaciousness of the corridor. The man spoke slowly and in a slightly more subdued tone as they moved toward a sunken alcove for more privacy.

"Now, I know that you never get a second chance to make a first impression but believe me, that's about the only way I could get done what it was I was needin' to do." He laughed and Mari and Jon laughed with him.

"You have a unique way of getting things done," Jon said.

"And a rather uncommon power of persuasion. You seem to have kidnapped me without even giving me your name, and even done so with the apparent permission of my husband," Mariana added.

"Little darlin'," the man said, "my name is Elmer Gibbons, and only because I know your husband to be a southern gentleman at heart, who will understand my apparent ill manners, would I even dream of bein' so forward."

They stopped at the bottom of the two steps that put them in the alcove, and the man now extended his hand and beamed a smile alternately between Jonathan and Mariana. The two shook his hand, and in the touching found him to be a warm and courteous person in spite of his unexpectedly blunt actions.

"I'm really not nearly as arrogant as my actions might seem," he said, shaking Jonathan's hand.

"I've found there's a very fine line between arrogance and sophisticated power," Jonathan answered.

"Well, sir, I do hope I'm on the right side of that fine line. Mr. Locke, I'm going to be bold enough to ask your wife to address the people here tonight. Now I'm in charge, which gives me the right to make that decision, but before I make the request I want to seek your permission to do so." His smile made it clear that he knew he was being clever. Gibbons' southern charm and calm courtesy were backed by a certain stubbornness. Everything about the man was flawless from his well-tailored beige suit, chocolate-colored tie and custom-made shirt right down to his brown shoes. In spite of the diamonds that covered its face, Jonathan knew somehow that the gold watch on Gibbons' left wrist was not worn to impress others, but rather was symbolic of another rung on the ladder of life put behind him.

Jonathan responded to the question. "Mr. Gibbons, you have my permission to present the question to my wife and, as she knows, she need not seek my permission to give you her own honest answer."

Gibbons looked at Jonathan's eyes a moment longer, respecting the spontaneity and thought behind his answer. Still smiling, he turned to Mariana.

"Mrs. Locke, I've read your book—the first one—*The Winter of Challenge*, and believe me, I'm most selective about who I will allow to speak in front of my people. Now, I don't *want* you to feel obligated in any way. And again, I do apologize for even approaching you this way, but I've learned that when an opportunity presents itself you'd better grab it before it gets away. That's what I'm doing, Mrs. Locke—grabbing opportunity. Now, I'd love to have you speak at the end of our program tonight—just for a few minutes, 'cause it's all I can spare. I'll pay you your fee. In fact, I'll insist on it, 'cause time and talent both have their price." He paused for a moment, not taking his eyes from her. Can you do it?"

He held up his right hand, the palm facing toward Mariana, closed his eyes for a second, then looked back at her. "Now, I know you *can* do it, so I should ask *will* you do it?"

"What time and for how long?" Her response was immediate, but she voiced obviously a question and not an acceptance. She glanced quickly at her watch.

"At exactly nine-forty and for twenty minutes."

She did not look at Jonathan for either approval or inquiry. "Mr. Gibbons, in view of the fact that you have the audacity to even ask under such circumstances, I would take pleasure in matching that audacity with the audacity of my own unexpected acceptance."

"Wonderful! What's your fee?"

The answer was as calm and uneventful as if she were asking for a cup of coffee.

"Four thousand dollars."

He listened to the answer as if he had been told the time of day.

"Fine. I'll have a check for you immediately after the meeting," he said. His eyes turned to Jonathan.

"Mr. Locke, I look forward to having you address one of my conventions in Kentucky one day, if you would accept. And by the way," he looked down at Jonathan's hands which were folded in front of him, "I purposely asked Mrs. Locke to speak tonight instead of you because I heard the news this evening and wanted to get her while she's still a private citizen . . . and before the fee goes up."

He smiled and Jonathan smiled back.

"Well, Mr. Gibbons, you won on one count but lost on the other."

"Oh?"

"You got Mrs. Locke *before* she became a public servant, but you didn't get her before her *fee* went up. Both your urgent need and her impending appointment just added an extra two thousand."

The man looked at Jonathan, then to Mariana, and then back to Jonathan. The smile vanished but came back after a moment of thought.

"Mr. Locke, I would have paid twice the price to be able to say that ol' Elmer Gibbons hired your wife's services the night before she became a member of the president's cabinet." He shook their hands warmly and thanked them both. Taking each by the arm, he proudly escorted them back to the crowd.

✦ ✦ ✦

Mikki found Mariana at seven twenty-five, and the words began flowing again. However, by seven twenty-eight, the sudden movement of people toward the entrance doors reminded the bubbly redhead that the conversation would have to continue later.

Jonathan was standing next to two attractive young women having his own conversation, and Mariana was saying a goodbye to Mikki when a woman in a black gown with coal-black hair turned from the entrance door and came back toward where the two women stood. Mikki noticed her as she approached, did a quick double-take, and extended her arms outward to the well-shaped woman.

"Jan, you little darlin'. You made it. I'm so glad to see you." The two gave one another a friendly hug. In the middle of the squeeze, the woman's eyes caught a glimpse of Mari standing a few feet behind them. For a second she had an 'I've-seen-you-somewhere-before' look.

"Hey, come over here a second. There's someone I want you to meet real quick," Mikki said, taking her friend by the hand. "Mari, this is one of my very best distributors and a very special friend. She just drove down from Philadelphia. Janice Alexander, I don't know if I've ever mentioned my squirrelly friend, but this is Mariana York . . . ah, shoot . . . Mari Locke. Mari's my very dear friend and ex-roommate when I used to work at Camelot Productions."

Mariana instantly recognized the woman. There had been but a brief meeting in Philadelphia a few years back in the office of Hank Culpepper and, by strange coincidence, she had thought of the woman earlier in the day while standing in the office of the president. It had to be the same woman, she thought, although by her appearance it was obvious that her circumstances had dramatically changed for the better.

"Hello, Janice," Mari said while the woman struggled within herself to recall where they might have met before.

"Good meeting you, Mari," she said as the two women exchanged a handshake and a smile.

Janice had a confidence about herself that was not apparent the day Mari had held the door open for her—the day she had been dismissed from Culpepper's sales staff. She wore a pin on the collar of her gown that had a single diamond in the center. Mari knew the pin to be a symbol of high achievement within the American Products organization.

"You're doing well with American Products?" Mariana knew the answer before asking the question.

"Extremely well, thank you. I've learned quickly by necessity and I had a wonderful teacher," she replied, looking at Mikki. Mikki Livingston smiled in response to the compliment, then placed her hand on her friend's shoulder in a joking sort of way.

"Okay, kid," she said, "remember the book I gave you to read when you were first getting started . . . the one you say probably saved your life?"

"The Winter of Challenge?"

"The Winter of Challenge," Mikki repeated. "Well, I hate to embarrass you, but sweetie, meet the author."

The mouth became rounded and the eyes opened wide. "Oh—my! "

She reached for Mariana's hand as though the first handshake had been just for practice.

"The Mari Locke. Mikki, you dumb bunny, when you said York . . . Mari York, it didn't register. I'm so sorry—"

"It's fine, Janice. It's not unusual, especially when Mikki introduces me."

Mikki's eyes flipped back and forth between her two friends as though she were watching a tennis match.

"Don't feel embarrassed, Jan," Mikki said. "I remember Mari when she couldn't write a coherent letter to her mother." The three laughed together and Mikki spoke again. "Jan was as bad off as you were, Mari. In fact, her past is a whole bunch like yours, right Jan?"

"Heavens, yes!" Janice Alexander answered. "I went through the same things you mentioned in the beginning of your book, Mari—the divorce, the whole mess. I tried selling real estate right after my separation and—"

"Janice, I think I know where we've met before."

"Oh?"

"Does the name *Culpepper* . . . Hank Culpepper . . . does that mean—"

"How do *you* know Hank Culpepper? He was my broker, but . . . but where—"

"The day he sent you away, Janice, I held the door open for you—the day you left the office carrying your things in a cardboard box."

Her face became grimly serious as though the memory transported her back in time to the actual moment, but she blinked and the smile returned, giving way to a broad grin.

"Oh, Mari, I can't believe the coincidence!"

"And I can't believe *you*, Janice Alexander. Look at you . . . at how far you've come! And you say it's going well for you?"

She closed her eyes for a brief second while a look of sincere gratitude crossed her face. "Really well, Mari, and in all seriousness, thanks in large part to you. Mikki didn't exaggerate—your book probably *did* save my life," she said. "Just knowing that someone else had had experiences like mine and had gone on to do something worthwhile gave me a whole new outlook on things."

Mikki noticed the doors beginning to close as the meeting started and missed a few lines of the conversation. "You two really do know one another?"

"Yes, Mikki, we really *do* know one another," Mariana answered.

There was a mingling of the minds for a few seconds before the two said what would be short-term goodbyes to Mariana and disappeared into the room where the amplified voice of the man she now knew to be Elmer Gibbons was signaling the beginning of the event.

Mariana noticed her husband finishing a conversation with Charlie Livingston and walked to a nearby chair to wait.

Her mind wandered back to that day two years before when she had encountered the tear-marked face of Janice Alexander at the very moment that her own life had been sent into a frenzied and uncontrollable spin by the words and actions of a person who was unsympathetic with her situation. She remembered the Janice Alexander then and thought of the same woman now. The hopelessness was gone. The woman she met tonight had a purpose and she was beyond being affected by the uncaring, impersonal decision of a Hank Culpepper. For Mariana Locke, the gratification was in knowing that their common experiences and the book she had written on those experiences had positively affected someone else. Janice Alexander had responded to a book written about the *real* world. She had not—and would not have—responded to a motivational speaker's hype on getting rich and becoming famous. That was the difference between what Mari and Jonathan Locke were doing and what the majority of other people who wrote and spoke on self-help subjects were doing. Jon and Mari looked at the negativity of the *real* world and chose to deal with *that*. They spoke on the never-ending war between good and evil; they did not speak on the necessity of staying positive in a mostly negative world.

Mariana York and the new Mariana Locke were now one and happy with the contribution each had made to this woman who now existed. She felt good about herself. She felt good about her contribution to the lives of other people. Her mind impulsively flashed a past thought to her present consciousness.

"To reap the great harvest of life, learn how to become the servant of many."

She had mastered that challenge and tonight would once again, with her words and insights, serve many. Tomorrow, the 'many' would be multiplied by a thousandfold as she took on far greater responsibilities. Her wandering mind was interrupted now by the figure of someone moving toward her. It was Jonathan. He had finished his conversation and Charlie Livingston was slipping through a side door into a convention meeting that would soon become Mariana Locke's audience.

"Shall we go upstairs and relax?" Jonathan asked, extending his hand out to her.

Her outstretched arm gave him his answer and the two went back toward the elevator and to the temporary privacy of their suite. It would be a privacy that would become less and less frequent as their respective schedules and new responsibilities increased, and they would both savor every such moment that life would be kind enough to give to them.

❖   ❖   ❖

Precisely as Elmer Gibbons had scheduled, the introduction of Mariana Locke occurred at nine-forty, and without any reference to her new, although currently tentative role in government, Gibbons handed her the lavalier microphone and gave her his best smile. Then, with a warm handshake and quick kiss on the cheek, he stepped down into the audience, leaving her to savor the continuing and thundering applause.

As the crowd sat back into their seats, Mari took a single drink of water from the glass placed on the podium for her, then looked out into the hungry eyes of the crowd.

"Thank you, Elmer. I want each of you to know that the man who introduced me a moment ago, Mr. Elmer Gibbons is, in my opinion, a man of ethics, a man of strong will, and a man who is blessed with a rare sophistication exceeded only by his unique qualities of leadership. And while it came as a surprise to me, I thank him for inviting me here to share some time with you.

"Of all the subjects I have covered over the years, subjects such as goal setting, time management, and personal development, among others, surely none are more important than that which I have decided to share with you tonight. For the next little while, I'd like to reveal to you what I consider to be the first prerequisite to success.

"I would suggest that the major key is not in learning how to set goals. The major key isn't in learning how to manage your time or in mastering the attributes of leadership. Every day, in a thousand different ways, people like you and me are trying to improve themselves by learning how to do things. We spend a lifetime gathering knowledge in classrooms, from books and from life's own experiences. All of us probably have all the knowledge we need to attract all that we want. We probably have all the knowledge we need to become all that we'd like to be. But in spite of the knowledge we spend our lifetime acquiring, most of us fall short of our goals and ambitions. We settle for a small, fractional part of what we could have otherwise had, in spite of the immense knowledge we've gathered in a lifetime.

"Now if, as someone once said, 'Knowledge is the forerunner of success,' why do most of us fall short of our objectives? Why, in spite of all we know and in spite of our collected experiences, do we wander somewhat aimlessly—settling for a life of existence rather than a life of substance?

"While there may be many answers to the question I've posed, the basic and fundamental answer is the absence of discipline in applying all that we know. That's the key word . . . discipline! In fact, we might add one more word to discipline . . . the other word is consistent . . . consistent discipline!

"You see, life is basically a process of gathering knowledge and learning to apply that knowledge in the world of life and business. But like anything that is newly learned, we must learn to use what we've learned. Better than knowledge is applied knowledge. And, once we've applied our knowledge, we must study the results of that process, and then study those results. If the results are poor, we refine our application of what we know and try again. Finally, by trying, observing, refining and trying again, our knowledge will inevitably produce for us worthy and admirable results. And, with the joy and the results of our efforts, we continue to apply, refine, learn and observe, until we become swept into a spiral of achievement and progress. The ecstasy of that total experience makes for a life of triumph over tragedy, dullness, and mediocrity.

"But for this whole process to work for us, we must first master the art of discipline . . . of consistent discipline. It takes a consistently disciplined human effort to master the magic of setting goals, or the results will be sporadic and elusive.

"It takes a consistently disciplined human effort to truly manage our valuable time, or our inconsistent attempts will find our time subtly stolen away by those to whom we feel obligated or whose incessant demands are stronger than our own.

"It takes discipline to want to try when that nagging voice within our own minds whispers to us about the painful consequences of possible failure.

"It takes discipline to admit our errors and to recognize our limitations. The voice of the human ego speaks to us all. It beckons to us to magnify our value beyond that which our results would suggest that we deserve.

"It takes discipline to be totally honest, both with ourselves as well as with others. Be certain of one thing—every exaggeration or distortion of the truth, once detected by others, destroys our credibility and makes all that we say and do subject to question. The tendency to exaggerate, distort or even withhold the truth is an inherent part of us all, and only an all-out disciplined assault can overcome this tendency.

"It takes discipline to plan; it takes discipline to execute our plan. It takes discipline to look with full objectivity at the results of our applied plan, and discipline to change either our plan or our method of executing that plan if the results are poor.

"It takes discipline to be firm when the world throws opinions at our feet. And it takes discipline to ponder the value of someone else's opinion when our pride and our arrogance leads us to believe that only we have the answers to our personal challenges.

"With this consistent discipline applied to every area of our lives,
we can discover untold miracles and uncover unique possibilities and
opportunities. With the discipline of setting aside thirty minutes every
day for reading, we feed valuable data into our mental computer that
enhances our value, sharpens our skills, polishes our sophistication, and
provides answers to current and future questions.

"Now, if it is discipline whose magic thread is interwoven among
all worthy human actions, then what is this thing we call discipline?
One good answer to this question might be that discipline is a constant
human awareness of the need for an action and a conscious act by us to
implement that action. If our awareness and our implementations occur
almost simultaneously, then we've begun the valuable process of disciplined human activity. If there is considerable time passing between the
moment of awareness and the time of our implementation, then that is
called procrastination, an almost exact opposite of discipline.

"The voice within us says, 'Do the deed.' Discipline then says,
'Do it now and to the very best of your ability—today, tomorrow,
and always—until finally the worthy deed becomes instinctive.'
Procrastination says, 'Later will do, tomorrow will do, or perhaps when
I get a chance.' Procrastination also says, 'Do what is necessary to get
by or to impress others. Do what you can, but not what you must.'

"We are constantly confronted by these two ever-present choices:
the choice between disciplined existence, bearing the fruits of achievement and contentment, or procrastination—the easy life for which
the future will bear no fruit, only the bare branches of mediocrity. The
rewards of discipline lie in the future and are great. The rewards of
the lack of discipline are for today and are minor in comparison to the
immeasurable rewards of consistent self-discipline. But for most, we
choose today's pleasure rather than tomorrow's fortune.

"Surely the creator who sits upon some distant throne looking
down upon the lives of his human creations must often smile at the
folly of our deeds. Perhaps he even speaks to himself the words once
written by James Allen in his book, As A Man Thinketh, who said,
'They curse the effect, but they nourish the cause.'

"Now, let's take a closer look at discipline . . . at the three steps for
becoming disciplined. First, true discipline is not easy. Most people
would have to admit that it's easier to sleep until ten o'clock rather than
to get up at seven. It's easier to go to bed late, sleep late, show up late
or leave early. It's easier not to read. It's easier to turn on the television
than to turn it off. It is easier to do just enough than to do it all. Waiting

is always easier than acting. Trying is an easier approach than doing. Wouldn't it be fascinating if we wouldn't have to make the bed, or do the dishes . . . or pay the taxes? For whatever the reason, the system in which we find ourselves is designed to make the easy things the most unprofitable, and the most profitable seem also to be the most difficult.

"Life is, and always will be, a battle between the life of ease and its momentary rewards, and a life of discipline and its far more significant rewards. Each has it own price: the price of discipline or the price of regret. We'll pay one or the other. To choose the disciplined life today, to put aside ease and tranquility now in order to work smarter and longer than most is painfully difficult. Your friends are at the beach while you sit at your desk or in the library. That's difficult! But if you make the effort, if you'll pay the price of discipline now, you'll find that the future rewards will be worth the price. Now, for those who select the life of ease, for those who choose to coast now and work later, for this great majority will come the price of regret. Regret is when your friend says, 'I wish I had started earlier,' or when you lose your job, or family, or health. Regret occurs during a time of tragedy or despair when we pause to look back at what could have been, or should have been said . . . at what we would do if given another chance. 'What we wish we had done' is the voice of regret speaking in a sorrowful tone at a time when there is no going back, no second chance, no 'What I would do differently.' Choose one or the other, but both will have their price. The price of discipline or the price of regret: one costs pennies, the other—a fortune!

"Okay, we've suggested that the first lesson on discipline is that it's not easy. Now, here's the second: discipline must be a full-time activity. We've said earlier that the best form of discipline is consistent discipline. You see, the discipline that it takes to make your bed every day is the same discipline necessary for success in the world of business. If we're willing to give ourselves the liberty to be disciplined in one area of life and undisciplined in another, then the area in which we remain undisciplined will create habits that destroy our self-discipline in the areas we consider to be important. Consistency cannot be inconsistent.

"Discipline is the mind being trained to control our lives. Discipline is a set of standards which we've selected as a personal code of conduct, and it's our willingness to impose upon ourselves the requirements for honoring those standards. Once we've adopted those standards of behavior and conduct, we are committed to honor them; if we do not, then there is no disciplined activity. We find ourselves announcing our standards and our commitments to our relatives, our *friends and our associates, but living in a way that is opposite to what we've said. This leads to a loss of credibility among those who watch our inconsistencies and, more important, to a loss of confidence within ourselves. But if there's anything worse than one who is inconsistent in applying his or her self-imposed disciplines, it's one who has never even considered the need or the value of discipline at all. They seem to wander aimlessly, changing procedures, changing standards, changing loyalties and shifting frequently from one commitment to another, leaving behind a trail of broken friendships, unfinished projects and unfulfilled promises—all because of a discipline that was either non-existent or imposed so infrequently as to be rendered ineffective.*

"Well, now that we've determined that discipline is not an easy matter and that there is little value in part-time discipline, let's look at the third step for learning how to become a disciplined person. This third step is not meant to be instructional, but it is meant to be one of life's unique promises. I give to you tonight a single, but very important phrase: 'For every disciplined effort, there is a multiple reward.' That's one of life's great arrangements! It's like the Law of Sowing and Reaping. In fact, it's an extension of that biblical law which says that if you sow well, you'll reap well. An effort, a disciplined effort, in the spring . . . in the season of opportunity, will produce a reward come the fall. Now, here's the unique part of the Law of Sowing and Reaping. Not only does it suggest that we'll reap what we've sown, it also suggests that we'll reap much more. If you plant a cup of wheat in the spring, the Law says you'll get a bushel of wheat in the fall . . . if you've had the discipline to plant in the spring, and if you've had the discipline to protect your crops through the hot season of summer. Life is full of laws that both govern and explain human behavior, but this may well be the major law worth studying and mastering. For every disciplined effort, a multiple reward. How clever! If you render unique service, your reward will be multiplied. If you're fair, and honest, and patient with others, your reward is multiplied. If you give more than you expect to receive, your reward is more than you expect. But remember, the key word here is discipline.

"Everything of value requires care and attention. A child requires discipline—consistent, unwavering discipline during his or her early years or the sporadic, inconsistent teachings of the well-meaning parents will create confusion and unpredictable behavior. Our thoughts require discipline because, left to their own, our thoughts will wander as though hopelessly lost in a maze. And remember, confused thoughts produce confused results.

"It takes discipline to change a habit. Habits, once formed, become like a giant cable, a nearly unbreakable human instinct, which only long-term disciplined activity can change. We must unweave every strand of the cable of habit slowly and methodically until the cable that once held us in bondage now becomes nothing more than scattered strands of wire. It takes the consistent application of a new discipline, a more desirable discipline, to overcome one which is less desirable. And remember the law: For every disciplined effort, a multiple reward.

"Learn the discipline for writing a card or letter to a friend. Learn the discipline for paying bills on time, or being on time, or using your time in a more effective way. Learn the discipline for paying attention, or paying your taxes, or paying yourself. Learn the discipline for having a regular meeting with associates, or with your spouse, or child, or parent. Learn the discipline for learning all you can learn, or teaching all you can teach, or reading all you can read. For each discipline, a multiple reward, For each book, new knowledge. For each success, new zeal. For each challenge, new understanding. For each failure, new determination. Life is like that. Even the bad experiences of life provide their special contribution.

"But a word of caution here for those who neglect the need for care and attention to life's disciplines: everything has its price. Everything affects everything else. Neglect your own discipline and there will be a price that must be paid. All things of value will be taken for granted with the passing of but a little time. That's what we call The Law of Familiarity. Without the discipline for paying constant, daily attention, all things become vulnerable.

"Be serious! Life is not a practice session! Don't be like the football teams who sometimes treat their Sunday afternoon contests casually, waiting for the two-minute whistle before getting serious. You may find that when the great referee of your life finally gives you your final two-minute warning that you're too far behind to ever catch up.

"And remember, a lack of discipline in the small areas of life can cost you heavily in the more important areas of life. You cannot clean up your company until you've learned to apply the discipline for cleaning your own garage. You cannot likely be impatient with your children and patient with your distributors or your employees. You may have difficulty telling others to recruit more or sell more when that instruction is inconsistent with your own conduct. You cannot admonish others to read the good books when you do not have a library card.

"Look around you at this very moment in time. What might you be doing that needs attention, that needs a new discipline, a new commitment, or a new decision? Life is too valuable for you to allow good ideas to be taken casually, as though the words or questions were meant for someone else.

"Perhaps you're on the threshold of giving up, or starting over, or starting out, and the only missing ingredient to your incredible success story is a new and self-imposed discipline that will make you stay longer, try harder and work more intensely than you ever thought you possibly could. And remember, the greatest, the most valuable form of discipline is the one that you impose on yourself. Don't wait for things to deteriorate so drastically that someone else must impose discipline into your life. Wouldn't that be tragic! How would you possibly explain why someone else thought more of you than you thought of yourself . . . why someone else forced you up early and into the marketplace when you would have been content to sleep in and let success go to someone who cared more about themselves than you cared about you?

"Your life, my life, the life of each one of us on this spinning blue-white planet is going to serve as either a warning or an example—a warning of the consequences of neglect, self-pity, or lack of direction and ambition, or an example of talent put to use, of discipline self-imposed, and of objectives clearly perceived and goals intensely pursued.

"In the end, when the conversation is over, or when the training class has ended, or when the book has been placed back upon the shelf, it is your own discipline that will be the magic catalyst that gives substance and depth to your plans and dreams. In the ideas and training provided by American Products lie the keys to the good life . . . the fundamentals for success, happiness, and pride in your own magnificent accomplishments. Once you've gathered up these ideas, these new insights, it will take your own discipline to make the basic fundamentals your own instinctive responses to life's challenges and life's opportunities. The ultimate question cannot be whether you are going to make the fundamental disciplines your own—the question is when?

"With the intense and consistent application of worthy disciplines we have the individual and collective capacity to change ourselves, our income, our attitudes, our lifestyle and our effect on other people. We can change opinions and we can change directions. We can change leadership. We can even change the direction of our nation. We have the chance. We have the capacity. We have the answers. And, we have the ability.

"The elements are all there, including the freedom to try—or even not to try. Only the discipline is missing, and that element and the decision to use it, lies within us all.

"The choice is ours. The time is now. I wish for you that you might seize the moment and make the choice . . . not the choice to try, but the decision to achieve. You are blessed with all the attributes for succeeding, not the least of which is the opportunity given to you simply because you are active participants in one of America's great success stories— American Products. I am proud of you, and I give you a challenge: Tonight, this moment, here in this place, become proud of yourselves!

"Thank you, Elmer Gibbons . . . my friends here tonight—Mikki and Charlie Livingston, Janice Alexander . . . my husband, Jon . . . and each of you. Thank you for inviting me."

Jonathan Locke sat in the back of the room watching as the gathering erupted with the spontaneity of a crowd of hockey fans as their team scores a winning goal. There was the rhythmic applause and the ever-present American Products theme song that was becoming symbolic of an American Products celebration. Jonathan stood, but he did not applaud. His wife would not expect it for she had his constant applause in the form of a love that was built on the foundation of friendship and a deep and unshakeable professional respect. He watched with a barely perceptible smile as Elmer Gibbons came back onto the platform, took Mariana's hand in his and raised the joined hands high into the air. He was celebrating a personal victory all his own. Of the crowd of over a thousand people, only Jonathan would know that as Gibbons took her right hand with both of his, he placed a neatly folded check into her hand as he whispered a private 'thank you' into her ear.

"Boy, what I wouldn't give to be able to speak like that!" The voice came from a young man who had been sitting a few feet away from Jonathan and had now moved closer to verbalize his feelings to anyone who might be willing to listen. Jonathan smiled at him. The man was in his early twenties and wore a pair of blue slacks and a blue jacket that didn't match. The brown shoes were badly worn but highly polished and he stood watching the applauding crowd that continued its rhythmic response to the ten or twelve people who were filing onto the platform at Elmer Gibbons's request. They were no doubt the local leadership of American Products.

"Someday I'm gonna be up there—you bet I am!" The young man spoke, almost to himself. He looked at Jonathan now. "Do you really believe that?" Jon asked.

"Well—maybe I'm just dreamin'," he said, "but I would if I could."

Jonathan looked at him again, and this time saw much of himself as he had been a long time ago.

"May I share an idea with you?"

"What's that?"

"It's not *I would if I could*; it's *I could if I would*."

It took a full minute for the young man to sort out the slightly complicated message. It was almost as though he had ignored the comment, moving slightly away from Jonathan, his eyes soaking in the events but his mind pondering the subtle message he had just heard. He came back toward Jonathan slowly as the applause began to subside.

"Sir, my name is Dwayne Karns . . . How did that go again?" He extended his right hand and Jonathan responded.

"Dwayne . . . My name is Jonathan Locke. I said, it's not *I would if I could*; it's *I could if I would*." The handshake gave added significance to the words.

"I'd never thought of it that way before," he said and slowly moved away into the mass of people as though the event had never happened. Somehow, Jonathan Locke had the distinct impression that a unique seed had been planted—a seed that might well take a decade to germinate.

The southern accent and the authoritative voice of Elmer Gibbons made a final remark that boomed through the elaborate PA system and the evening officially ended. Jonathan stood at one end of the room and his wife at the other, both saying hellos and goodbyes and signing their autographs. By ten-thirty, as if by grand design, Jonathan and Mariana Locke and Mikki and Charlie Livingston emerged from the room at the same time. Joining arms, they walked down the wide corridor toward the restaurant. It would be a long evening of stories, updating, remembering, examining, comparing, sharing and laughing. There were names that couldn't be remembered, dates that couldn't be agreed upon, and the mingling of stories that caused both joy and sorrow. And then, the final revelation by Mariana Locke to her friend Mikki of the events that afternoon at the White House with the president of the United States of America. She had been strangely reluctant to share the news, somehow fearing that Mikki and Charlie had heard it and had chosen not to discuss it for some silly reason. Mari had not wanted to boast, and had had difficulty finding a way to share her news without sounding pompous. It was one of the few remaining self-imposed limitations that she had not yet mastered, and yet it was a virtue—a willingness to consider carefully the emotions and sensitivities of others as much as her own.

The moment she heard it, Mikki climbed upon the cushioned bench of the oval shaped booth and hugged her dear friend with a total outpouring of joy. Mariana cried tears of both regret and happiness—

regret for ever doubting a friendship as unique as this, and happiness that her own well-measured discipline had forced her to do what, at the moment, was difficult for her.

The night finally gave way to morning, and at two-twenty Mariana and Jonathan waved as their friends pulled the Eldorado out onto the Parkway and toward the bridge leading across the Potomac. Jonathan looked down at his tired but obviously happy wife who held a small box with blue foil paper and a white ribbon in her left arm.

"Is it heavy?" he inquired.

"No, on the contrary, it feels almost empty," she answered.

"What do you suppose it is?"

She looked up smiling as they walked to the door leading to the lobby. "That crazy Mikki," Mariana said. "Charlie said it was just a few things she had found a few years ago after cleaning out the old apartment we shared in Philadelphia. It's just some old odds and ends."

"Wrapped like a gift?"

"That's Mikki, Jon. She has a way of making the common seem uncommon. That's one of the reasons I love her so much."

The night ended and the morning of a uniquely busy day would be upon them in a few hours. But neither thought to consider the time, for hours with rare friends should not be restrained by impending responsibilities, and both Mari and Jon were wise enough to know that the time ahead of them would be imposing its great demands on them both.

CHAPTER EIGHTEEN:
The Conference

"Ladies and gentlemen, the president of the United States." Robert F. Reardon entered through a side door to Mariana's left and stepped up onto the slightly elevated platform. He walked the few steps to where Mari and Jonathan sat, shook their hands, then turned and stood before the half dozen microphones. He looked out across the stone-faced press corps and waited for everyone to return to their seats.

Mariana had been silently observing these men and women for several minutes before the arrival of the president. After smiling or winking at a few people she recognized, she had spent time studying the expressions of those whose words contributed so much toward the mood of the nation. On some faces she saw pessimism, while on others indifference was clearly visible. A few joked and smiled, but most sat studying her, making comments to a colleague behind insincere smiles. These were faces she had seen all her life—faces on television that looked so much different when confronted in real life. She was discovering that TV newspeople had a lower body, just like other humans, though one saw only heads, arms, shoulders, and an occasional chest or stomach when they were on camera. Mariana couldn't help smiling to herself when she noticed that Phil Worthington, who had been doing network news reports since World War II, was wearing white socks with a black suit.

The president's opening remarks immediately shifted her attention away from the audience.

"Good morning. As is often the case, I am certain it would be inaccurate for me to begin by saying, 'I suppose you're wondering why I invited you here this morning.' There have been a number of rumors in recent weeks about the administration's interest in organizing a cabinet-level position empowered with responsibilities of a very significant, although unusual, nature. We have now spent a number of months getting to know congress, finding out what we can and cannot do, proposing legislation, and have even succeeded in getting a *few* bills actually *passed* up on the Hill."

A trickle of laughter flowed through the audience.

"There have been solutions proposed on financial matters and international matters. We have attempted to legislate morality by tackling such issues as gun control, women's rights, drug abuse, abortion, and racial equality. On the international scene, we are working to find a common ground between opposing parties. Through negotiation, compromise and an appeal to justice, fairness and reason, we strike a delicate, although precarious, peace—often between peoples whose historical tendencies have been the annihilation of the other side. We seem, at best, to alienate one side while making a shallow friendship with the other, and we call it compromise.

"At nearly every turn and on virtually every issue, whether at home or abroad, laws are passed that help the few at the expense of the many. We find ourselves often attempting to legislate everything for everyone, but in the final analysis, we are discovering that we have helped no one.

"Now, as I travel around this nation of ours, and listen and talk to people, I find one common thread woven throughout the conversations, the speeches, and the letters . . . whether that input comes from Boston, Miami, Los Angeles, Seattle, or Omaha. The theme is the same, and that theme is this: America is quickly becoming a nation without hope, without dreams and without ambition. Success has been made so difficult to achieve through legal means that more and more people are turning to illegal methods to pursue their fortunes. For many Americans, the reality of the way things are has become so difficult to deal with that the only option available to them is the temporary escape offered by drugs and alcohol.

"We have become so promiscuous and so grossly irresponsible that most forms of normal and ethical behavior have given way to that which is expedient. While all of this sounds perhaps like a condemnation of the American people, I would rather suggest that it is a condemnation of government. Over the past years, we have slowly allowed ourselves to become influenced and intimidated by special interest groups or by organizations supposedly designed to protect the rights of the individual. As a result, we have passed an unprecedented number of laws of such a ridiculous nature that now very *few* people have rights . . . very *few* people have freedoms . . . very *few* people have hope.

"What I want to go on record as saying is that when a nation— supposedly 'one nation under God'—that becomes so immoral, so irresponsible, so uncaring and apathetic that they do whatever they darn well please and demand that the government should pay for it . . . when a nation has become so massively inconsistent with the principles upon which it was founded, then I say we are a nation on the very threshold of collapse. When the rights of the criminal become as important as the rights of the victim, then I suggest we are moving in the wrong direction. When congress may begin its day with prayer, but our children in school may not, then I suggest something is wrong. When *any* group of people, whether it is a minority or a majority, adopts the belief that government owes them an income, or a job, or a free handout of *any* kind simply because they are part of a particular group, then I suggest that government has somewhere in the past given out the wrong signals. Government owes every person one thing only, and that is a fair chance—an equal opportunity for each human to make something of themselves. Beyond that, any government does not, in my opinion, owe anything to anyone who is physically or mentally able to take care of themselves.

"Government has its responsibilities; there can be no question about that. Government owes to every citizen the right to express himself freely, unless the individual's free expression suggests, either overtly or covertly, the overthrow of that very government which owes to them that right of free speech.

"Government owes to each citizen the right to an equal education, but not the burden of a drive by bus to a neighborhood foreign to his home.

"Government owes to business a climate in which it can stretch its muscles, expand, create, compete, promote, explore and study, so that through its successes it will provide more opportunity for more people to pursue their own individual success within that business. When the system works right, some employees will even leave and use their own gift of creativity to become an honest competitor offering better-quality products and lower prices. That, you see, is nature's way of sustaining balance; it is the strong becoming stronger so that the weak might survive and one day take their first step on the ladder leading to success. To have government interfere with nature's divine intent will surely invite disaster.

"Today, however, I am inaugurating a program of fulfilling new needs and responsibilities heretofore neglected. The needs to which I am referring include the need for more *hope* in our individual and collective future. There is also the human need to learn the value of a positive and healthy self-image. And, too, there is the need for training the young as well as the old on the value of setting goals, of discovering and pursuing ambitions that lead to a more productive life, independent of any government assistance. These principles are being taught in America today to a small minority of our people. They are taught to executives in corporations and to an inner-elite which uses these principles in their daily lives. And because they are used, the affluent become more affluent, the wealthy become more wealthy and the ambitious become more ambitious. Now, unfortunately, these principles are taught in private seminars and the vast majority of the American people are unaware of their existence or, even if they *are* aware, do not take advantage of them . . . though the material they choose to pass by is the very material that would provide the answers they need.

"Therefore, with the introduction of a new cabinet post called the Department of Human Development, I am initiating a government program that will bring these private seminars and the material that these seminars include to the American people . . . to *all* of the American people. As the first Secretary to be called to this very important position, I am nominating Mariana Locke—author, lecturer, and businesswoman— who, with her husband Jonathan, has been a principal of Camelot Productions, a seminar production company based in California.

"No doubt you are going to wonder just what this new depart- ment is going to be doing—what its goals and objectives are. To help answer that, we've prepared an outline of what we anticipate the role to be. Each of you has been given a copy of that outline for review this morning. In the weeks ahead, we shall be giving you more specific information as the plans are developed. It's going to take a while for various materials to become available; this is an area, as I say, that has been completely neglected except within a small sector of the business community. However, beginning today, and as I indicated in conversation with Mrs. Locke only yesterday, I am putting the government in the people-development business.

"So that you might get to know her better, I'm going to ask Mrs. Locke to spend some time with you this morning. Some of you may have read her books or perhaps have heard her speak. If so, then you know what she teaches and what her philosophy is. My purpose in creating this new cabinet post is so that *all* Americans might be given the chance to learn from that philosophy.

"I'm certain that Mariana will do her very best this morning to answer any questions you might have . . . oh—and please remember, Mrs. Locke first learned of this yesterday; we've only had the chance for a very brief conversation. I assume the shock has worn off sufficiently by now . . ."

The president turned toward her, smiled, then looked back at the press to thank them. Then, with a simple 'Welcome to Washington, Mrs. Locke,' Reardon walked over to her with an extended hand. Mariana stood to accept the handshake and stepped up to the podium. From the corner of her eye, she could see the chief executive stop briefly to shake her husband's hand before quickly disappearing through a door on the opposite side of the room from which he had entered.

There was no applause—only the sound of rustling movement as the reporters made themselves more comfortable. The photographers moved in slouched and hurried motions for their first pictures of this personality who was unknown to them. It was obvious to Mari that the questions she assumed they would ask were being held until later, and that she was expected to speak. There had been no detailed briefing of what she was to do; only her own experience told her how to respond to the situation. There were more warm smiles than she had expected, but somehow she knew instinctively what this was going to be like.

"Good morning, ladies and gentlemen," she said. "The thoughts going through our minds this moment give us a great deal in common. I do not know any more about you than you know about me. In the time ahead of us, however, we will no doubt become increasingly familiar with one another. I'm certain you'll be doing a great deal of study into where I've come from, what I have done, what I think, and how I am likely to conduct myself in any government position to which I might be nominated or confirmed. Let me make just a few comments here about some of the events in my past that will no doubt be of interest to you. By covering them this morning, perhaps it will help to clarify a few questions. First, I do not have the normal qualifications or experience of one called to such a position of responsibility. I have no background in government service, which I consider to be an asset. Second, I have a minimum of formal education to bring to this office, which I have found in dealing with people and their needs is also an asset. Third, in my fairly recent past, I have a divorce—which you may find to be good copy, although the reasons for it are, in my opinion, very valid and quite personal.

"You are probably going to find my views on government and people to be considerably different than most. I deeply believe in the individual responsibility that each person has—to themselves first and second, to their country—a responsibility for making something worthwhile of his or her existence. If an individual truly *does* take advantage of opportunity and does well in life, then that person has the full and total responsibility for taking *credit*. If the individual does not do well in life—particularly in America—he or she cannot, in my opinion, blame government . . . nor anyone else, for that matter. I will admit that the tendency exists for us to blame someone outside ourselves for our actions, but to engage in *that* foolish mental exercise is to assure the continuation of circumstances as they are.

"It is my intent, should my nomination be confirmed by the Senate, to make available to every American the basic information one needs to hear, read, and in some way experience, if life is going to improve for that individual. I believe that we become what we think about—that thought has some mysterious way of producing circumstance, and that to change how we live, where we live, what we *do*, and what we *earn*, we need to begin by changing our *attitude*. I believe that a collection of individual attitudes further creates a *national* attitude and that to a very major degree, much of our current national challenges were produced by an attitude. A plunging stock market is an attitude phenomenon. Climbing interest rates is an attitude. Inflation is an attitude. Poor quality in our educational systems is an attitude. Just as our attitude and our moods change as individuals, so do our attitudes and moods change collectively. I noted yesterday that the stock market dropped seventeen points. The financial analysts reported that the reason was the uncertainty over the action that might be taken by the Federal Reserve Board regarding interest rates. I ask you, ladies and gentlemen, to ponder that statement. Are we to believe that several million people holding stock chose to sell it within a few hours because they all had a common fear at the same time? I think not. I think that a few people somewhere near the top of the financial structure became worried or apprehensive for some reason and, by expressing that apprehension, a chain reaction of thought was triggered that produced a . . . well, the familiar *domino effect*. In other words, a single and relatively unimportant event or fact produces a thought . . . which produces apprehension . . . which becomes worry. Then, we begin taking negative action in response to these worries. Of course, the negative action then automatically produces the very thing we worried about. Being well-educated humans, we then conclude that the event itself caused the negative results. I find this a bit . . . well, I suppose *stupid* might be a good word.

"It is my opinion that the material that my husband and I have found to be so very effective within the business community also has great value within the public sector. Therefore, I shall be studying ways to make that material available to anyone who wants to have access to it, and investigating what it might require to break down our anti-quated superstructure of educational administration in order to have some of this material taught in schools.

"As you might guess, there are a number of unanswered questions regarding exactly how we're going to implement some of the programs I have in mind. This new position is an entirely new thrust for all of us. Therefore, rather than attempting to get too specific right now, I think I shall end my remarks at this point, and in accordance with the agenda for this press conference, open up the remainder of the time for ques-tions from—"

As if on cue, several dozen of the hundred or so in attendance came to their feet in a simultaneous "Mrs. Locke!" She had asked that she be free to handle whatever questions be thrown at her, and Fletcher Kennedy had agreed.

She saw Leonard R. Bernstein in the front row and pointed at him, smiling.

"Yes, Mr. Bernstein."

She would have staged it this way in advance if she had been given the choice. Leonard R. Bernstein had been the *NBC Washington* corre-spondent since as far back as she could remember. He rarely smiled on camera, but was courteously returning her own smile now. The red bow tie he wore had become his trademark—not always red, but always a bow tie.

"Mrs. Locke, in reading some of your books and articles, you've commented on several occasions that it is your belief that television is largely responsible for a decline in morality in this country. Do you still think it is true—and do you think it is fair?"

"Let me say, Mr. Bernstein, that the truth is seldom fair—especially to those sensitive to the truth. If truth is the objective, then fairness becomes irrelevant. Now, the issue would seem to be whether the statement you've attributed to me is accurate . . . does television contribute to immorality? First, let me say something in defense of your industry. It is *not* television teaching *immorality* that is the problem—it is *part* of the problem, but of equal importance is the fact that there are so few voices teaching *morality*. I recently read that a study indicates that by the time a young child enters the first grade of elementary school, he or she has been witness to twenty-two thousand murders on television. Now, if you're going to show that much violence, Mr. Bernstein—not you, of course, but your network programmers and producers—then I suggest that you ponder the effect of such staged human conduct on the audience who watches it. You see, if that many murders had been seen by the young viewer by watching six years of network news, then we would have to condemn the society that *commits* those twenty-two thousand murders. You would have merely reported on such sad human behavior. It is when so much of your prime time programming contains repeated scenes of violence, sex, and questionable human conduct deliberately written by television writers and acted out by actors that your conduct needs to be questioned. Therefore, to directly answer your question, the answer is yes, I believe your industry is largely responsible."

She paused and the group spoke in unison again. She pointed to a completely unfamiliar man well back in the group who had risen to his feet a split second sooner than the rest.

"Yes, Mrs. Locke—Eric Wiggins of *The Washington Post*. The president commented this morning that . . . and I use his words . . . 'We are a nation on the very threshold of collapse.' Do you share that same view?"

"I do. *That*, Mr. Wiggins, is the reality of things; but it need not remain that way. A writer once said that the only thing necessary for the triumph of evil is for good men to do nothing. But to change our current direction, we must begin by knowing where we really are, and I believe that we are headed toward an eventual collapse . . . a major change in life as we've known it to be. However, by implementing some very positive and worthwhile programs designed to perpetuate and encourage hope rather than to promote despair, I know we can reverse the trend."

The next question, from a young man with an arrogant look on his face, was one she knew would eventually arise.

"Mrs. Locke, does it occur to you that by instituting government programs that withhold the truth from the American people, even though the truth might be *negative*, that you will be guilty of managing the news in the same way that Mr. Goebbels, the German propaganda minister in World War II, painted false pictures to the German public?"

She paused for a moment, her eyes not leaving the young man who had asked the question. She thought about how quick he had been to determine her guilt.

"Might I ask the name of the judge who has proclaimed me guilty?"

His arrogance was made more noticeable by the defiance in his voice. "Lester Manly of the *International News Network*, Mrs. Locke, and my question was hypothetical."

"Well, Mr. Manly, I would never consider any program designed to hide the truth, whether the truth be negative or positive. My affirmation of the president's earlier remark that 'we are a nation on the very threshold of collapse,' is not one of the more positive statements I have heard, and yet it was stated here for you to hear. The programs I envision will not be designed to *manage* the news, merely to present another voice . . . a voice of hope and encouragement that provides the American people with a whisper of inspiration amid a flood of human desperation."

The youthful voice came again from the same young man who now only partially stood.

"Then you wouldn't consider the government involvement in a program of teaching your philosophies to the public to be a government-sponsored program of brainwashing the people to your own personal views?"

He sat down, folding his arms and slouching into his chair until he almost disappeared from her view. She felt a rush of anger which she fought to control. The smile which came to her lips was designed to camouflage the inner emotion.

"Well . . . uh—Mr. Manly . . . the public has been listening to *someone's* views for a long time now. Our freedom of speech and of the press, granted by the First Amendment to the American Constitution, allows a number of views to be promulgated. The views I've heard lately, and those that I've read, are not of the type that make me feel encouraged about our future. In essence, the views . . . *my* views, as you call them, are merely the other side of the coin. As a journalist, you have the license to affect public opinion with each article you write. If you, and a significant number of other members of the media, tend to be skeptical, excessively investigative, and largely pessimistic in your personal views, then those limiting views are going to show up in the general opinion of the public. You must understand, sir, as must all members of the media, that your role in forming public opinion is not at all unlike the role of a parent in forming the personality and attitude of a child. Each day, each of you is affecting the public. My question to you is very simple—look at what you're saying and how you say it, and then ask *yourselves* if this is the kind of journalistic language likely to encourage and inspire the public. If not, could you say it, perhaps, in a different way that lets you report the *facts* while providing hope for a better future? You see, government has *its* right to speak and to provide views as well, Mr. Manly, and I am merely going to work on programs that are factual but encouraging, that promote dignity rather than scoff at the human dilemma. I say, Mr. Manly, that America need not be the way it is. To paraphrase someone, 'The press tends to look at things the way they are and ask why. We are going to look at the way things could and should be, and ask why not.' I do not consider that line of thinking to be brainwashing."

Lester Manly continued to slump in his chair as she pointed to another of the raised hands.

"Mrs. Locke—Alex Dreyfus of *Newsweek*. Could you tell us, please—since your firm creates the sort of materials it sounds as though you're going to be putting to use in your programs within the government structure, do you plan to use the programs of Camelot Productions, and if so, would this not be a conflict of interest?"

She smiled warmly at the man and then answered. "Yes, Mr. Dreyfus, any products produced by Camelot Products and sold to the government at a profit *would* create a definite conflict of interest and *would* therefore be unacceptable . . . both to the public and to me. Mr. Locke will continue to serve at Camelot. Since I've not yet had the opportunity to discuss the issue with him, I'm not certain whether he would object to making a profit or not . . ." She turned briefly and smiled at Jonathan, who laughed but did not respond. Then she turned back to her audience who seemed to enjoy her first attempt at government humor.

"No, Mr. Dreyfus, any materials produced by Camelot for use in any government program would, I suspect, be made available at cost. Or perhaps, in order to avoid any question at all, we may decide to have other vendors manufacture the materials."

Her slight pause indicated the conclusion of her answer and the chorus of "Mrs. Locke!" rang out again. She pointed this time to the silver-haired William Abbott, whom she recognized from *The Los Angeles Times*.

"Mrs. Locke . . ."

"Good morning, Mr. Abbott." Her unexpected greeting and broad smile brought a warm chuckle from most of her audience, and Abbott smiled in return.

"Good morning," he answered. "Mrs. Locke—the . . . I suppose you would call it the . . . the seminar business, is exploding across the country, and more and more people are becoming involved in so-called self-help or personal development programs. Since your company is but one among possibly hundreds involved in this relatively new kind of business, would you care to speculate on why *you* were chosen as the nominee from the many others?"

She looked down for a moment, then back over her right shoulder toward where she knew the president had disappeared moments before, and again looked back at Abbott, the smile returning broadly. "Well, I suppose you would have to ask the president that question; but in his absence, I might offer a speculative answer. Both Mr. Locke and I have attempted to be a bit more realistic in our attempt to change people's lives. We've taken somewhat of a dim view of the fact that changing one's life—and hence one's circumstance—is an easy matter." The smile disappeared now as she carefully and deliberately chose her words.

"There are those—both authors and speakers—who *perform* rather than *inform*, and who provide interesting and sometimes humorous entertainment as they are called upon to share ideas with groups at conventions and other public gatherings. Some of these people teach that affirmations—that is, repeating some positive kind of statement over and over again—will somehow change one's life. There are others who resort to such things as self-hypnosis as a means for transforming oneself from being . . . uh . . . somewhat average to being instantly wealthy and famous. While some of the things *might* work well for a few, they certainly appear to be somewhat ineffective for the masses and seem to provide, at best, only a short-term means of escape from the real world. After you've hypnotized yourself into the delusion of any antici- pated immediate success, there is still the real world—with real people and real challenges—to contend with. You see, you might walk about with a strange gaze in your eyes wildly anticipating your imminent success, but those who watch you may not understand your strange behavior and begin instead to avoid you . . . as they well should . . ."

The audience broke into open laughter. Even Lester Manly sat erect, a broad grin on his face as he looked at the man next to him who sat stone-faced, as though her words were directed at him. She laughed with them, glancing behind her at Jonathan whose own laughter and simultaneous uncrossing and re-crossing of his legs signaled a loosening of the tension within the room. Mariana let the laughter subside before continuing.

"Our experience—my husband's more so than my own, indicates that such forms of wild enthusiasm and somewhat unorthodox approaches to the field of behavior modification offer, at best, a form of temporary anesthesia and give false hope to those seeking to truly improve themselves. We believe that there are no easy solutions to changing oneself or one's circumstance. It takes a number of things. In the interest of time this morning, I cannot elaborate, but things such as the recognition of the need for change, combined with a new commitment, uh . . . self-discipline . . . planning . . . and consistent execution of newly learned skills, are of paramount importance. In general, we believe it to be unlikely that a human life that has been generally neglected for thirty years or so can be changed in a thirty-minute motivational speech. After the *speech* is over, now what are you going to do about correcting the thirty or more years of *neglect*? Hopefully, we will or should be doing more than waiting patiently for the motivational speaker to come back to town.

"To be more specific in answering your question, Mr. Abbott, I suspect that our views are somewhat more conventional, more realistic than some of the others, and probably more in line with the president's views."

She kept her eyes on her audience as she paused to correct a thought, then looked upward from the podium and continued. "The president has, I believe, taken somewhat the same approach in *his* attempts to correct the nation's economy. He has inherited the results of those who preceded him, who had sought short-term solutions to age-old challenges, who had at times and in the interest of popularity, done that which was expedient rather than that which was necessary. *This* generation—*our* generation—is now being called upon to correct the ills and the errors of the past. While this is certainly not an easy or a popular task, it is one that was both inevitable and predictable. I can recall other prominent citizens, both within government and from the public sector, who recognized the imminency of our current challenges, and who often commented on the fact that some *future* generation of Americans would have to be called upon to make sacrifices . . . that the erosion of our economy, and the combination of inflation and the import-export imbalance—to say nothing of the staggering national debt—would soon take its toll. *That* generation of Americans is *here*! Our children, our parents and certainly ourselves have been called upon to make the necessary sacrifices.

"Long ago, the voices of inspiration spoke to us, and their warnings went unheeded. They cautioned us against excessive spending and we continued to spend; they cautioned us against the dangers of a diminished national defense system, and we allowed that system of defense to reach what are now dangerous proportions. Those voices of inspiration called out to us from every corner and we failed to listen. We were caught up in the endless wave of prosperity and abundance; we were too busy having a good time to pay any attention. Now, the quiet voice of inspiration is silent, and the void is filled with the shrill and penetrating voice of desperation. Our neglect leaves us no choice other than to respond. It is not *this* president whose policies have caused high unemployment and interest rates, or who has given to us the many and diverse challenges which divide and demoralize us; but it is this president, as well as those who follow him as *future* presidents, who must bring us to the inevitable day of reckoning with policies and programs which, while unpopular, are both necessary and difficult. We chose, you and I, to turn a deaf ear to those who earlier admonished us, to those who spoke at a time when the sacrifices would have been easier to bear, to those who offered what I call 'the favored voice of inspiration,' and now we have no choice.

"So you see, the steps necessary to change a nation whose health has significantly diminished through years of neglect are similar in nature to those steps necessary to *restore* . . . or *discover* prosperity and contentment to the life of any given *individual* whose accumulated years of neglect and inattention have produced a hopeless or mediocre condition. Change takes time. The restoration of health takes time. The regaining of prosperity, whether by a nation or an individual, takes time. And the changing of one's attitude, circumstance, and lifestyle takes time. You cannot demand your share of the American dream today, or this month or even this year, when the previous thirty . . . or forty . . . or more years have been devoted to the planting of seeds which were clearly destined to produce just the opposite result come the time of harvest. You may *want* your personal fortune and happiness now, the nation may *want* its times of prosperity now, but we will, as we always have, reap what we've sown.

"The president's policies in restoring health to government are similar to *my* policies in the area of human behavior . . . I would call it a policy of hope and encouragement coupled with an acceptance of reality, and tempered by a commitment and a determination to change ourselves from what we are to what we can be, from a time of challenge to a time of rejoicing. The American dream requires only a reawakening of the American spirit, and I am convinced that our decade of challenge and uncertainty that began in the early seventies is now giving way to a time of growth and a time of new opportunity . . . for each of us individually, and for our nation collectively."

She paused, her eyes remaining on her now silent audience. There was something about her words—about her—that filled the room with an indefinable air of respect and a strange feeling of pride. There was the intense feeling that all *would* somehow be well again.

Sensing the need for a lighter word, she leaned slightly to her right, her eyes catching William Abbott's, who sat with a strange, but deeply respectful smile.

"Mr. Abbott, if you will excuse my five-minute answer to your five-second question, I trust you see somewhat more clearly why I was selected from those who serve in a similar capacity of giving hope and encouragement to others."

She smiled.

It began with two men in the third row. Slowly, the silence gave way to a reluctant but certain applause that spread like a wave throughout the room until all were on their feet, standing and applauding the woman who moments before was unknown to them, but whose words and conduct, and whose sincerity and intensity had captured their respect and brought tears to the eyes of a few who had not been touched with such uncommon sophistication from within these walls in more years than most of them cared to remember.

She had not thought of what she had said, or why it had brought such a response. An audience such as this, in a place such as this, did not respond in such a way, she thought. She did not know that it was not just what she said, but the manner—the totally unexpected manner in which she had said it—that created the spontaneous outpouring of respect. To them, she had been an unknown personality, a woman selected for a position of great responsibility for perhaps the wrong reasons . . . the political reasons . . . the appointment of a woman in order to fill a campaign promise. This unique person had in a few short moments converted skepticism into enthusiastic support.

Mariana Locke did not become emotional. She was deeply moved, but she did not cry as she had always done before during times of emotion. She stood firmly at the podium and uttered an almost indiscernible "thank you." She savored the moment as the applause continued for a full half-minute.

As had happened once before, a single and insignificant figure did not join the salute to the words and charm of Mariana Locke. The woman sat ten rows back, near the far wall to Mari's left. In her hands she held a single piece of paper in preparation for a confrontation that would change the mood of the room as she tested the woman who had just accepted the subsiding applause of the gathering.

"Mrs. Locke—Gloria Simon of the Human Liberties Protective League. While we're all impressed with your eloquence, I would like to ask a question whose answer requires a bit more than mere rhetoric. Some time ago, in a speech you gave in Los Angeles, California, at a time when you did not have your current political aspirations, you said, and I quote, 'If there is anyone here tonight who feels that the government or those of high achievement should be forced by law to give the fruits of their efforts to those who sit and feel sorry for them-selves . . .' Well, you asked that they leave the room. I find it difficult to understand how someone with views such as this might intend to serve all the people in a position with the proposed title of The Secretary of Human Development."

Mari listened courteously and attentively, then began her answer.

"Well first, Mrs. Simon, I—"

"And when you've finished I have another follow-up question." She remained on her feet, her arms folded and her chin thrust slightly upward.

"First, let me say that I don't believe your quote is quite accurate. My—"

"I was there, Mrs. Locke. Please don't resort to the 'I've been misquoted' scenario."

"May I finish my answer as I have given you the courtesy to finish your question?"

She paused, and the silent Gloria Simon stood motionless. "I clearly recall the event you are referring to, and while you seem certain that those were my words, I can assure you that such words, taken out of context, do not present an accurate assessment of either my views or my character. I will, however, clarify my position on the subject you refer to. I cannot accept the suggestion that government serve as a financial income source for those who are able but unwilling to put their skills or talents to work in the American marketplace. There—"

"Did you not state in Los Angeles that dependence is a dangerous human condition?"

"Isn't it?"

"Dangerous? I fail to see how, Mrs. Locke."

"Except in those cases where aging or physical or mental conditions prevent human productivity, dependency is, Mrs. Simon, a dangerous human condition. Dependence on someone else suggests weakness. The alternative to dependence is independence, and I suggest it is a preferable alternative. My responsibility in life, or at least one of them, is to free myself from depending on the efforts, promises or charity of someone else. Someone else may well offer me charity or urge me to depend on them, but with my acceptance of their offer, I sacrifice something far more valuable—my freedom to act and to choose, and my responsibility for my own actions. If my fate is in the hands of another, and if my dependence upon that other person ends in disappointment, then I will find fault with and place blame upon that other person. I will blame government or the company I work for, or my neighbors or relatives or perhaps my husband. I will seek to place blame *anywhere* except where it *belongs*. Such is the curse of dependence and it is, yes—dangerous. Dependence fosters fear and uncertainty. Dependence robs us of our dignity and encourages laziness. Dependence permits one to feed off the productivity of another, and soon the one who *gives* is as weak as the one who *receives*. I will permit myself, Mrs. Simon, to depend on only one thing, and that is on my government to give me the freedom to speak, to write, to try, and to be held fully accountable for my own actions. With that, I shall plot, scheme, and contrive ways to win back my other freedoms until once again I emerge fully independent. But with dependence, we *lose* our freedoms. We must measure our words, guard our opinions, limit our questions, restrict our views, and compromise our beliefs lest our own expressions threaten those on whom we find ourselves dependent. Yes, Mrs. Simon, dependence is indeed dangerous, for it threatens the bonds between those who offer and those who accept, and surely the day will come when the dependent one will deem the independent to be his enemy. Dependence is a deception that gives a temporary and deceptive security, and I call to the world—to each one here and out there—to seek your independence, and reject those who seek to take care of you, lest your *caretaker* become your *jailer*."

"Mrs. Locke . . . Mrs. Locke . . . Again, your rhetoric is most admirable, but I can't help but believe that perhaps you're just a bit out of touch with reality. There are over twelve million people out there who have, because of the policies of this administration, become dependent on their government for food and shelter. There are the minorities, Mrs. Locke, who have difficulty finding a job in *good* times and who, when they *are* employed, are underpaid. And then there are those in prison—incarcerated in antiquated and overcrowded facilities unfit for human habitation. It seems to me, Mrs. Locke, that the view from your half-million dollar home on the hill of Southern California has distorted your view of those who *really* need your help. It seems to me that you and Mr. Locke, and your friend, Senator Elliott Brendis, have only the interest of those who are *affluent* at heart, and the rest of us—those who are poor, without jobs, and without any substantial support from government assistance programs—are going to be offered tape programs and books, all containing philosophies that seldom work for anyone but the ambitious or the wealthy. It is my humble opinion . . ."

"Mrs. Simon—"

"I am not finished, Mrs.—"

"Mrs. Simon, you never *will* be!" For the first time, the reserved personality of Mariana Locke gave way to an obvious firmness, and the strength and volume of her voice stunned the audience who had gathered for a routine introduction to a new cabinet appointee, but who now witnessed an unexpected confrontation at a time and in a place most unexpected.

"Mrs. Simon, is it possible that you might condense your speech and revise it in the form of a rational question that I can respond to?"

Gloria Simon remained on her feet, a look of vengeful satisfaction on her face. She paused but a moment, smiled slightly at a woman who had turned to look at her, then spoke.

"Yes, I have a question for you that I'm sure will be of interest to us all. Is there anything, anywhere in your programs—assuming you *have* some tangible programs in mind—that will give meaningful assistance to the poor . . . the minorities of America, so that this position . . . this . . . this Department of Human Development as it is called, will function as more than just another government bureaucracy?"

"No."

"I beg your pardon?"

"No, there shall be nothing in our programs designed to provide meaningful assistance to the poor . . . or to the rich, the unemployed, the criminals, or the elderly, or anyone else for that matter."

Gloria Simon's eyes widened, her mouth opened, and she smirked at several of those who had turned toward her awaiting her response.

She was like an actress playing the role of one who had discovered a damaging and secretive fact about someone they sought to destroy.

"Then just what *do* you propose to do, Mrs. Locke? What *are* you going to offer the minorities of America? *That* is your purpose, Mrs. Locke, and *that* is my question."

With a look that combined both smugness and contempt, she sat down and glared at the woman who looked downward at the podium, fumbling with a single sheet of paper that the president had left behind. For but a millisecond, Mariana felt the surge of anger and unpreparedness she had felt many times before, many years ago. It was an unpreparedness reminiscent of the day she sat before Culpepper who had challenged her existence and her beliefs. That was then, but this was now. She raised her head to look at her audience. Breathing in slowly and deeply, she then spoke—not to Gloria Simon, not even to those in the room. She looked at them, but her words were directed toward all who would hear what she was about to speak.

"Today, at this moment, a confrontation takes place with each of you as a witness to that confrontation. It is not, as it appears to be, a confrontation of personalities with opposing views. It is, rather, a confrontation of ideologies each with its own inherent promise, and each with its appeal to a particular class of people. One ideology promotes the belief that those who are in need are the masters of those who have the capacity to *fill* that need. The other promotes the belief that *no* class is the master of the other, and that neither class is responsible *to*—or *for*—the other, but that we all are, in the final analysis, responsible to ourselves for our existence, our future, as well as our current circumstances. There is a movement underway in America . . . a subtle movement toward the displacement of wealth and power from the hands of those who *have* into the hands of those who *have not*. I suggest to you that it is a dangerous movement. Let it be clearly understood that I harbor no prejudice toward any group of people. I do not recognize minorities, nor do I recognize majorities. I care for the individual and I care in proportion to how much that individual cares for him or her *self*. I care about the untapped potential of the individual mind, whether that mind—that unlimited, restricted, but unused brain—rests within the head of a member of the minority or the majority. I care about a member of any minority having a fair chance to escape his or her circumstances and move upward to new plateaus of self-discovery, human fulfillment, and achievement. But as much as I want it to be known that I care about all individuals, I want it clearly known that I care even more about the collective body of productive individuals living together in a free land, who by their collective efforts and combined talents have produced a society that permits a member of the ghetto community to rise above their limitations and go on to become a member of Congress, a business executive, a publisher, author or *whatever* they choose to become. You see, I believe it is right to care more about *America* than about *Americans*.

"I believe that if we will devote ourselves to taking care of America, then America—a healthy, productive and free *America*—will take care of those among our ranks who *cannot* take care of *themselves*. And yet, there are those within our ranks who seek to weaken the goose that lays the golden eggs by proclaiming that those who have little must, through threat, coercion, demand, boycott, demonstration or whatever means may be at their disposal, be given a portion of wealth by those whose efforts have created wealth and fostered a strong America.

"I suggest to you that we are becoming a nation that, in our zeal to eliminate discrimination, is beginning to *discriminate against talent*. We have closed our doors to talented individuals because quotas and restrictions permit only the admittance of minorities. Schools, institutions, and research projects are turning away extraordinary talent because that talent is a member of the majority, and majority positions are supposedly 'up to quota.' Recently, an unusually talented young man was barred from participating in a program of major national interest because he was not a member of a minority. Should we not be *promoting* talent, rather than discriminating *against* it? Discriminate against talent, and you discriminate against creativity, productivity, progress and profits. I find myself sometimes confused and sometimes perplexed at the capacity of the media to uniquely make the minority look like the majority. I say to you today, at the great risk of making myself rather unpopular and at the risk of embarrassing some politicians who, in their pompous and selfish fashion, speak only what they think large voting blocs want to hear, that we must begin again to reward those who are *productive*. We must be willing to follow our elected leaders and to minimize our condemnation of their policies. And finally, we must turn away from those who want to return to programs of unwarranted social charity.

"You ask, Mrs. Simon, what I am going to do or to offer the minorities of America. My answer is simple—I intend to give America hope in *itself* by giving *people* hope and encouragement and instruction designed to lead toward their discovery of *self*. We're going to teach people *to hold up their head* rather than *hold out their hand*. We're going to teach people to accept full responsibility for their actions. We're going to help people to find within and for themselves what they want to do with their lives, and then point them in that direction and encourage them to continue that journey. People with direction and ambition and enthusiasm don't look for jobs; they create their *own* opportunities. Jobs are, in my opinion, resting places for those who have not yet found *themselves*. Government shouldn't need to create jobs, Mrs. Simon. Change the attitude of the nation and the nation will produce more jobs than people can fill. Show one person how to capitalize on their talent, teach them the merits of free enterprise in a capitalistic society, and that *one* person will, with his or her new enthusiasm, create a *thousand* jobs.

"Now, I am very sorry for taking more of your time than the schedule had allotted, but the question posed here today required more than just a cursory answer, and—"

"Would you permit me just a final question?" The voice belonged to William Abbott.

"Yes?"

"You've been unusually candid today, Mrs. Locke. Do you think that perhaps your candor will have an adverse bearing on the U.S. Senate's willingness to confirm your nomination?"

"My frankness is necessitated by my own conscience, Mr. Abbott. I do not exist to impress *anyone* or any organization, but to speak what I conceive to be the truth. What the Senate will do, the Senate will do. Thank you."

With that, she turned toward Jonathan just as Fletcher Kennedy entered from the side door. There was a polite exchange of words and instructions while behind them the applause gained in volume. She turned, spoke another "thank you," smiled, and walked through the doorway, guided in that direction by Kennedy.

Within moments, she and Jonathan found themselves in a limousine being whisked from the White House grounds and toward the hotel. It would be a ride without conversation, for Jonathan knew that she needed time to ponder what she had said, and what she wished she *might* have said. He sensed that she was not happy with herself. It was a time for playing the tapes over again—a time for introspection and evaluation.

She spoke but once as the limousine pulled from the highway into the driveway that led to the hotel. Her statement was in the form of a final remark *to* herself, *about* herself.

"I've spent over thirty years speaking in riddles and parables— being nice and saying what sounded good to other people. For that, I alienated others *and myself*. I will never again speak anything to anyone simply because they want to hear it or because I am afraid of the truth. My life and peace of mind are more important than my position."

She turned to look at her husband.

"Of all human virtues, Mariana, the truth is second to none. You don't apologize for it, nor for the consequences. Truth needs no explanation; it merely exists."

CHAPTER NINETEEN:

The Return

T he voice on the phone was that of a man named William
Sorensen. He was the White House Chief of Staff and was
calling to advise her of the tentative plans for the coming week
that would require her presence in Washington.

"We have a team to build around you," he said, "and programs and
plans to mold."

"Has the president been fully advised of my remarks during the
press conference?"

"Of course. He saw most of it on the closed-circuit television system."

"And he did not object to my remarks?"

"Why would he object?"

"Directness is hardly a way to gain popularity in Washington," she said.

"This administration would prefer accuracy to popularity. I thought
that was clear to everyone by now. But no, the president rather enjoyed
the way you handled yourself, and with no detailed briefing."

She laughed. "Would a briefing have prepared me for Gloria Simon?"

"Gloria? She means well. She just has her priorities a bit confused.
Anyway, we'd like to plan on spending several hours with you
tomorrow morning, but we'll need an early start. Could we send a car
by at . . . say five a.m.?"

"Five?"

"Relax. You'll get used to it."

"Mr. Sorenson—this may be a bit out of line, but just how certain can we be . . . I mean, well—the situation with the Senate confirmation . . . are we being a bit assumptive?"

"Assumptive? What do you mean?"

"Well, believe me, I'm pleased that the president enjoyed my remarks this morning, but isn't there a rather distinct possibility that my confirmation by the Senate is still in question?"

There was a slight pause as though he had hesitated to swallow a mouthful of coffee.

"Mrs. Locke, you'll be going before the Senate before you know it, and if you'll merely conduct yourself in the same confident and professional way you did today, you'll be fine. Believe me, your Senate confirmation was assured before you were ever called to Washington. Just trust me on that."

He spoke as though her expressed concern was irrelevant, as though any opposition would be as eventful as a fly landing on a roof.

"You sound very convincing, Mr. Sorenson."

"You're critically important to our plans, Mrs. Locke . . . critically important. I want your mind free to develop some creative plans for changing the attitude of this country, so just operate under the assumption that you're going to be in Washington for at least a few years."

"I like your attitude, Mr. Sorensen."

"And we like yours—which ought to make us all get along rather famously. Now then, you'll be ready at five?"

"Of course."

"Good. Just remain in your room until the man who will pick you up rings you from downstairs. Are there any other questions . . . Your accommodations are comfortable?"

"Very, thank you."

"We'll see you in the morning. 'Bye."

There was a click and Mariana Locke placed the phone down gently. Sliding herself down into a fully horizontal position on the bed, she laid her head on the pillow still folded under the bedspread. Jonathan had gone to the lobby to meet with someone he hadn't seen in a while, and had encouraged her to sleep if she could. Suddenly, sleep seemed welcome.

Outside, the sky was clear and the sun warm in spite of the season. A strong wind blew and the glass in the window made a slight clicking sound as it fought against the power of the wind. The drapes were drawn nearly closed and the beam of sunlight slipping through the opening shot across the room and spread its halo-like appearance against the double-door entrance to the room. Her head was still filled with a feeling that the events of the past seventy-two hours were somehow a childlike fantasy. And yet, there was a strange awareness that what was happening *should* be happening . . . as though she knew within her that her presence here and for this purpose was destined . . . almost a part of a grand plan.

Her eyes slowly closed, then snapped open again as the wind gusted and the occasional clicking of the glass in the window increased its rhythm. Her eyes looked straight ahead across the room and her brain slowly painted mental pictures of what her eyes saw. At first, it was but an indefinable silhouette, but then she remembered. It was a small square box . . . the box that Mikki had given her the night before. The blue foil paper seemed to shimmer in the semi-darkness. Her curiosity told her to open it, but her body and her mind told her to sleep.

In a moment, her awareness of her existence slipped away, and the body went slowly limp. It was a good sleep—an unusually resting sleep where neither the past nor the future mattered. There was but *this moment*—this resting, relaxing moment of peace and serenity. She was entering a place in time where only those of tranquility were permitted . . . a rare place . . . a place where only the chosen may visit.

As it had happened before, the voice of the man spoke to her as if from the inner confines of her own mind. The eyes were closed, but she could feel the narrow beam of sunlight stretching across the room, and could sense the occasional tapping of the branch against the window. His presence was seen moments before she could detect the sound from his moving lips. At first, only two colors were discernible—a shimmering redness against a backdrop of pure white. Then the features became clear . . . the slight smile showing the whiteness of the teeth . . . and the apple . . . that unusually dark redness of the apple contrasted against the whiteness of the suit he wore. The first sound from the lips that broke the peaceful silence came as a rush of air, a muffled whisper, until finally the voice was heard. It was a soothing, quietly authoritative voice.

"Mari . . . Mari. If you can hear me, raise your right hand slightly."

She was still lying motionless. Her eyes were closed, for his presence required neither auditory nor visual confirmation of his existence. It was as though her mind had eyes of its own . . . eyes not requiring the miracle of lens and light for relaying minute electrical impulses to the brain. The impulses were somehow sensed, and the same miracle worked for the words he spoke. Her *mind* sensed his thoughts, and all the movements of speech . . . the lips, the gestures . . . were strangely unnecessary. The communication was from within. The figure before her, this bearded, eloquent man in white, seemed to be nothing more than a physical personage that gave necessary form and substance to the intelligence *within*.

His words activated her senses and her right hand moved slightly, giving physical confirmation of her awareness of his existence.

"Well, Miss Mari, you've given us great cause to be ever so proud of you," he said.

The feeling within her was the feeling that makes one smile, and her lips responded.

"As I said to you during an earlier visit, your talent will create a place for you, and indeed it has. You are living proof that the miracle works."

Her mind forced the thought and transmitted it to him without the necessity of words.

"The miracle?"

"The miracle—yes."

"Have we talked about the . . . the miracle before?"

"Indirectly. The miracle, very simply, is the change that comes from working on one's self and in learning to work in the realm of *ideas* rather than in the realm of *things*."

She continued to listen rather than speak.

"When first we met, you were wandering, my little one. You had married prematurely and for the wrong reasons. *You* had not chosen your career—*it* had chosen you. You were told to attend college because everyone of substance attended college. The question was, For what purpose? To prepare for what? To gather knowledge, yes, but *what* knowledge, what specific field of study? Being uncertain, and forced into a decision, you impulsively chose to become a teacher. Why? Because your body chemistry and your mind and your destiny were structured for you to become a teacher? No! You made that monumental decision for but one simple reason—because a decision was necessary, and therefore you had set out on a path that would lead you in a direction unsuited to your skills. You, as are all others, were uniquely blessed with a talent and a purpose; but the blending of talent and purpose merging together with the proper opportunity takes time. Just because you were twenty years of age does not mean you were fully ready to make a final and irrevocable decision of what your life's work was to be. However, your system of education, your society and system of ethics dictate that you must be ready, at age twenty . . . or thereabouts. Like most, you were *not* ready and, like most, allowed yourself to become committed to something that, at the very moment you were *forced* to decide, seemed proper. Then the inevitable day of reckoning finally arrived. Your *happiness* now forced you to put aside both marriage and profession, leaving you with nothing. You had no direction, no foundation. You had only what your mind interpreted to be failure and you sat idly, feeling sorry for yourself.

"Well, that is when we found you, Mariana. We found you by watching your mind search for an understanding of things. You had nothing, but you felt deep inside that you were capable of so much. You certainly had great cause to do what most people do with their lives at an early age. You could have committed yourself to staying married, or you could have ended the marriage and resigned yourself to remaining in your profession, to 'make the best of it,' so to speak. You could have also put aside teaching and accepted something that just—well, something that just *came along*. You could have wandered from job to job, trying to find happiness with someone else's structured system—someone else's idea, or company, or opportunity. And that's where we chose to inter- vene. We planted ideas in your mind, Miss Mari . . . the seeds of ideas and insights, and the miracle of the seed worked as it always works. You found your *own* opportunity. Through an intense desire to make something of yourself, you set an ambitious goal of your *own* choosing and committed yourself to its achievement. And, regardless of the challenges—the Culpeppers, the Gloria Simons, and the ever-present self-doubt—you remained the captain of your ship, the master of your soul, and the maker and shaper of a new condition, a new environment and a new destiny.

"I give to you today a new phrase, Mariana. One of my colleagues calls it the *push-pull* law. In essence, it means if *you* will, through your own efforts and initiative, push yourself toward a rewarding and fulfilling life, *we* will, in our own good time, intercede and assist by pulling you toward the very thing you desire."

"Pull—How—What do you mean?"

"Ah ha! Therein lies the key to both fortune and contentment. Only *you*, Mariana, along with a handful of others, will understand, and until now even *you* could not have *fully* understood.

"But after today, we shall have no secrets between us; today is the day of full disclosure.

"You see, the *pull* will only work for those who committed a significant period of time and effort to providing their own discipline in developing *their* part of the formula. The *push* you have done for yourself and *by* yourself, and for that you receive the miraculous gift of the *pull*. The *pull* comes in many forms and dimensions. The *pull* can be a whisper, an intuition, a thought out-of-the-blue, if you will. It is what you call a *hunch*. It is an instinct, an idea, a spontaneous burst of insight or understanding, or a full awareness and understanding that something is *right*. You may not be able to explain it to others; in fact, you seldom can. The *pull* is that still small voice from within. It is God speaking, Mari. It is the total wisdom and intelligence of the universe speaking to you in one collective and fully authoritative voice. We even speak to those who are not yet ready. However, those who have not developed their own self-mastery of the *push* seldom listen. Those who are among the uninitiated feel and sense the pull, but their lives are being run by logic—by what they have learned from the limiting forms of teaching provided by the secular teachings of . . . of *people*. It is an interesting case study in the blind leading the blind.

"Tell me, have you ever felt the sudden, instinctive and unexplainable urge to call someone on the phone? Then, without pausing, you pick up the phone and call that person only to have them say in a somewhat shocked but obviously sincere way, 'I was just thinking about you'?"

She mentally nodded in agreement.

"That was the *pull* speaking, Mari, but most who sense its voice shrug it off. Opportunity speaks in the voice of the *pull*—so does insight, fortune and earthly serenity. We speak quite often, Miss Mari, but nearly everyone is far too busy trying to become successful, and therein is the great human dilemma. You don't try to become successful—you are *led* to success. It is there waiting, but it will retreat at every conscious human attempt to try to seize it. It is the great paradox of all human existence. That which you want you chase away simply by *insisting* that you want it. You must first—and I've shared this with you before—*you must first become the kind of person that nature requires for success.* To do otherwise is analogous to planting seeds in concrete; your seeds may be good, your intent may be honorable and your effort may be intense, but you have omitted one of the essential parts of the formula—you substituted soil with cement!

"Mariana, you have spent a goodly number of years in self-preparation, and the past few years you have totally devoted to your own wise response to the *pull*. In past conversations, I gave you mental seeds of ideas and insights. I have surrounded you with a number of those who, by your very association with them and theirs with you, have fed you a daily diet of an ever-growing knowledge and awareness of life—its mysteries and its purpose. You have learned well. You have grown well. You have been found worthy of awareness. You are among the chosen few. As was written on the document I handed you on our very first visit, *Behold, I have chosen thee . . . I have refined thee in the furnace of affliction.*"

Her mind flashed now for the first time since she became aware of his existence here in this room with her, although her body seemed to continue to sleep. She had been absorbing his words, but her own mind had been almost completely passive, responding little and thinking even less, only absorbing the words of the man. But now, and for but a fleeting moment, she remembered the envelope and its contents. She remembered the ribbon . . . the ribbon whose redness was like that of the apple he held in his hand. And there was a handkerchief he had tossed onto her bed. What had happened to them? He had not taken them back and . . . and . . . they were not there when she awoke the next morning . . . at least she couldn't remember seeing them.

It had happened twice before. In his presence, she seemed unaware of her physical life. When she was with him, she was *totally* with him. And when he was *gone*, she had no recollection of his having existed. It was as though a veil had been drawn between their two worlds.

His next words helped unravel the mystery of her thought. "Mariana Locke, it is time that you enter a new phase of your life. It is time that you become consciously aware of my existence *after* I've departed, and more important, that you become conscious of and informed of the details of the *conspiracy* and those engaged in it."

He stood looking down at her and she could somehow sense the very depths of his soul. It was as though his wisdom was being transferred into her own brain—an intermingling of one mind with another until both became one. She felt a strange warmth as the combining of thought with thought and concept with concept began. Suddenly her physical eyes opened and she found herself with the urge to speak with him as one human would normally converse with another. She looked directly at him as he polished the apple against his sleeve.

She asked the question just as he raised the apple to his mouth. "*What* conspiracy?"

He closed his mouth and lowered the apple in response to her question. It seemed to her that he had started to bite into that strange apple a hundred times before, but had never quite succeeded.

"The *conspiracy* that we conceived twelve years ago in response to the decline of our *creation*."

"Creation? Noah, you bring up new mysteries even before you've cleared up the old. What conspiracy—what creation are you talking about?"

"Patience, little one. Our creation is in two parts. First, the creation of mankind in whom we took great pride. Second, the creation of a land . . . of a nation unlike any other nation in the earth-world. Your nation, Mari. We caused it to be, you know. Your founders knew that. In fact, that was the first great conspiracy, the first time we chose to intercede in the affairs of mankind. We provided the pull to such men as Franklin and Jefferson. Under our direction your nation was formed, and we even received some degree of credit for it. You proclaimed yourself to be 'one nation under God,' and you even stamped 'In God We Trust' on your coin of the realm. As surely as we are again interceding now, so did we do so then. We appointed worthy individuals to band together and rise up against the King of England. We arranged, in accordance with our clever but necessary conspiracy, to give equality and freedom to all. But, as someone cautioned, all things of value are threatened with ultimate extinction from the very hour of their inception. Only evil has its own assured longevity. Goodness and virtue must be nurtured and defended or evil will prevail. As I once said, and you quoted in one of your speeches, the only thing necessary for the triumph of evil is for *good* men to do *nothing*."

"Edmund Burke may have said it before either of us, Noah. As I recall, he died in 1796."

"Yes, I know. Edmund was one of my better students . . . so terribly clever."

"Pardon me. I should have known that if you advised Franklin and Jefferson, that you might also have advised Burke. After all, they *were* of the same generation."

He smiled somewhat proudly, looking upward for a moment as though recalling a past event he had long since forgotten. Finally, he came back to the present moment. He looked back at her, breathed deeply and stroked the apple twice against his lapel.

"And so here we are, Mariana—back again for perhaps the final time to restore some resemblance of our original intent for your people to live individually and collectively as a free nation. I am here, as I was then, to single out unique people whose calling is to partici-pate in the restoration of morality, equal justice, common sense and freedom, that all mankind might have access to their fair share of dignity and opportunity."

"But the conspiracy . . . what *is* it?"

"It's what *all* conspiracies are, Miss Mari . . . well, not quite. A conspiracy is a gathering of individuals coming together for an *evil* purpose, which would make the *conspirators* evil. We are coming together for a positive and essentially *constructive* purpose, but the *word* somehow seems appropriate. It must be sufficient at this moment for me to merely advise you of the need and the existence of our undertaking. Soon, very soon, you shall be given the details. My purpose now, however, is to bring together your subconscious awareness of the thought—seeds I have planted in your mind with your *conscious* awareness and recall of that event. It will cause you some confusion, no doubt, as it has the others, but it—the confusion, I mean—will be very short-lived.

"Before, when you would awaken following my visits, you had no recollection of my having been there. Yet my words had their effect— the *seeds* had been planted. Now, when you awaken, *you will recall all that we've ever discussed*. Even now, you sit erect, your eyes are open and you are conscious of my existence. Now, however, I must arrange for your subconscious to combine with the conscious so that your mind fully relates to *me* and *our* world together, and *you* and *your* world of people and business, so that in *your* world you are aware of *me*, and when with *me* you have full knowledge of *all*. Then my visits with you and with the others will be on the conscious level, as is your earthly custom. Does that make sense, Mariana?"

"No."

"It will."

"When?"

"In a few moments . . . after I've departed and you are fully aware of your return to the physical realm."

"But the conspiracy! So far you've only been ambiguous, Noah. I'm to be a part of a . . . a conspiracy, but to conspire for the purpose of *what*?"

"Saving mankind, and saving your nation and your freedoms."

"But that's not enough, Noah. You said that this will be the day of full disclosure, yet you continue to be secretive."

"The day is not yet over, Mari. First, you must enter *Phase Two*."

"Phase Two? Noah, for pity's sake . . ."

"Mari, *please* be patient. Phase Two is when you fully awaken after my departure and, for the first time, have total recall of my existence. Believe me, it's painless . . . confusing perhaps, but painless and quite necessary."

She looked toward the ceiling as a deliberate gesture of her bewilderment. Noah smiled at her and put the apple to his mouth.

"May I ask you just a few incidental questions?"

He stopped just short of biting into the apple to answer her question. "Of course."

"Who are the *others* you refer to in this—this conspiracy?"

"You will meet them shortly."

"Do I know them?"

"Some, yes. You are familiar with them, but we cannot discuss that further. It will only add to the confusion of the moment. All things in their own due season—remember?"

"Yes, Noah, all things in their own due season. But another question . . ."

"Yes?"

"A few moments ago you spoke of the . . . I think you called it the *first* conspiracy. You said it was clever and necessary. Obviously you're referring to something that has to do with the Revolution of 1776?"

"Obviously."

"Why was it, as you said, necessary?"

"For the same reason that it is *now* necessary. The world needed a place where there was an abundance of all things. It needed a place relatively uninhabited . . . a place devoid of any unfair system of government tyranny, where men and women could become somebody simply because they were willing to commit themselves to an honest task and see it through to its conclusion. That was America, your *United States.* We watched your ancestors struggle against the mother country. We observed the massive tax burden imposed upon your people. We observed the armies of England imprison those of righteous intent who sought only freedom of speech and freedom of religion. And then, seeing your founding fathers struggle with their conscience as they deliberated on the question of total independence, we . . . well, to be specific, *I* was elected to intervene. I met with Mr. Jefferson in much the same way that I've met with *you,* as well as many others. I was most intrigued with the innate brilliance of Jefferson. And that Mr. Franklin of yours—what a delight! He did have some rather odd ideas, however. Like that idea of using the turkey as your national bird. Imagine! Anyway, our intervention in the affairs of mankind at that time was essential. The world would soon need a pillar of strength built upon freedom and fairness. We knew it well in advance, so we engaged in the first great . . . well, what I referred to earlier, Mari—the first great conspiracy."

He looked down at the apple that he held in his right hand and began rotating it with his thumb and fingertips much like a ballplayer would casually inspect a baseball.

"Times are a bit different now, I will admit. Then, our conspiracy was for the purpose of *establishing* your freedoms and independence. Now, our intervention, this *second* great conspiracy, is for the purpose of *preserving* your freedom and independence, for you are about to lose it through careless neglect and misuse. You have become a selfish, greedy and apathetic people . . . not *all* of you, but enough to threaten your own national stability."

He looked up at her quickly, his eyes widening into an intense and serious stare. "You know that, don't you?"

Her answer was immediate. "Yes."

"Yes," he said. "I am reminded of a man—Edward Gibbons was his name—who wrote an interesting book in which he outlined the five underlying reasons why a great civilization collapsed. First, the undermining of the dignity and the sanctity of the home, which is the basis for human society. Second, was higher and higher taxes, and the spending of public money for free bread and circuses for the populace. Third, was the mad craze for pleasure, with sports and plays becoming more exciting, more brutal and more immoral. Fourth, the building of great armaments, when the *real* enemy was *within*—the decay of individual responsibility. And finally, the decay of religion whose leaders had lost touch with life and with their power to guide the people."

Mariana had closed her eyes as he spoke, as though she were listening to him read from a book. When he had finished, she opened her eyes and looked up at him.

"Gibbons summed it up very well, Noah. Who is he? I've not heard of him."

"Most people haven't, Miss Mari. He's not of your generation. The book was entitled *The Decline and Fall of the Roman Empire*, and it was written by him in 1788."

"We—we humans never seem to change ourselves, do we?"

"History shows that you make bold attempts, but usually you do not take life seriously until you are on the threshold of destruction."

"And that's why you've come back again?"

"That's why I've come back."

She thought for a moment. "I'm thinking of something a man said to me once. We were talking about people helping people so that we can all live a better life. He said, 'Let humanity figure it out for them-selves.' I don't know why that comes to my mind just now, except that whoever you are, Noah, and wherever you come from—and I can only speculate—I'm a bit surprised that you still have any interest in what we do *with* . . . or *to* ourselves."

"Indeed, all things in their own due time, Miss Mari, but like promises, potential and good intentions must soon be matched by results . . . and your time grows short. With time, I would have thought you would learn that no human differences are as important as you seem to make them, yet you seem so insistent on *changing* one another. Why can you not become . . . well, *fascinated* with something or someone you don't understand, rather than bothered? Why is the truth so difficult to tell? Why is plenty never enough? These are interesting questions, Mariana Locke, but unfortunately your government and your people have learned to ask *different* questions. You ask, 'How can we get more?' You ask, 'How can I receive twice as much pay for half as much work?' You look to government for all forms of assistance. If they give, you demand more. If they do not, you condemn your leaders. Do you not understand that any government that has become so all-powerful that it can *give* you whatever you need or demand has also become so all-powerful that it can *take away* everything you *have*—including your freedoms, your hope and your human dignity?"

She did not answer.

"You asked why this last great conspiracy is so necessary. It is necessary because *this* conspiracy becomes the *ultimate weapon* in changing and preserving your republic. We do not want you to destroy yourselves, either slowly or in one cataclysmic blast. Therefore, we are invoking direct intervention—*final intervention*.

"Two hundred years ago we guided the minds, the words and the pens of a handful of great men. The result was your Constitution and your Bill of Rights. It was a grand idea, Mari—a true masterpiece of literary creativity. The grand idea, that masterpiece, was created that it might accomplish good among mankind. But instead, your lawmakers and your politicians have allowed it to evolve into an institution. Now, with the passage of time, the idea has lost its magic; it has become an institution more interested in its blasted protocol and procedure than in functioning as a breeding ground for good ideas.

"In essence, the conspiracy in which you shall participate is essential to protect your land, your freedom and your independence not from a threat *outside* your borders, but from the threat *within*. Your country and its destiny lie in the hands of those who serve in positions of government and business. To change the *direction* of your nation, one must change the *quality* of your leaders . . . and not just a few, but *many*.

It is not your laws that are faulty, little one, it is your *lawmakers* and those charged with interpreting and *enforcing* the law."

Noah checked his line of thought as he was about to speak, and his expression changed from intensity to a look of slight concern. "Goodness! I have gone on far too long, and there is much to do this day."

"You're not going, are you?"

"I must, but we shall be together again before this day is finished. For the moment, I ask that you just lay your head back, my pet. There is sometimes the need for talk and sometimes the need for silence, and the moment of silence is upon us."

She smiled at him as he flipped the apple in the air, grabbing it with a smooth motion of one hand. Following his instruction, she relaxed and lowered her head. In an instant she remembered nothing.

After a time she was jarred awake by the ringing of the phone. "Yes, this is . . . Oh, Jonathan . . . What time is it?"

She asked the question at the same instant she looked at the watch on her left wrist. He told her it was three-thirty, and that he would be a while longer. They agreed on an early dinner and the conversation ended. She sat erect on the side of the bed and raised her arms high above her head. She had gone to sleep without intending to and had slept far longer than she should have. Her thoughts immediately returned to the press conference and the response of the media to the things she had said. Her mind speculated, pondered, and reflected, but it did not recall the events or the words that had occurred while she slept. There was, in her mind, no knowledge of this man who entered her mind, nor any knowledge of the subjects they had discussed. There were only thoughts of her impending responsibility as the nominee to the president's cabinet.

The ray of sunlight illuminated the blue foil paper of the box Mikki had given her the night before. She smiled to herself and her mind flashed the last thought she had had before falling asleep. She weighed the decision of a shower before opening the package or opening the package before she showered.

She stood up and walked toward the dresser. She turned on the lamp to brighten the room and looked down at the box. She felt more than curiosity. There was somehow a magnetism about it . . . a compelling desire to open it.

The shower would wait.

CHAPTER TWENTY:

The Awakening

S he removed the white silk ribbon and expensive blue foil paper with the same care that she knew Mikki had used in wrapping it. The box itself was not an indicator of the contents, unless Mikki had decided that Mariana had the need for two dozen Misty Breath Fresheners from American Products. She picked up the box and walked to the small table near the window and sat in one of the four lobby chairs, placing the box on the table. For a moment, she sat back in the chair, yawning and rubbing her eyes lightly to remove the final vestiges of sleep.

The thought of a dream came into her mind—not the remembrance of the dream itself, only the faint recall that she had had a dream about something. She felt uncomfortable whenever she couldn't remember her dreams, as though a secret part of her brain had a life and a mind of its own. She shrugged away the thought and sat forward on the chair. She folded open the flaps of the box that had been tucked inside one another as if to prevent the contents from spilling out. She raised her small frame slightly and leaned forward a bit more. Removing the folded balls of newspaper that held one of the items securely inside the box, she smiled as she noticed the newspaper . . . it was the *Philadelphia Enquirer*, the newspaper she had once read so thoroughly. A headline on one of the crumpled sheets read "Nation In Greatest Economic Crisis Since Depression."

With care, she removed what appeared to be the only item inside. It was the cup with the penguins she had used when sharing the apartment with Mikki. Her memory fed her the same thought that it had had years before. The leader of the penguin procession slouched forward from the burden of leadership . . . the willingness of the uncaring, incapable and ambivalent to follow any form of leadership, *wherever* that leadership might take them. Then there was the last penguin . . . the youthful one, who didn't seem to care—not because it *didn't* care, but because it hadn't been asked by anyone to show that it *did* care. The youthful penguin would one day lead the procession to places it had never before been.

She stared at the cup for a full minute, thinking of the Mariana York who once drank from that cup, and thinking of the Mariana Locke who was now preparing herself to drink from a new cup. She found herself wishing she could repaint the procession of penguins to show the youthful and vigorous penguin in front.

Leaving the thought behind and pushing the cup aside, she placed the box on her lap and slowly removed the paper and tissue wads that had protected the cup. In the bottom of the box were the remainder of the items Mikki had packed. There was a small, transparent plastic box with a few long-forgotten items . . . a bracelet given to her by one of her students, a pair of earrings, a necklace with a silver chain and two rabbits dangling at the end, and a mustard seed set inside a small plastic square. She remembered with affection the origin of each, and thought of the woman to whom each had been given—a woman who, in many ways, no longer existed.

At the bottom of the box she found a brown five-by-seven business envelope with a broken metal clasp and removed it. She carefully picked up the wads and strips of packing paper and tissue that had protected the cup and stuffed it back into the box, clearing the tabletop of the mess she had created. She sat back now, looking down at the brown envelope on her lap. She picked it up with her left hand and pulled open the flap with her right. The right hand then slid into the opening and pulled out a ribbon . . . a red ribbon. It looked like a ribbon that had been used to secure a gift. It was tied in a simple bow with a loop that seemed to have once held an item closed. The hand slid back into the envelope and touched a cloth. It was a neatly folded cloth . . . a handkerchief from somewhere in time.

She found herself removing the contents without thought, for the envelope contained only miscellaneous items of questionable value. She squeezed the envelope with both hands and peered inside, finding only two smaller envelopes. The smaller of the two was from the office of the County Recorder. It was her divorce decree. Folded inside the document that announced the *dissolution* of the marriage was the document that had *confirmed* and verified the beginning of that marriage . . . her marriage certificate. Both the documentation for the beginning as well as for the end, had been folded, filed and forgotten. Her eyes scanned the words imprinted on each. The wording on the marriage certificate was both official and reverent, with a border of scrollwork with angel faces along the edges. A slogan printed in gothic letters at the base of the certificate was man's declaration of commitment and permanency . . .

"*That Which God Has Joined Together, Let No Man Put Asunder.*"

The second document made a mockery of the first. The official signature finalizing the divorce was barely legible. "*That which God had joined together*" had been officially put asunder by Wendell C. Pettibone, Chief Clerk. In retrospect, the hypocrisy of the system brought a smile to her lips as she picked up the second envelope.

She was still smiling when her eyes caught the details of the envelope she now held in her hands. But the smile was quickly gone, forced from her lips by the rushing feeling of confusion and shock. The words her eyes absorbed had no meaning until her mind repeated the words back to her.

"*A Gift, To Be Used and Shared*"

To her conscious mind, the words were insignificant and meaningless, but she was sensing a physiological response that seemed to have no valid origin or purpose. In an instant, she forgot where she was—only the words, her eyes and her mind existed. She stared as if in shock. Her brain switched in a rapid staccato from past to present, flashing pictures that made little sense—pictures that emanated from her own brain that didn't seem to have been placed there by any of her own experiences that she could remember. The room seemed to move in a clockwise direction—slowly at first, then faster and faster still until she found herself clinging firmly with her right hand to the rounded edge of the wooden table in front of her.

She closed her eyes, breathing in deeply and slowly. She could not identify the cause of what was happening to her because of the nearly paralyzing influence of the effect, and in the microseconds that her spinning brain *did* permit a logical analysis of what was happening, she imagined the event to be physiological.

The eyes remained closed, the room slowed down from its high-speed orbital spin, and the logical brain slowly began to function and to analyze.

She looked downward again, the eyes slowly opening once more and focusing on the envelope that now lay in her lap. She saw the mental picture of an envelope, framed and hanging on a wall—Jonathan's office wall—an envelope that had aroused her curiosity but that she had never asked about. Her hand slipped away from the edge of the table and she picked up the envelope for the second time. It was of unusual size—slightly larger than the usual letter-size envelope. The words across the front were written with what looked to be a fountain pen. The wide trace of ink that had flowed from the pen had left scroll-like words that reminded her of historical documents she had seen in the National Archives in Washington. "*A Gift, To Be Used and Shared.*" This time, the words and the combination of eyes and brain flashed images of a man whose features were clear and distinct. She saw the face as though she were gazing at a black and white glossy photograph. It was a distinguished face. The man was smiling slightly, the parting lips displaying the perfect white teeth that contrasted with the coal-black beard. He looked very much like Sebastian Cabot, she thought. Then she heard the voice—that soothing and reverent voice that somehow provided a feeling of reassurance and insight.

She remembered a sentence—"*Your talent will create a place for you.*" Another sentence—"*You can have more than you have because you can become more than you are.*"

The left hand plucked the envelope from the right and flipped it over. Across the back were the written words that flashed to her another mental picture.

"*I have chosen thee—I have forged thee in the furnace of affliction.* "

The eyes stared forward, but looked within. They saw the dimly lit room of her apartment in Philadelphia. She saw the full figure of the man now, standing before her, as if he were there with her this very moment. The mental images flashed in rapid succession from the past to the present . . . from the envelope she held in her hands now, to the envelope she had held in her hands as she sat on a bed, bewildered and confused, listening to the words of this man—this . . . what . . . did . . . he . . . call . . . himself? What was she thinking of, anyway? Was it a dream she was trying to recall? How could something be real and yet be so difficult to recall? What was happening to her?

The room began moving again, but she fought to slow it down. She breathed in deeply and fixed her eyes on the picture hanging on the wall across the room. The room wanted to move, but her fierce concentration held it back until something within her snapped. It was as though a spring had uncoiled, and the sudden and fast moving procession of thoughts rushed from the ambiguous past into the present with such rapidity that she found it nearly impossible to assimilate them all.

She saw a mental picture of herself, sitting in bed, reading the book . . . Jonathan's book. She saw the room and the man with the beard, dressed in white. She saw the apple and heard clearly the 'plop-plop' sound as he flipped that unusual apple from one hand to the other. There was the man . . . kneeling toward her, the outstretched hand holding the envelope . . . with . . . the red ribbon. The eyes flashed in sequence from the envelope in her hands to the ribbon on the table—from the crying and confused young woman looking at the handkerchief the man had tossed at her fingertips to the now intense woman whose eyes looked upon the handkerchief lying on the table just a few inches away. Her hand reached out for the white cloth and pulled it toward her. It had been folded into a rectangle, but as her hands unfolded it, the image she caught with her eyes transmitted an impulse to her brain. She saw but the single letter monogram . . ."N," and the letter translated itself into the single word that flashed from somewhere within the inner chambers of her own head. The word leaped from the subconscious to the conscious—from the past to the present—with the suddenness of a cat springing upon its prey, and her mouth moved in sequence with the name her mind-voice spoke.

N . . . Noah! Noah . . . Noah . . . Yes . . . Oh—God—yes . . . It *was* Noah, and it *had* happened. The past was now the present, and the secret stored deep within some untapped mental storage circuit of her brain had received the final trigger impulse that now released the absorbed and carefully filed data from deep within. She sensed the awesome experience of mental ecstasy, and felt totally overwhelmed by the magnitude and import of what she was remembering. Her mind raced like an uncontrolled locomotive from one experience to another—from one conversation to another. She remembered now the words and the phrases that had, over the past four years, made her sense a feeling of déjà vu. Sometimes the words and phrases were uttered by someone else; other times it was her *own* thought or her *own* voice that had stopped her thinking processes cold with the familiarity of a thought.

She remembered now the ever-present sensation of having "forgotten something," that in spite of her phenomenal personal growth and progress, there had always been that inexplicable sensation of something missing . . . forgotten . . . something that she once had that was of immeasurable value but that had been left somewhere in the dusty catacombs of the past, lingering there, serving her in a way that she couldn't understand.

She was being *driven* by something, and *toward* some predestined purpose beyond her ability to identify. There had been an indefinable spirit within her—a spirit that had transformed her appearance with the passage of time until at last she had emerged as a woman with both charisma and purpose. Before, her urges and intense and insatiable appetite for achievement were *within*, and defied explanation. Now, they were rushing to the surface with the explosive intensity of an erupting volcano, and she felt a joy that she had never before experienced.

Her thoughts moved now from ambiguity to an ever-increasing clarity. This man—Noah . . . *he* had been the force behind her progress and change. *He* had planted the . . . the "thought seeds" as he called them. It had been *his* words that instilled a new confidence and a new attitude—*that* was why she had felt so different the day she had returned to Jonathan's office to thank him for the book and to express to him what she thought the book had done for her. But now—now she had a *new* perspective. Jonathan's book had only been a trigger; it had set the thought processes in motion and it was *Noah* who had launched her into a new and intense activity.

The substance of that first conversation was coming back to her now. He had forced her to find her—*her obsession*! Before, she had been employed because of need and because her college credentials had confined her to a narrow set of selections, and she had been doing something she did not want to do. He drove her to find something she *did* want to do, and *that* was the turning point. A thought rushed now to her consciousness, but she could not recall its origin . . . the thought was of the three things—the three activities that mostly determine the quality of life . . . what you *do* . . . who you do it *with* . . . who you do it *for*. Who had said that? Was it Noah's thought or was it her own?

Noah had led her to the "what to do." That, in turn, had put her in touch with people of unusual personality and character. What she had *learned* from working with people, the products and the services provided by Camelot Productions had made a much greater contribution to her life than what she had *earned* at Camelot, therefore the "who you do it with" was a by-product of the "what you do." But what about the third element—the "who you do it for?" Her current intense activity at Camelot was fundamentally for two people: first, for herself . . . and second, Jonathan. Was it through Noah's planning and guidance that she was led into a personal relationship with the man who was now her husband, or was that *also* a by-product of the first element? And there was the . . . the mystery of this thing . . . this . . . this . . . yes, this . . . this *conspiracy*!

It was with the flash of thought about the conspiracy that it hit her . . . another morsel of emerging subconscious thought rising to the conscious level of her mind.

Noah had just been *here*—in *this* room . . . *moments ago as she was sleeping!* Her eyes jumped to her left and she looked toward the bed where she had been lying, and at the very place where she knew now that he had been standing. With her mind's eye, she could see him . . . she could hear him as though he were there.

The excitement of what she was remembering gave way for a split second to a moment of doubt. It was too unbelievable to be real, yet it was far too detailed and specific to be a dream. Her eyes flashed back to the table, and the proof of the existence of Noah, and of these unbelievable shreds of evidence that lay on the table before her.

The envelope . . . the ribbon . . . his handkerchief . . . tangible bits of evidence confirming the reality of the events and the words as she was now recalling them. The possibility that it was a dream was itself unrealistic. Her hands fondled the envelope and the nearly overwhelming excitement of the magnitude and authenticity of her discovery came rushing back to dominate her mind. She found her mind chronologically skipping from one recalled event to the other. There was the first visit from Noah as she slept, at a time when she was groping for reasons and answers that would both justify and clarify her existence. It had been a conversation that had gone on well into the early morning hours, and her mind pondered now the totality of the event rather than the specifics. Then there was the visitation only moments before, and the conversation regarding the conspiracy. But somehow—where was it—when . . . the *other* visit?

The thought pictures flashed again . . . Culpepper . . . the disappointment . . . the loss of self-confidence, and . . . the reassurance! That was it! Again, as she slept. *Always as she slept.* Why had he come to her only when she was sleeping, and . . .

He was coming back . . . today . . . but . . . where and how? The mind of Mariana Locke wandered on, recalling the other visits from Noah, and remembering the many things he had taught her. It was as though a switch had been turned on within her brain, and a tape recorder was playing back events that had been experienced but not remembered.

✦   ✦   ✦

Jonathan sat at the long conference table of the conference room. The doors had been secured with specific instructions to hotel security that he was not to be disturbed. It was the room he had used on occasion for executive meetings with his national staff when the corporate office of Camelot was in Washington. He knew that his wife would not question where he was or what he was doing, and their private suite provided for them during their trip to Washington to visit the president was only three floors below where he now sat. He had always disliked the secrecy that had to exist between he and Mariana regarding his role as a participant in the project, but it was painfully necessary. It was the only element of untruth that he had ever allowed to exist between the two of them, but the need for secrecy was absolutely paramount.

The man who had entered the room moments before sat at the center of the elongated table directly across from Jonathan. It was the thirty-ninth meeting they had had this way, and there had been four others while Jonathan was yet in Phase One. The hour was growing late, and the time for implementation of Phase Four was imminent. The planning had been meticulous, the seeds had been planted carefully and in great abundance, and the season of harvest was nearly upon them.

Jonathan's mind wandered momentarily and his face reflected his thoughts more than he had wanted.

"You look somewhat troubled, my good friend. What is it?" Jonathan shrugged his thought away and smiled. "I think I have a slight case of the guilties," he replied. "It's sometimes a bit difficult to withhold the truth from Mariana, and I'm sometimes concerned about her feelings when she finally learns it."

"Well, 'finally' is nearly upon us," the man said, twirling the apple in his right hand as he spoke.

"Which is the reason for my concern," Jon explained, looking down toward the table and back to Noah.

"I think you greatly underestimate your wife. When in possession of all of the facts, she will clearly see and accept what you've had to do. Anyway, if we choose to forgive you, be assured that she will do exactly the same. You have no cause for concern."

"So, Phase Three is today. That decision is final?"

"For Mariana?"

"Yes."

"Oh, absolutely," Noah said without hesitation. "She will be the first to move from Phase Two to Phase Three on the same day, but our schedule demands that we move hastily, although deliberately. I have no reservations regarding her worthiness or her ability to handle it."

"Neither do I, but you'll have to admit it's a lot for one human to assimilate in forty-eight hours . . . the appointment to the president's cabinet, and now this. Especially Phase Two and Three on the same day . . . and so close to Phase Four."

"Jonathan, Jonathan, if she were not capable, she would not have been chosen. Don't you see? By virtue of the fact that she *was* chosen, she automatically received the assets of character necessary for all aspects of the assignment . . . *and* for understanding *your* actions and behavior. If that were not so, we would not have chosen her."

"Noah, more than my concern over all of this is my feelings about myself. I've been deceptive, but I also know it's for a worthy cause, and I know she'll fully understand and accept that. But I will *not* take lightly the fact that circumstances have placed me in a position of having to be less than totally truthful, and my acceptance of the Law of Sowing and Reaping will—and *has*—caused me a bit of anxiety. I'll control it, and grow from it, but I will not overlook the violation."

"You take these principles rather seriously, don't you Jon?" Jonathan crossed his legs underneath the table while he folded his hands on top of the table and leaned forward slightly toward Noah. Looking directly at him, he smiled warmly and spoke. "Samuel Johnson once said that 'the chains of habit are generally too small to be felt until they are too strong to be broken.' Yes, I take these principles *very* seriously. You found me when I was struggling to find myself, Noah, and you've taught me to respect truth and honesty and all the other virtues that hold society together and keep it from destroying itself. You also taught me well the power of habit, and I'm a great respecter of what good habits can do *for* you, and what bad habits will do *to* you. If I overlook this one violation of that which is right—justifiable as it may be—then there will be other justifiable exceptions, and we both know . . . ." He stopped in the middle of his sentence, sat back in the chair and smiled.

"Why did you stop?" Noah asked.

"You enjoy testing people, don't you."

"Not testing, Jon . . . merely *leading* you to discipline yourself. I'm most pleased with your ability to identify the seed of future difficulty and to speak out against it. We need say no more about the matter. Now, are the principals in the project fully informed of their respective responsibilities in Phase Four?"

"Everything is in place and everyone is fully advised. Mari was the final piece of the puzzle, and we'll be taking care of that within the hour."

"And Brendis?"

"The congressional participants have been notified, as have the executive and judicial placements. Our media people in the seven principal cities are ready. We've overlooked nothing. The conclusion is now inevitable and probably just in time. The intervention was nearly too late—you know that, don't you?"

"Our interventions are *never* too late, Jon, or we never would have implemented the plan. If we act at all, it is because we are destined to succeed. We've been trying to teach you humans that for centuries."

"I don't follow you."

"Jonathan . . . surely! On my second visit with you, remember? You are never given an idea or an intuitive thought of any kind without—"

"—also being given the powers to implement and succeed."

"Right!"

They both smiled and Noah flipped the apple high into the air. It fell perfectly into his cupped hand while his eyes remained firmly fixed on Jonathan's.

"I've never thought about angels being show-offs," Jonathan remarked.

"And I've not thought about humans being insubordinate." The two had become close friends in the years since Noah first appeared in the sleeping mind of the young man named Jonathan Locke. He was thirty-two then, and working in a nine-to-five environment that he had not chosen for himself. His dreams and ambitions of his earlier years had all but evaporated into an uneventful life of existence without substance. Within him, he had always had the belief that he was capable of far more than he had ever achieved. He had married at an early age, but the financial pressures brought on by his inattention to financial responsibilities and his inadequate income took its inevitable toll, and the marriage ended. The miracle and ambition of youth had given way to the routine of maturity. He had reluctantly accepted a sales position with a small company that marketed motivational tapes and seminars but had become quickly disillusioned with the process of selling success when his personal finances were in such turmoil. The hypocrisy affected him, and while he spoke the words of his presentation well, the sincerity was lacking and his customers somehow felt it and, more often than not, chose not to buy—not because they were not interested, but because they were not affected or persuaded by a sincere and honest appeal.

It was at the end of his sixth month with the small company that the owner died in an accident, and his widow, who received a large insurance settlement, met with Jonathan on a cold winter afternoon in Philadelphia, and handed him a document that gave him the rights to continue the business and to receive full ownership of the business provided he would agree to pay her one thousand dollars at the end of the first year. She had met Jonathan only twice before, and saw something in him that he had not yet seen in himself. It was her encouragement that convinced him to accept the offer, and she worked with him for several months—guiding, instructing, and encouraging. She taught him the basics of operating a small business, of the value of keeping accurate records and of the wisdom of investing a small portion of one's income—*no matter how insignificant the amounts might be.*

"You can admire the oak tree in your neighbor's back yard, or you can plant an acorn in your own," she had said one morning. "If you choose to admire the fruits of someone else's effort and to covet *their* rewards, you will live a narrow life full of anger and frustration. But if you choose to *plant*, you must also choose to stay and commit yourself totally to your project, for *your* rewards will take time, and your patience in *yourself* and in the merit of your *project* will be tested by adversity at every turn—not intentionally . . . not by anyone or any particular thing, but merely by time, for it takes *time* for acorns to become oak trees."

It was from her advice and counsel that Jonathan began the growing experience. It was from the few months spent in conversation with her that he learned that just because the body stops growing, the mind must never stop its process of expanding and accumulating wisdom and experience. The woman who gave direction to his life, and who challenged him with a meaningful purpose, went away without explanation. They had been sitting in the office discussing an obstacle that Jonathan couldn't understand or overcome. She had been exhorting him to concentrate on his objective and not to dwell excessively on the obstacles.

"Obstacles are things people see when they take their eyes and their minds off their goals," she had said just as the phone rang. Her conversation with the caller was short and her decision was immediate.

"I must go now, Jon," she said. "Stand guard at the doorway of your mind. You'll *make* something of yourself, if you'll just *be* yourself." With those words, a smile and a firm squeeze of his hand, she was gone. He later found that her home had been vacated and sold, and there was no explanation, no communication—nothing. For nearly ten years now, he had kept in his desk a check for her. One thousand dollars, payable to Vera Stevanus. This check had become symbolic, for he knew somehow that he would never see her again.

Jonathan Locke responded quickly to his new challenge and opportunity and Camelot Productions grew and prospered. It was shortly after

Jonathan took control of Camelot that Noah had visited him for the first time, and he soon evolved as a brilliant businessman, writer, and lecturer. Within a year he was designated as the project director by Noah, and was fully informed on the details of the project. Other than himself, Jonathan knew that one other major participant in the planned conspiracy would have to be found, and that only Noah could himself conduct the important search for this person whose role would be as important as his own. The search had taken nearly another year, during which Jonathan found the many others who would play important roles in forming the nucleus of the project team. He passed the names to Noah, who then visited each as he had visited Mariana, and Jonathan before her. Slowly and methodically, the participants were singled out and the mental seeds planted, and now the years of work were nearly complete. Only Jonathan, Mari, and the other major participant had entered Phase Three, but the remainder of those selected would be moved forward in the hours ahead.

Noah stood at the conference table now, looking directly down at Jonathan. There was a certain set to his jaw that signified readiness and determination. The apple was now in his right hand, which he held limply at his side, the fingers of his left hand hanging lightly on the edge of the table.

The two looked at one another for a full half-minute, their only communication being one of mutual contemplation and reminiscing.

It was finally Noah's voice that broke the silence, and he spoke in a near whisper.

"Jonathan, Mariana once spoke to me about . . . well, her question was *why* she was chosen as a participant. Have you ever asked *yourself* that question?"

"You mean . . . why *she* was designated? But we've—"

"No, not her . . . *you.*"

"I've wondered . . . yes."

"Why haven't you asked?"

"Because I assumed when you wanted me to know . . . Let's put it another way: all things in their own season, all things in their own due time."

Noah smiled. "I trust that I do not use that to excess?"

"Excessively, no. Effectively, always."

"Do you know its origin?"

"The Bible?"

"The Bible." He looked toward the wall, but with a gaze that went far beyond the limits of the wall. His voice became slow and deliberate as he spoke the words.

"To everything there is a season, and a time to every purpose under heaven. A time to be born and a time to die. A time to plant and a time to pluck up that which is planted. A time to kill and a time to heal; a time to break down and a time to build up. A time to weep and a time to laugh; a time to mourn and a time to dance. A time to cast away stones and a time to gather stones together; a time to embrace and a time to refrain from embracing. A time to get and a time to lose; a time to keep and a time to cast away. A time to rend and a time to sew; a time to keep silence and a time to speak. A time to love and a time to hate; a time of war and a time of peace."

Noah continued looking toward the wall for a moment longer as though listening to the echo of his own words in his mind. He raised the apple with his hand and began the familiar flipping motion again, then stopped, looked down at the red apple and then at his friend.

"And now, Jonathan, we are given yet another season. It can be said that there is a time to neglect and a time to restore, and indeed the time and season of restoration is upon us. It is time, I believe, to take leave of this place and visit your wife."

Jonathan stood. "You'll want me to go ahead of you?"

"Of course. I won't be long, and I'll travel in the usual way."

"Anything I should say—or not say?"

"Be yourself, Jonathan. This step is relatively incidental. Anyway, this is the day we've planned for so long. It represents an arrival . . . a milestone of major significance, so remember to keep your eyes on the goal, Jon, not the obstacles."

"I'm fine, Noah. I'll see you shortly."

With that, Jonathan stepped back from the table, turned and quickly disappeared through the door behind. Within seconds, he stood at the house phone adjacent to the elevator and dialed the four digits that would ring his wife's phone. On the fourth ring he heard her voice.

"Are you okay?"

There was a moment's hesitation. "Yes, I'm fine." The words did not equate with the emotion he detected in her voice, although he knew the reason for her obvious disturbance.

"You weren't still asleep, were you?"

"No . . . no, I slept for a while, but I'm awake now. Just a bit groggy, I guess."

"I'll be there in less than a minute."

He placed the phone back in place at the instant the doors opened on the elevator and he hurried his step and slid past the emerging passenger. The elevator was on its way up and he wanted to go down, but it would give him an extra minute to collect his thoughts. He was not questioning whether Mariana would *accept* the full explanation and forgive him for his secrecy, but he *did* feel uncomfortable because of the confusion she was experiencing and would yet experience at such an unbelievable and complex set of circumstances.

The eventual ring of the elevator bell as it finally arrived at his floor was symbolic, for it represented the beginning of an event that would defy any rational explanation except for those few singled out for participation in this extraordinary mission. Fourteen steps later, he stood at the doorway to suite 964 and paused one final time.

Noah was right—Mariana would be told and she would accept and understand, and the implementation would move forward with flawless efficiency, without notice, and in exact accordance with the master plan.

Inside, Mari Locke had used the two minutes to organize her thoughts and put away the items of evidence that had triggered an onrushing of her new awareness. She had not had time to ponder what she might say to her husband. She could not think about how *he* might respond to her incredible revelation until *she* could respond in a more rational way. She needed more time to think, to sort out her thoughts. But there was no more time. He was here, she thought, as she heard the key slip into the lock.

Without their mutual knowledge, each was harboring a pretense and a preoccupation, and each struggled for words and made artificial movements that were obviously unnatural and immediately detectable by the other. He had the advantage, for he knew the thoughts in her mind and the experiences responsible for those thoughts. He knew the depth of her confusion, for he had once felt it. He understood the sense of aloneness, for he too once held a new knowledge and because of the uniqueness of the circumstances, felt unable to share it with *anyone*. He sensed the almost overwhelming sense of responsibility that she must feel at this moment, for he once felt that only *he* had been singled out for participation in such a momentous, although mysterious, drama.

Each avoided the eyes of the other, something that had never before occurred between them. It was the discomfort from that seemingly unimportant act that caused Jonathan to break the silence and relieve the tension.

"Are you okay?" he asked for the second time in less than five minutes.

She had been standing in the center of the room, but turned now and walked away from him without answering and sat on the chair she had used when she opened the wrapped box. Jonathan watched for a moment and came to sit in one of the chairs at the table, rolling the chair to his right to get closer to her.

"Mariana, listen to me. This is going to be difficult, but . . . but I understand."

She detected his discomfort, and for a fleeting second, forgot her own burden.

"Jon, what's wrong?"

"Mari, believe me, what you feel right now . . . what's happened to you today has a rational explanation. It may not seem so at the moment, but you're about to understand it all."

She sat upright and grabbed his right hand with both of hers.

"What do you mean?"

"You've had something happen to you—something that just . . . well, just doesn't happen to people, yet it happened to you. Is that right?"

"How do you know . . . what . . . ?"

"I know everything that *you* know, Mariana—even *more*. And I've known for some time."

"Jonathan, what in heaven's name do you mean? What's going on?"

The third voice came from the darkened entryway, and they both turned to see the man with the white suit and the beard walking slowly toward them.

"I think it might be best if I offered the advantage of an outside voice," the intruder said.

"Oh my God!" Mariana stood erect, looking first at Noah then at her husband who stood up far more slowly than she had, and he put his left arm around her waist. "I don't understand," she said.

"Why don't the three of us sit down and relax—if that is possible," Noah suggested.

Jonathan placed his right hand on her shoulder and eased his wife's tense body back and downward toward the chair, watching her eyes shift in rapid movements back and forth between the two men. Noah continued his slow and deliberate movement toward the chair directly across the table from Mari, with Jonathan seated on his right. The expression on the face of the woman was one of total confusion—a look that neither Jonathan nor Noah had seen on her normally attractive and relaxed face before. The eyes were widened and her mouth was slightly open as though it wanted to speak but could not.

"Mariana, I must ask that you not speak for the moment," Noah said, "which should not be that difficult for you given your current state of shock. Allow me the time for a brief explanation of these most unusual events, and at the conclusion of what I trust will be a . . . a few moments of full disclosure, you may then, as you regain your composure and your control of your emotions, ask any questions you may have until you have a full explanation of the events that *have* and *will* transpire."

"Now, if I ask you a question during my explanation, you may answer, but not with a question of your own. Do you understand? There was no response for a few seconds, then finally a deep breath, a glance at Jonathan, a slow and deliberate closing and reopening of the eyes and a barely detectable, "Y—Yes."

"Good!" Noah smiled now, raised his hands on the top of the table, put the red apple carefully down on the table directly in front of him, and folded his hands before speaking. Slowly and softly the words came. She listened with the total attention of a munitions expert disarming a bomb, and Jonathan watched and listened. It would be the moment of full disclosure, a time of full and complete revelation of the meaning and purpose of the incredible sequence of events that would alter the direction of the nation.

CHAPTER TWENTY-ONE:

The Disclosure

The thoughts firing through her brain were as confused and disarranged as they had been at that time when she had first been confronted by the strange gentleman. Mariana Locke fought within herself to remain coherent as the words of the explanation began.

"Mari, what is happening is real, not imaginary," he said. You are not dreaming, though you are having great difficulty at this moment in distinguishing dreams from reality, and separating the truth from the imagined. You find yourself recalling a thousand thoughts that are real, yet the events *behind* those thoughts seem to have never happened in your real world. It is truly as though your imagination is gaining control over your orderly mind.

"You are further confused as to how it is possible that Jonathan should know of things that transpired between you and I—things that *we* discussed literally in your mind while you slept. How could he know of such events? What role does *he* play in this bizarre sequence of events?

"And you are afraid, for indeed it would seem that some form of plot is being thrust upon you, without your conscious knowledge and consent—a plot that threatens the very foundation of your private world."

Noah picked up the apple from where it rested and moved it to the center of the table. As Mari's eyes followed his deliberate movement, it occurred to her how that strange apple seemed to have become a symbol of this unusual man's existence. She had seen him holding it, flipping

it, examining it, polishing it. The object summoned up countless memories, all of them now as real as his very existence at this precise moment.
Noah watched her glance from the apple to him and back again.

"Let me pose two basic questions to you, Mariana. I am sure that you
have many, but allow *me* to ask *and* answer two questions. In so doing, it
is quite probable that I will answer most of your own.

"First, where have I come from? While it is not necessary that I
should answer that question totally, I will say only that this spinning
sphere is not my home. My home is beyond this place and time, but we
have inseparable bonds that make *your* interests *my* interests.

"Second, why have I come here? *That* is the question that must be
answered. Why have I been sent to intervene in the affairs of mankind? I
have covered that subject in detail with your husband, Mariana, on that
day several years ago when I revealed my purpose to him as I reveal my
purpose to you today.

"To answer that question for you, I must tell you that your
government and the laws that merged your peoples together in a
common bond over two centuries ago were inspired by an order of
thinking vastly superior to your own. The hand that molded *this*
planet is the *same* hand that guided the pens that inscribed a parchment paper with your Declaration of Independence, your Bill of
Rights, and even your Constitution.

"If you will research the writings of Jefferson, whose mind fathered
your free nation perhaps more than any other, you will find a curious
phrase written by him to one Dr. Benjamin Rush on the twenty-third of
September in the year one thousand eight hundred. The words tell more
than any of your historians have considered. He said, '*I have sworn upon
the altar of God eternal hostility against every form of tyranny over the mind of
man.*' Your Mr. Jefferson meant that phrase literally, Mariana.

"I tell you now that your country was christened by the hand as
well as by the word of God as surely as we sit together in this hour. The
origin of true freedom—the United States—did not *evolve;* nor was it the
splendid minds of righteous men who formed it. Oh, they *organized* it all
right, but they were instruments . . . each of them.

"You see, when your world was created, it was the intent of the
Creator that it be a place of beauty and harmony. It was to be an experiment of sorts, as well as a testing station . . . a place where we could send
those who needed to gain a new level of understanding.

"It was interesting the way your world was arranged. Some of those
who sat in on the planning sessions wanted it to be a place of continual

goodness, of everlasting love and goodwill, free of any difficulty or challenge . . . a place of perfection, if you will. But then, *that* is the state of
things in the world where I reside, so it would be a bit foolish having *two*
realms, *each* in a state of perfection. I pointed that out to the Creator and
it was then that he called a conference to discuss the issue of your world.
It was at this conference that the new concept emerged.

"Without boring you with excessive details, I suggested that perhaps
evil should be introduced as a choice to exist along with good, and that
those who come into this world be given free choice to select between
good *or* evil. In that way, we would have a means of separating the
strong from the weak. The plan was accepted, refined and implemented.
One individual who resided in our world had always done things
contrary to the wishes of the Creator. He became a troublemaker, and
even succeeded in attracting his own following. Because he was so profi-
cient at being a rather nasty person, he and his band of followers, along
with their unsavory philosophies, were sent to occupy your world along
with those of good intent who already resided here. *They* were, and are,
referred to as *the adversary*.

"It was a terribly clever plan. But with the passage of time, things
seemed to become excessively imbalanced. Far more people were being
drawn toward the philosophy of the adversary. They began to dominate.
We hoped that the trend would reverse itself, but it did not. That is when
the Creator decided to send his oldest son to your world to restore more
of the original philosophy. It was our *first* attempt at direct intervention,
and it began to have an effect.

"But then the trend toward the gathering strength of the adversary
began anew. Once again, we were called into a hasty conference. This
time, it was concluded that what was needed was a . . . a showplace—a
land within your own world where admirable philosophies would have
a fair chance to work. That is when I was first chosen to visit your world,
Mariana. Your nation—America—seemed to offer the best chance for
the success of our new concept. It was a *new* land, inhabited by those
of worthy thoughts. For whatever the reason, most were blessed with
a spirit of adventure and seemed to be genuinely intent on finding the
proper environment in which to worship their creator.

"Well, as your knowledge of history will confirm, Miss Mari, it did
not take long for the corrupt concepts of the adversary to follow the early
inhabitants to America. The influence of greed, unfairness and corruption
again made its appearance, and your people fought back in anger and
chose to declare their independence from those who sought to control and

enslave them. By the time I had arrived, the first meeting of the colonial dissenters was converging in Philadelphia. It did not take long for me to observe that Thomas . . . uh . . . Mr. Jefferson was emerging as the great writer, thinker and persuader among the gathering. It was then that I appeared to and counseled with the young Jefferson in the same way that I first visited you, Mariana . . . and you, Jonathan.

"After many, many months your laws were finally formed, and your government finally and fairly established. I remained for several years, often meeting with those who were chosen by your own kind to serve as leaders. The balance between good and evil had been firmly rees-tablished, and we were indeed proud of the way your land responded. For the first time, a nation—an entire *nation*—had been founded upon the principles of fairness, so that goodness would have an equal chance against evil and against the nearly overwhelming attraction to the prin-ciples of the adversary.

"I left your world in a spirit of hope and joy, and the Creator was indeed pleased. That was one hundred and seventy-six of your years ago, Mariana. Now, I have returned again. I return at the direction of the Creator to intervene in your worldly affairs for the *second* time. I do so because in this one hundred and seventy-six years since my last visit, you have again permitted evil to gain the upper hand against good.

"It isn't entirely your fault. Because of the way we designed things, it is the natural inclination of the human mind to lean toward negativity. It is your very nature to *doubt*. It is your nature to *worry*. It is likewise your nature to be greedy and dishonest. We tilted you toward *losing* the battle here on Earth. However, it was pointed out that perhaps we went a little too far, so it was decided that we would intervene one more time.

"Now, let's move along to the details of the intervention itself. We long ago discontinued the *miracle* routine. It was terribly dramatic, but people seem to forget so very quickly. Parting large bodies of water is very impressive, but the people themselves learn nothing from it. We've had our designated leaders over the years do some very clever things. They've turned wooden sticks into serpents, a few fish into many . . . things like that. But what good did it do? Well, learning from the past, we've now chosen merely to guide and direct thoughts. We did that with the founders of your nation, and it proved very effective. Even now, among the nations of your world, you are still the most affluent, still the most free, and certainly the most emulated. But now, we've decided to implement something so very basic, so simple that it nearly went over-looked. It is a product of my own personal design . . . something I've chosen to call the *multiplication factor*. It is going to transform your land as though we ourselves had directly intervened with a miracle of our own; but *you* will be the *workers* of the miracle, and in so doing will grow and benefit and learn, so that never again will our return or our intervention prove necessary. Oh, I am so terribly excited for you . . . so terribly excited indeed!"

Noah took the apple and placed it in his right hand. Polishing it briskly against his left sleeve, a beaming smile appeared on his face for the first time since entering the room to sit with this man and woman. But in spite of his relaxed posture, his worldly hosts remained silent.

"Very well, then. Let us get into the specifics. Do you agree that an excessive number of your people have *given up on themselves*?"

Mariana had become nearly frozen with intensity as she listened to Noah speak, and could not respond immediately. "Yes—uh, yes . . . I do."

"And do you agree that an excessive number of your people have *given up on America*—or have at least become apathetic about it?"

"Yes."

"Then I must tell you that I am here to start the process of correcting *both*. We shall begin by giving our attention to the repair of the people. You do not change the nation by changing the *government*. You change the *people*—or at least their *attitudes*—and the government will care for itself."

He looked at Jonathan, then at Mari, and in her eyes he could see that the bewilderment was still there.

"Mari, my dear Miss Mari, I am afraid you find this perhaps too incomprehensible. Let me chronologically cover a few steps with you . . . from the beginning until now. As I speak, please feel free to interrupt if you find it necessary. If I find your inquiry to be out of sequence, I shall ask you to bear with me. I do think that might be better.

"Now, let me see . . . As I recall, it was twelve years ago—plus or minus a few, perhaps—I was . . . well . . . *appointed* to direct this most important mission here on Earth—to give hope back to your people and to restore respect for your government in their hearts and minds. As I said earlier, I was to refrain from *direct* intervention. There are to be no miracles in this process of restoration—this *conspiracy*. It is to be *your* work.

"Since my purpose here permits me to serve only in an advisory capacity, I needed to find the right person to begin the project. The first person with whom I worked would become absolutely critical to the success of the conspiracy, for this *one* would lead to *many*. I would indeed need someone of youthful years—one with the vitality and curiosity of the child, but with the mature sophistication of a wise king. Much would be demanded of this person.

"Fortunately, it did not take long," he added, looking at Jonathan. Mariana followed the direction of his glance, and inside her the answer began to emerge that would solve the clouded mystery of the role of her husband in the bizarre event.

"You are quite correct, Mari," Noah went on. "The young man is your husband. He was blessed with an abundance of talent, and I soon visited Jonathan for the first time, just as I had visited you much later. Like you, Mariana, I planted mental seeds in the mind of Jonathan and continued for nearly a year to work on developing his skills without his conscious awareness that I was serving as his teacher and advisor.

"Now—and this is very important—we call this stage of communion between me and one of your kind *Phase One*. This is the stage where you, Mari, were being taught and guided while you slept, but upon awakening had no conscious knowledge of anything that went on between us. During Phase One, my objective is quite simple: I implant worthy ideas and insights into your mind . . . or perhaps it would be more correct to say that I *reawaken* emotions and knowledge that resides within the human mind from the time of birth."

Noah paused for a moment and leaned forward with his elbows on the table while his hand twirled the red apple.

"Is this making sense, Mari?"

For the first time her face showed a slight smile and her body relaxed visibly as she changed positions in the chair.

"Yes," she answered.

"Very well. If I lose you, stop me."

Mariana turned to look briefly at Jonathan who smiled encouragingly.

"Mari, you are certain that you are clear on Phase One?"

"Yes, I think I am. It's where I was until about an hour ago. It's where I've been for about . . . *five years*."

"Correct. Instilling confidence, sensitivity, and a keen awareness of life takes time. Learning to develop an appreciation of freedom takes time, and so does the development of the art of effective communication. Moreover, you needed time to develop and polish your writing and speaking skills, as Jonathan needed time to master *his* innate talents. Both of you had spent so many years neglecting yourselves that not only was it necessary for me to polish your *skills*, I also had to work very hard to undo the *past* . . . those limiting habits which you humans are so quick to develop.

"Well—you, Mariana, have now left Phase One and entered Phase Two just an hour ago. Jonathan, of course, had been in *Phase Two* for much, much longer than you. This stage merely describes the moment that you are permitted to consciously recall my visits with you while you were yet in Phase One. It is that period of time given to you to adjust to and reconcile this most incredible event. It isn't easy, I know. The uninitiated would not understand these rather unusual procedures. They would not believe it if you tried to tell them, and being unable to share such a . . . a . . . well, almost a miraculous phenomenon can be a major burden to have to bear.

"As I might have expected, Mariana, you have spent less time in Phase Two than any of the others—partly because of your uncommon adaptability and partially due to necessity. Within one hour of entering the second phase you have come to the point where you are about to enter *Phase Three*. Very simply, little one, that means that you are allowed to become aware of the specific details of the last great conspiracy, of which you are already a part. You will be playing a major role in that conspiracy, Mari, and the importance of *your* role is second only to that of one other."

Mari made an immediate assumption and glanced again at her husband.

"No, not Jonathan," Noah said, dispelling her conclusion. "Jonathan's role is separate from yours and from the other individual that I referred to. In fact, it is separate from *all* those who were chosen to participate. He is *responsible* for their participation, but separate *from* them. Jonathan is responsible for all those who are chosen . . . except for you and for the role of the other participant I referred to. *You*, Mariana Locke, were chosen by *us*, as was he with whom you will be working, and your husband, Jonathan. Three of you are principals in our last great effort to lead mankind back to themselves, that they might fulfill their destiny.

"Before we go any further, I must clarify a most important point. It was not our intent, Mari, that you should develop a personal relationship with Jonathan. *That* was an occurrence set in motion entirely through your own efforts. As I once discussed with your husband, I am obviously capable of interfering in the affairs of state *and* the affairs of the mind, but *never* the affairs of the heart. I must admit, however, that at the moment I feel some concern over what today's revelation might do to your feelings for Jon. He *had* to maintain secrecy, Mariana, even from *you*. He had no choice. Unfortunately, he had a pre-existing commitment greater than any other responsibility."

Mari's eyes traveled down to the hands folded in her lap. She looked at the ring on her finger, and dwelled for but a moment on what the ring represented and the vows made at the time it had been placed there. Her eyes shifted to Jonathan's at the same time her hand crossed the table to touch his arm. Finally, she spoke the words Noah had hoped to hear.

"I'm still bewildered by what you're describing . . . by what is happening. But my love for Jonathan can't be changed because of any single event. Our lives are too inseparable. We are one mind in two bodies, and I can only imagine the mental burden he's had to bear . . ."

Noah put his hand on Jonathan's left shoulder and gave a gentle squeeze. "I told you that if she were not capable of understanding she would not have been chosen. I told you!" he said, the music in his voice reflecting his inner joy.

Jonathan took his wife's hand in his, looking at her through moist eyes. "Had I any choice, I would have told you."

"I only wish I *understood* all of what you *are* telling me."

"Can you *accept* it?" Noah asked.

She pondered the question for but a second. "Yes, I can accept it."

"Then for now that is all that is necessary."

She was finding it easier to be herself now. "But this conspiracy . . . this *Phase Three*, as you call it. When am I to find out the details of *that*?"

"Soon, Mariana—soon." Noah tilted his head backwards slightly and looked toward her down along the lines of his face like a man peering over his glasses. "We must precede that monumental step with a few other insights, and we must see to a few details first." Noah paused, grinning impishly at the woman. "And once we've done all that, we must begin our final discussion on the implementation of *Phase Four!*"

Her eyes shifted toward the ceiling in a gesture of disbelief and her head nodded from side to side. Noah and Jonathan laughed at her gesture of animated confusion.

"You have my sympathetic understanding," Noah assured her as the laughter ended. "Adjusting to the . . . the . . . what must be the unbelievable shock of being called to the office of your president, and being asked to shoulder the responsibility of such a burdensome position is quite enough by itself. You must—or should—be given the time to adjust to the shock of that, my little one. But unfortunately, there is no more time. We must move in haste.

"Let me now tie together many different questions in your mind by making a very simple statement," he suggested. Noah began polishing the apple against his sleeve—slowly and methodically, with the long, smooth movement of a violinist moving his bow across the strings of his instrument.

"Your calling to this position in government is a fundamental part of the project that we've been working on all these years. The two are inseparable."

"What do you mean?" Her eyes darted from the bearded philosopher to her husband and back again.

"The conspiracy, Mari. The conspiracy . . . the project . . . our visits together in Phase One; it's all interwoven—inseparable. Once you understand the project, you will understand all. Right now, your mind and your thoughts are like the unassembled pieces of the jigsaw puzzle scattered across the top of the table. You could begin assembling the component parts at random, or I could show you a picture of the completed puzzle by explaining our plan. Then all else will be answered."

"When does *that* happen?"

He smiled at her but chose not to answer. He glanced at the highly polished apple in his hand and raised it toward his mouth. His movement made her want to do something to stop the act that seemed so imminent.

"Noah!" she cried out like a mother warning a child of an impending danger.

He stopped to answer, not with words, but with a slightly startled look. Mariana felt a twinge of embarrassment, but the thought of the man biting into the very object that had become a symbol of his presence seemed somehow sacrilegious.

Noah glanced at the apple, then at Mari.

"I wouldn't have bitten into the fruit—not yet," he assured her, having finally understood her thought.

"You wouldn't? Why?"

"Well, at least for the moment, this red fruit has significant sentimental value," he said, holding the apple at near arm's length from his face and gazing at it affectionately.

"You're fond of that apple of yours, aren't you?" Mariana asked the question hoping the answer would provide an insight into the full story behind it.

"Let's just say it's an old superstition. This apple has been with me since I first accepted the assignment," he explained. "You're joking! What—twelve years?"

"About that, more or less."

"And yet it looks as though—"

"—it's just been picked from the tree? Yes, I know. But as you will one day understand, in *my* world nothing ages."

He stared at the red fruit for several seconds then, as if spotting a slight blemish on its skin, carefully placed the apple against his sleeve and gave it one long, slow stroke downward on his sleeve. His deliberate act seemed to please him for as he looked at the apple again, he smiled.

"There *is* a story behind that apple of yours, isn't there?" Mariana finally asked.

"All things have their own story," he replied. "But yes, I suppose this one is a bit unique. I remember the day I picked it up . . . and the first day I visited with you, Mariana. Somehow, it is you."

Then, without thought, he fired a question at her—an unexpected question. "How do you tell an apple to grow?" he asked. His words flashed a picture from the past, a vivid picture that until now she had no memory of—no *conscious* memory. But now the memory of the first time he had asked her the question was as clear as the current moment, and her response was instinctive.

"It just grows—by itself." The words surprised her, and she felt a warm flush on her cheeks.

Noah smiled, glanced at Jonathan then back at her. "Does your answer sound familiar to you?"

"Yes."

"Good. You see, my little one, you must not permit yourself to be disturbed by these strange events—incomprehensible as they may be. That you should be here, that your new calling to this position of great responsibility in government has been given to you, that you have the love and companionship of Jonathan . . . these things and more should give you cause to rejoice, and rejoice you surely shall once you unravel the mystery of my presence, and of Jonathan's role, and of the details of our project."

Noah paused as though reminiscing, then continued. "Do you . . . *can* you identify the greatest benefit you've derived from the time we've spent together?"

It was an odd question, she thought, but then somehow she had grown accustomed to Noah's unexpected queries.

"You helped me to identify what I wanted to do—to write and to teach."

"Yes, Mari, your all-consuming obsession. *That* is what converts the human existence from the dull and routine to the life of substance and achievement. Until humans find their *true purpose* . . . until they find what they deeply and genuinely want to do they will achieve very little. That, Miss Mari, is the gift that I gave to you, and the gift that you and Jonathan and the others will be giving to anyone who will listen, for your land and its people are in great need of its message. You will not be using the same techniques as I, but your purpose will be as my purpose has been. You will be guiding others, not through the delicately manipulative processes of the subconscious, but through the teaching of worthy principles to the conscious minds of people everywhere. You have been led to a position of great responsibility and influence, and from that seat of power and along with others called to positions of influence, you will be teaching people to *find themselves* . . . to discover *their* purpose . . . to think constructive thoughts and pursue worthwhile objectives. Of course, by not tapping into the subconscious as I have tapped into yours, your task will take longer . . . *much* longer. But the *result* will be the same; your efforts are going to transform the prevailing individual and collective attitude of your people . . . and to a far greater extent than you could possibly imagine."

It was as though he were instructing them and thinking aloud to himself at the same time. He reminded her somehow of a man who was living his final hours, entertaining thoughts that came into his mind about the past as well as the present, and speaking those thoughts in whatever order they occurred.

"Now, a few moments ago you asked when you would learn of the full details of our project. I say to you that it shall be before this day ends, Mariana. But the revealing of the depth of our conspiracy must come to you while we complete its final stages.

"You must meet one or two of those who are participating, and you must learn of your responsibilities in your new position.

"The balance of the day is laid out for us and the schedule is extremely tight. Both you and Jonathan have a trip that you must take, and I will be joining you there later. Your husband will inform you of many of the details that time does not permit me to discuss with you.

"My blessings upon you both," he said. Noah took one step backwards, and with that he was gone, as though he had never been in the room with them.

"Where are we going?" Mariana asked as the private limousine turned into the exit ramp leading to I-95 South.

"Fort Lee." Jonathan looked away from her and out the window.

"Where's that?"

"Virginia—about forty minutes away."

"Jonathan?"

"Yes?"

"What's wrong? What is the secrecy about? And why are you so far away from me?"

He turned toward her with a look of preoccupation. Taking a deep breath, he reached out for her hand. "Several things, I suppose," He touched the silver button on the armrest next to him, and the glass window that separated the passenger compartment from the driver slid upward in one smooth, silent motion giving him the privacy he knew he would need for the discussion that would follow.

Jonathan turned his body toward her now, and she turned slightly to her right to face him.

"Jon, I really don't know what to make of this," she began. "There are still so many unanswered—"

He squeezed her hand and interrupted. "By the time we get to where we're going, I will have filled in most of the blanks," he assured her. "Even then, I can understand your dilemma. It's almost like watching the landing of a flying saucer, having a conversation with little green aliens, then trying to convince yourself that the whole thing isn't real . . . even though the object of your confusion is still sitting there on the ground humming and blinking."

"Where is Noah—? Well, I think I know where he's from, but even that is incomprehensible," Mariana said, her head shaking from side to side in lingering disbelief.

She thought for a moment, then spoke again. "And this limousine, Jon. Within two minutes of Noah's . . . well, his rather unique way of leaving us, we rush outside through a side entrance of the hotel and the limo is conveniently waiting there . . . the *same* limo and driver that's been transporting us around since we got off the plane at Dulles Airport and took us to the White House is *now* taking us to a place in Virginia where only God knows what other bizarre things will happen."

"Well then, let's clear up some things that will help you to understand. First, there are one hundred and twenty-eight similar to you at this moment in time," Jonathan began.

"Similar to me? How?"

"Who have been mentally prepared as *you* have been mentally prepared . . . as I have been mentally prepared. All but a very few are now in Phase Two. They've been fully prepared with correct principles, wisdom and understanding, and have been carefully guided to positions of great influence. *Their* talent has created a place for *them*. And there will be several thousand more like them very soon. They are in state legislatures, federal courts and state courts. They are in the media in great numbers—in publishing and television, and as editors of periodicals and schoolbooks. They've been placed in highly responsible and influential positions in business, and in positions of responsibility in many of the leading universities. They're finding their way into state and local offices such as school superintendents so as to massively affect the quality of education.

"Each of them has an attitude of optimism tempered with a sense of reality. There's no delusion among them. Each of them is fully capable of establishing clear and concise objectives, and know of the value of the single-minded purpose. They have mastered the art of communication, and their written and spoken words both inform and inspire. They pursue personal perfection in all things. They are honest, true, benevolent and loyal to their commitments. They know that you cannot strengthen the weak by weakening the strong. They understand that you cannot permanently help people by doing for them what they could and *should* do for themselves. And, they believe that character cannot be built by taking away one's personal initiative and independence."

He paused now to study her reaction. Mari remained silent, needing more to absorb rather than to inquire.

"But it has all worked out," Jonathan continued. "All is in place now. The foundation is in place. The organization is complete. The leader is ready and at the helm. As Mr. Churchill once said, 'The die is cast.' "

"I think I understand better," Mariana said. "Something you said before, about the 'positive' conspiracy. You've managed to infiltrate high levels of government, business and the media with people whose attitudes are conducive to the principles you teach, haven't you?"

"Exactly. It will take time for the *effect* to appear, but the *cause* is now in order."

"But the system—the established bureaucracy—it's going to fight us, you know . . . not consciously, not as though they are *aware* of a conspiracy, but because they're so entrenched in their ways. Of course, if there are enough of us in positions of influence . . . "

Jonathan interrupted his wife by placing his hand on her arm and leaning slightly toward her.

"Mari, believe me, we've been very sensitive to the need for sufficient numbers of our kind of people in key positions. There aren't as many as we would *like* just yet, but only because we've spent most of our time just developing the nucleus. But believe me, that nucleus is stronger and in greater positions of influence than you imagine."

"Knowing the two of you, I *can* imagine. After all, you've just used me to infiltrate the president's cabinet. You can't go much higher than that."

"No, not much," Jonathan agreed, flashing a smile that told her he was harboring a thought that she would find exceptionally intriguing. He was playing games with her sense of curiosity and she knew it.

"What's the look for, Jon?"

"I beg your pardon?"

"Will you stop it! You know what I mean. What have you two done?"

"We're fortunate to have people in high places," Jon said, continuing the game.

"All right. How high?"

"How high would you like? The Supreme Court? The senate majority leader? The chairman of the senate judicial committee? What else would you like?"

"You've got people *there* . . . in *those* positions? How—how could you have managed such things without people being aware of it? I mean, there hasn't been the slightest clue!"

"That's the way it *had* to be, Mari—not even the slightest clue. After all, what we're doing *is* a conspiracy. The fact that our *purpose* is right is irrelevant. We are, and have been for several years, conspiring to gain control of government for our own personal benefit. We all know that in this case the end justifies the means, but believe me, Congress would not have approved of what we've done. Therefore, the secrecy must be continued," Jonathan said.

Mari looked away from her husband for a moment to ponder the magnitude of what was happening. She spoke almost to herself. "You seem to have permeated every branch of government. We all know of the clear danger of a Communist infiltration of such magnitude. The McCarthy era painted the horrid pictures of how bad *that* could be, and . . . and I can only begin to speculate on how effective such a plan could be—a plan designed to produce *good* rather than *evil*."

Jonathan gave her time to ponder her thoughts, saying nothing until she had successfully assimilated, understood and accepted what had already been said.

Mariana broke the silence with a question. "Jon, there's you, Noah and me . . ."

"Noah is only the *influence* behind the project, Mari, so if you're trying to keep score, you mustn't include him."

"Okay. You said one hundred and . . . what?"

"Twenty-eight."

"And several thousand more to come?"

"At least."

"And Noah began the project—what . . . twelve years ago?"

"About that." Jonathan nodded in agreement.

"Then if it's taken twelve years to get a hundred and twenty-eight, how long do you think it will—"

Jonathan sensed the purpose of the question and interrupted. "It took that long for the *nucleus*, Mariana."

"How many people like us will it take?"

"Several million wouldn't be too many. However, I suggest you get on with more pertinent questions, my love. We don't have long, and you're going to have to be satisfied with what's happening so far or the hours ahead are *really* going to have you confused."

"Okay, let's begin with those currently involved," she said. "First, there's Elliott Brendis. I rather suspect he's involved somehow, although he may not yet be in Phase Three."

"Assuming he *were* one of us, why would he not be in Phase Three?" Jonathan asked.

"Because when he visited us in California, he encouraged you to seek public office. Surely were he consciously aware of the total picture in what Noah calls Phase Three, he would know that such a proposal was unnecessary."

Jonathan glanced at his wife and smiled.

"Is he part of the conspiracy, Jon?"

"He's involved," Jonathan confirmed.

She didn't move, nor did her facial expression change.

"Care to hazard any more guesses?" Jonathan joked.

Mari nodded thoughtfully. "I also think that somehow, in some strange way, American Products has something to do with your—with *our*—conspiracy. Don't ask me why, it's just something I sense. There's something there—I'm sure of it. There's something about the under-lying philosophy that permeates that organization that is consistent with everything you teach and everything you stand for, Jonathan. Somehow, whenever I'm at one of their meetings, I sense your pres-ence there . . . and Noah's. It's as though the two of you are guiding and directing everything from the atmosphere in the room to the words that are spoken."

"You're terribly perceptive—which is one of the reasons I love you so much. But you give Noah and me a little too much credit," Jonathan said.

"Then at least my *perception* is right." She studied him with intense concentration, knowing she was closing in on something. "Well—yes . . . we've had something to do with American Products, but not quite to the degree you may think."

"How did—? Well, go ahead . . ." She turned fully toward him now, her right shoulder resting against the back of the seat, giving him the few seconds he needed to collect his thoughts.

"We found a lot of good people there, Mari. Their philosophy of life and business is the very philosophy that keeps this country together. Many of their top people are terribly influential. Former President Carl Williams, for example, is a good close friend of one of the top ten distributors in American Products—D.L. Baker."

"Is Baker part of the conspiracy?" Mariana asked.

"Yes."

"And—surely not Williams?"

"No, there's no need for his involvement, at least for now. But who knows . . . with the plan set the way it is, he may very well become a part of the project at some future point.

"What do you mean 'the plan set the way it is'?"

"The multiplication factor. It's what the whole project is based on. But I don't want to get into that quite yet."

She turned away from him and sat staring out the window while her right hand toyed with the gold chain around her neck. In a moment, a smile came to her lips and she looked back at her husband.

"I still can't believe this is happening, Jon. I'm . . . I'm expecting to wake up any minute now and find this whole thing was nothing more than a dream," Mariana said.

"You woke up several hours ago, Mari—remember?"

She laughed aloud. "You're right. I did, didn't I?"

It was obvious that she was adjusting to and accepting the incredible sequence of events of the past twenty-four hours. "Mariana—about American Products . . . " He hesitated, adjusting the watchband on his left wrist. "Watching them gave me an idea that led to the refinement of the purpose of the project. We used it as a testing ground. I was invited to speak at one of their functions several years ago, and when Noah moved me into Phase Two and then into Phase Three, I saw a certain parallel between our *intent* and their *system*. The whole question centered around whether or not it is possible to market and promote an idea. Studying them assured us that Noah's basic plan was absolutely correct—that our effort at saving a nation by motivating its people with the value of ideas was a strong approach. Believe me, Mariana, there's something massive happening here . . . something that goes so deep that it *cannot* be stopped. The culmination of its designed purpose is now a foregone conclusion."

There was silence now. Only the barely perceptible sounds of moving traffic and the smooth movements of the limousine as it rolled through the northern Virginia countryside distracted them from their thoughts.

It had been a monumental day filled with extraordinary discoveries and neither Mariana nor Jonathan Locke had escaped the effects of the shocking revelation that Noah's master plan had brought about.

But for Mariana, the day of unbelievable discovery was not yet ended. The limousine that had carried her from one dream to another slowed now as it pulled into a driveway. It stopped at an iron gate bearing a white sign with red letters that were partially hidden by an armed military policeman. The guard stepped forward as the car waited. The driver's window rolled down silently and electronically.

Mariana Locke's eyes moved from the guard to the sign, which was now clearly visible—

TOP SECRET CLEARANCE ONLY
EXECUTIVE ENTRANCE.

CHAPTER TWENTY-TWO:

The Conversion

The meeting had been arranged for five o'clock in conference room 201B of the Rayburn Building, and it was now ten past five. Time was crucial, for there was so much to do this day, and another meeting awaited Noah when this one ended.

This was not a meeting that he had planned on, but the unfolding of events made it clear that this confrontation would be painfully necessary. It would be as close to a direct intervention as he would get. In fact, he wondered now as he sat quietly awaiting the arrival of the woman if perhaps this act might possibly exceed the authority given to him back when the project began. But then he remembered that it had been done before. He would not be setting a precedent, he assured himself. After all, he would merely be confronting evil with good. He would be making an emotional appeal . . . a strong presentation of fact, logic and reason.

But suppose his appeal failed? Suppose she failed to respond. What then?

He knew in his mind what he would have to do. The project must be given a fair chance for success, and if he had to resort to the ultimate choice he would do so. Too much time had been invested, and too many plans had been carefully made. The implementation of the conspiracy was now on a hair-trigger, and this confrontation perhaps more than any other single event might well determine the success or failure of the conspiracy.

She was a formidable opponent, this spokesperson of the adversary.

His thoughts wandered for a few moments more, finally interrupted by the opening and closing of the anteroom door adjacent to
the conference room where he sat.

This would be his visitor, he thought to himself. He remained
seated at the end of a conference table, and stared straight ahead now
at the adjoining door to the anteroom, which was slowly beginning
to open.

A single lamp glowed to his right, giving only slight illumina-
tion in the conference room, and he saw the brighter light pouring
through the opening of the door ahead of him.

"Come in—please," he said, not yet seeing the person to whom he
had spoken.

The door was pushed fully open now, and the full figure of his
guest stood before him, the bright light behind her accentuating her
feminine curves. She stood motionless, not knowing whether to enter
the silent and dimly lit room before her, or to wait for some assurance of safety.

"Please, Mrs. Simon—it's all right. My name is Noah, and I assure
you that you have nothing to fear." He stood now as he spoke, but
remained behind the end of the table, holding his arm out to gesture
toward the chair at the opposite end of the table.

Gloria Simon closed the door behind her and cautiously moved
toward the chair. Her eyes flashed from object to object throughout
the room . . . the telephone, the lamp on the credenza with the
emerald green glass shade, the pitcher of water and glass at each end
of the table. Her eyes lingered for a moment on the apple sitting on
the table directly in front of the man, then darted briefly to the man
before looking back again at the apple.

She placed the black purse she carried onto the table and slowly
sat into the chair. Noah remained on his feet watching intently her
deliberate moves.

The silence continued as she settled into the brown leather high-back
chair and Noah resumed his seated position eight feet away from her.
His eyes peered into hers as they sat alone and in silence, each studying
the other as two adversaries reluctant to make the first advance.

A polite smile appeared on Noah's lips, although not in his eyes,
and he spoke.

"Gloria—may I call you Gloria . . . ?"

"Please."

"Gloria, what now occurs between us in this room is perhaps of greater historic importance than any event of the past two thousand years, and I trust that in spite of the informality of the circumstances that you will treat the occasion accordingly."

She placed an instant smile on her face that somehow seemed programmed not by emotion but by polite pretense.

"Aren't you being a bit overly dramatic?" she suggested. "I find your meeting place and the arrangements for it rather strange, but I don't believe I would call it *historic*."

"Then perhaps *others* will one day look upon this meeting between you and me as historic—not for who we are or where we meet, but because of where our words and decisions may lead future generations."

"Do either of us wield that much power? Really!"

"No, Gloria, not you and me. What we stand for . . . what we represent . . . *that* wields all the power that is. We are representatives . . . *instruments* representing opposing views, and one or the other of us will prevail."

"Then you do represent the views of the present administration?"

"President Reardon?"

"Yes. I gathered that you were somehow appointed as an intermediary to approach me to . . . well, in some way convince me to go along with the policies of the Reardon administration."

"Whatever gave you that idea?" Noah asked.

"Just a hunch. The person who called to arrange this meeting . . . well, let's just call it a hunch. Am I right?"

"Let us say that this meeting was called at my personal request, but arranged by others. Its purpose is hopefully to arrive at the truth, Gloria . . . the truth as it exists, not as we may *interpret* it to exist."

"And you, of course, have truth only on *your* side, and the object is to convince me that my views are in error. Isn't that the bottom line?"

"I can only say what I have often said before: the issue is not *who* is right, but *what* is right."

She flashed the instantaneous and insincere smile again. "Then if you don't mind, I will labor under the assumption that you were sent by the president to convince me of something, whatever it may be. I've had people try to win me over before, so I should warn you in advance that—"

"Please—that which we fight merely gains in strength, Gloria. I would not be so presumptuous as to assume that your views are subject to change through coercion or intimidation. I do, however, wish to learn more of how you do feel about certain issues and why you feel that way. Further, I *do* have a motive in mind, but my motive is my own. The president did not 'send me,' as you suggested."

Gloria looked at him, analyzing for a moment what his motives might be. "The people who contacted my office to arrange this meeting were certainly secretive—a meeting with a gentleman at the Rayburn Building, for an unde-fined purpose . . . and all they give is your first name . . . I mean really!"

Noah gave a short and courteous laugh, placing both forearms on the table and leaning forward slightly.

"There is proper reason for the relative anonymity and secrecy, Mrs. Simon, as you shall soon see. Tell me—what are the objectives of the Human Liberties—uh—"

"Human Liberties Protective League," she provided haughtily.

"I'm *sorry*—yes," he said, a slightly visible note of discomfort at himself showing on his face for not remembering.

"We're a national organization of individuals who work together to protect the rights of the individual against the power and influ-ence of the state."

"You are against . . ." He paused a moment as if to collect a thought, and resumed his words. "You are opposed to the state?"

"We are opposed to the misuse of power to the extent that people are subordinated to the state."

"The state, to use that term, means the federal government, I gather?"

"Yes."

"And you think it has excessive power, do you?"

"Absolutely!"

"So do I," Noah said, smiling fully for the first time.

"I beg your pardon?"

"Yes, it may startle you to hear it from me, but I do believe that government has so corrupted itself that in many ways it no longer represents the miracle that men of vision once designed it to be."

"Is that token lip service or do you really believe that?"

"I believe it, Gloria—absolutely."

He watched her relax now, and she leaned forward, one arm on the table, looking curiously down the length of the table at him.

"But if I am disappointed in what has happened to government, I am even more disappointed in what has happened to its people. What do you think of *that* remark?"

"I think it's fairly typical of a politician to pass responsibility onto the *people*. Make the people the scapegoat for government blunders.

That, sir, is the philosophy of the Reardon administration . . . the *rich man's* administration."

Noah leaned back in the chair, his fingertips on the edge of the table.

"Where do you think responsibility should be?" Noah asked.

"It's the government's responsibility to protect and provide for its people. That's why we have a government—to protect and provide."

"But aren't you . . . well, didn't you just say that your duty was to protect the rights of the individual against the power and influence of the state?"

"I did."

"Yet isn't it true that to make the government responsible for protecting and providing for the people is to give even *more* power and influence to the state?"

"I am saying that government is responsible for us, but not to the extent that it has burdensome power."

"You may be seeking a panacea that does not exist," he remarked.

"Perhaps—but it's up to the politicians to figure out how to do what must be done. That's why we elect politicians to office. We pay our taxes—you people tax us to death—so all that the people want is their fair share."

"Of what?"

"Of government help! What else are you there for?" she asked. Noah sighed and closed his eyes, withdrawing inside himself to collect his thoughts and to ponder what she had said. In a moment, his eyes opened slowly and he looked directly at her.

"I would like to speak for a moment—without interruption if that is possible," he said, his voice almost a whisper. "First, I am not a politician. I am not sent here by anyone with secular authority. I have a purpose, Gloria, and that purpose shall be served within the next several minutes. This meeting . . . this conversation merely represents a confrontation of opposing ideologies. It is your fundamental view that the government and its elected leaders exist to dispense whatever service and assistance is necessary to give the people whatever they want and need. Is that correct?"

She looked away from him toward the ceiling for a single second, then spoke. "That is one of the responsibilities of the government, yes."

"And I say to you that when it becomes the role of government to serve its people by *giving* to them what they may want or need, then the people will begin to look to *government* for their needs more than to *themselves*, and in so doing, lose their sense of self-responsibility.

I say to you that when the primary role of the state is to serve its people, then on that day the people will cease to serve themselves."

"My God, you sound like Mariana Locke," she muttered, folding her arms.

"Perhaps. But please, let us not inject personalities into our short time together."

"Wait a minute. I know you asked not to be interrupted, but—"

"You long ago violated that request, Gloria."

"Listen to me. You people are very good at talking about the people being responsible to themselves. I am telling you that the vast majority of the people out there are lost in the dark. They don't have jobs. They don't eat most of the time. Their rights are being violated in a thousand ways. This 'self-responsibility' concept of yours may be a nice idea, but it doesn't pay the bills."

"Gloria, you say the people are 'lost in the dark,' as you put it. Perhaps that is a good descriptive phrase, but for some reason you are suggesting that we give a flashlight to government, and let *it* lead the people. Have *you* ever been in the dark trying to follow someone ahead of you who held the light? The person who holds the light can see, but *you* can only follow, feeling helpless and stumbling blindly over obstacles you cannot see. I am suggesting that the purpose of government, of *your* organization, or *any* individual or group of individuals who seeks to help the unfortunate should be to *enlighten the individual*. Learn to hand people their *own* flashlight, Gloria. Let them control their *own* destiny. Let *them* decide when they want to leave the darkness, or *whether* they want to leave, but do not ask them to *follow*. That is the fallacy of your thought, Gloria. The more you give to another person, the more they will *demand* to be given. With each gift or offer of generosity must come responsibility. If you *accept*, you must *commit*."

Gloria Simon sat silently in the chair, her fingers tapping lightly against her opposite forearms, as the arms remained crossed. There was an uncommon intensity about her, a combination of arrogance and defiance. She tolerated his words, but she did not seem to find truth in anything he said.

Noah knew that from the very foundation of the world there was good and evil; truth and deceit; love and hate. He knew that all of life and nature were in constant opposition. Life was both Cain and Abel—a battle between the victor and the vanquished. There would always be both freedom and servitude, and in each group would be human beings disenchanted with their status. Before him was a woman who sought to give rewards to the undeserving, and to combine all of the goodness of the world and divide it up equally among all the people so that prosperity and happiness might be the universal right of everyone. Noah smiled to himself at the thought, but knew that while some among humanity sought total equality through the redistribution of wealth, it was not God's plan for his people to exist without choice and division.

Noah knew that the philosophy of Gloria Simon was the philosophy of the adversary . . . the philosophy of evil. It was a condition of human existence that the Creator had long ago rejected, and no power on Earth would change the nature of the plan. He knew that *how* people were was because of *what* people were, and that *what* they were could be changed for the better only by changing thoughts and attitudes for the better.

He looked at her with respect, in spite of the fallacy of her views, for she was a woman of both beauty and skill. He knew that she was the chief adversary of an erroneous philosophy, one that had become so popular among the masses that it now threatened the very fiber of a nation that had been designated for greatness. He knew that the doctrine of evil—the doctrine of the adversary—had gained the upper hand, and that the Creator had not yet decided to give up on his experiment. He also knew that a correction would have to be made. The power and influence of evil would need to be slightly diminished for this one final time.

A smile came to his face. It was a genuine smile that mirrored the love that he felt in his heart for the woman who sat before him in spite of what and who he knew her to be.

"Gloria, you are an uncommon woman," he said.

"You needn't try to win my support by compliments," she said. "That, too, has been tried before."

"Then you will not consider a more rational philosophy toward helping those who have not yet found themselves?"

"Your approach, Noah, is no more rational than my own."

"And you know who I am—who I really am, and what and whom I represent?"

"You have created your following, and I have mine," she said. "I am the spokesperson of one philosophy and you are of the other, and it will be interesting to see which view prevails."

"I agree, Gloria. It would be an interesting contest. Unfortunately, it is a battle which must be fought at another time and in another place."

Noah leaned forward now, his hands outstretched on the table before him, his eyes fixed firmly on hers. A light from above reflected in his eyes as he tilted his head slightly to the left. Even as his head moved away from the reflection, the light in his eyes remained, intensifying until she could not look upon him. The light somehow caused his being to glow with a power she had never before experienced. She could not move now or speak; she was helpless to prevent the act that was so imminent.

His right hand raised a single inch from the table top, his index finger pointing toward her, and with that single and insignificant act, it was finished. The conversion was accomplished, and the camp of the adversary had been infiltrated. The conspiracy had created one of its own kind whose words would gain the audience and respect of those most unlikely to accept the words and admonitions of a Mariana or a Jonathan.

It was the same body who sat before him, but the mind had been transformed. For Gloria Simon, there would be no Phase One, Two or Three. The miracle was complete and a new spokesperson had been gained. It was the only direct intervention that Noah would resort to, and even now, he did so with both reluctance and regret. But in his heart he knew the future regret for not doing it would have been even greater.

He would not need to tell her of the conspiracy, for it was not his intent to make her part of it. He sought only to win her support to make her *views* compatible with the views of those in the conspiracy. His eyes studied her now, and the kind smile that appeared on his lips was matched by one of sincerity showing in her eyes.

"Perhaps we could make some adjustments . . . some compromises," she suggested slowly.

"Adopting something that you once rejected because you now believe it to be true is not compromise, my dear. To hide from truth, to refuse to seek it, or to admit that it is bigotry is the very heart of all that is evil," he said.

"You do understand that the president has some philosophies that are very difficult for those at the bottom of the economic ladder to accept, don't you?"

"Truth, like success, Gloria, flows downhill. This country is in need of truth and justice, not political rhetoric and foolish programs designed to give people false hope. There is precious little time left to correct the errors of the past. Your elected leaders cannot continue to promise all things to all people simply to gain votes or to be popular. Somewhere, sometime, someone must have the courage to speak the truth and to do what is right."

"Yes, I understand. I'll admit that there must be give-and-take on both sides, and I can only tell you that I will do what I can, wherever and whenever I can."

Noah stood up, and Gloria seeing that the meeting was ended, stood with him. He walked from behind the table and along its length toward her, and each extended their hand toward the other.

The two stood face to face in a gesture of friendship. It was indeed a day of monumental importance, for today there would be a voice of reason and hope amid the turbulence on *both* sides of the philosophical and political spectrum.

CHAPTER TWENTY-THREE:

The Departure

Mariana Locke sat four levels down in the underground bunker within the walls of Fort Lee. She watched quietly as Jonathan unlatched his briefcase and removed several papers, which he laid in front of him on the table. So far, he had said nothing to enlighten her on the reason for their trip, nor why they were in such an unusual location. From the moment that the iron gates opened at the main entrance, each movement further into the compound added to the mystery.

She had sat in the limousine as it rolled slowly inside a concrete building with airplane hanger type doors that had opened slowly like the yawning jaws of an alligator. The car had carefully moved into the center of the massive building to park within the yellow lines that seemed to mark the exact center of the concrete floor. They had sat unmoving for a full minute as the huge doors behind them slowly closed. Then there had been the unexpected jerk of the floor beneath them, which had caused her heart to leap into her throat, and she had watched in silent fascination as the section of floor ahead, behind and on either side of them sunk slowly downward.

The vertical journey seemed to take several minutes. She had looked upward through the glass sunroof of the car to watch the opening where the floor had once been shrunk away until it was smaller in size than the sunroof itself. Finally, the vertical movement had ended in a near-silent lurch. As the wall ahead of them slid open, the driver pulled the car fifty feet forward into a narrow opening that seemed specially designed to accept the size of the limousine with only a foot ahead, behind and on either side. And then the entire cubicle had moved to the right for what seemed like thirty seconds, coming to a final rest in a fifty foot square concrete room with green paint on the walls, ceiling and floors, and yellow lights providing only enough luminance to pinpoint the single door ahead of them.

Without a word being spoken, Mariana and Jonathan Locke and the driver who escorted them had stepped from the limousine for the first time in over an hour. They moved through three separate cubicle-like chambers, each requiring that the doors behind them be closed and sealed before the plastic card which the driver inserted into the slot on the wall would open the metal door ahead of them.

And now they sat alone in a room that seemed designed for a business meeting. The driver had activated a control panel on the wall with a key he carried within the glove of his left hand, and a row of amber lights glowed across the otherwise blank face of the panel. He then prepared coffee for them, and still without a word, exited through the door on the opposite side of the room through which they had entered.

Jonathan glanced at his watch and then turned to face the control panel on the wall. His wife leaned forward, elbows on the table, her hands clenched together and her chin resting on the joined hands. She watched her husband prepare two cups of coffee, finding the cream and sugar without searching, as though he knew from experience where everything in the room could be found.

Her words were more of a stated observation than a question. "You've been here before, haven't you?"

"Yes—many times. Particularly over the past year. Each time I came back to Washington I seemed to end up here at least once."

"Aren't you going to compliment me on my patience and self-control?" She smiled at him as she asked the question.

"Patience and self—? Oh, of course! I am impressed, but then again that's *you*, my love."

"Do I wait much longer . . . I mean, will the ceiling open, or what? This is all so . . . so unreal, Jon. Whatever happened to my uncomplicated, open-book husband?"

He gave her a flashing smile as he set the coffee in front of her. "You're handling it very well, and your 'open-book' husband is about to give you the whole book so that you can read the parts that weren't in the original copy.

"As for how long you may have to wait . . . probably another ninety seconds," he remarked, glancing again at the control panel whose lights had flashed from amber to red, and sequentially from red to green.

Obviously something was happening, but the flashing lights were as mysterious as had been every other event of the past six hours.

"What's happening—or shouldn't I ask that either?"

"Our guests are arriving. The lights represent each of the fourteen doors or levels we passed through to get here," Jonathan explained.

She took a sip of the coffee, her eyes watching the lights flash in succession—left to right . . . amber . . . flash . . . red . . . flash . . . green . . . sequence to next light.

With four stages of lights remaining, she suddenly reached for her purse and removed her lipstick.

"Is there anyone that you *wouldn't* touch up your lipstick for?" he inquired fondly.

She continued to look into the mirror while answering him. "The day I begin to neglect my appearance will be the same day I begin to neglect my thoughts."

The door at the end of the room slid open almost without a sound and two men stepped out. The first man carried a black briefcase, while the other carried a large black bag that reminded her somehow of the bag she had once seen an artificial plant salesman carry.

"Good evening, Mr. Locke."

"Good evening, gentlemen. This, of course, is Mariana Locke, my wife."

The same man who had spoken to Jonathan greeted Mariana politely. The other looked toward her, nodded and smiled. Mari had not noticed that the light sequence had resumed, moving again as it had before. She watched in fascination as one of the men moved about the room opening panels in the walls, flicking switches, and connecting what appeared to be electronic equipment to whatever was in the single black bag he had carried in.

The other man pulled out a phone from beside the light panel and spoke in a slightly muffled voice. "Twenty-six connected and green at. . . . " She missed his last words as he turned away from her to glance around at the doors that were now sliding open again.

Mariana Locke sat upright, her eyes moving in staccato bursts from her husband to the newly arrived visitors emerging from the sealed room. The first two were not known to her—they were much like the men who arrived only moments before. But behind them stood. . . . How could *he* be here? How could he be in the presence of . . .

"Good evening, Mr. President," Jonathan said.

"Good evening, Jonathan," Reardon said, walking quickly toward her husband and shaking his hand. The handshake between the two continued for several seconds as the president put his left hand on Jonathan's shoulder in a gesture of obvious friendship. They stood looking at one another, each with a confident and victorious smile. Then their hands separated, and the man swept past Jonathan, moving directly to Mariana with his hands outstretched in a warm gesture of greeting.

"Mariana—Mariana! How very good to see you," he said.

"Mr.—Mr. President . . . good evening."

She spoke to him, but her eyes flashed past him to look upon Noah who stood in a far corner smiling his best smile, and holding the ever-present apple in his right hand.

Jonathan looked at the expression on his wife's face, then toward Noah, who nodded reassuringly toward Mariana, as if to tell Locke that his wife would be all right.

Mariana's eyes detected everything, but her mind understood nothing. She could not conceive of the answer behind the presence of these three men together at the same time and in such an unexpected place: Robert F. Reardon, the president of the United States; Jonathan Locke, her husband—a man who only a few days ago harbored no secrets . . . a man she thought she knew; and Noah, the person who had worked a miracle in her own life. Each of these powerful and talented men who had played such a significant role in her life were now standing before her, joined by the common bond of the conspiracy . . . the plan that somehow she was to be part of.

The mind of the startled woman rushed back in time and presented her with quick-changing images. She focused on the moment that she had walked through the door of the Oval Office into the outer office following her meeting with the president. It was—when? Yesterday? The day before? So much had happened she was losing track of time. Suddenly she remembered an incident of such seeming insignificance that her brain nearly failed to recall it. It was the moment that her husband paused momentarily to re-enter the privacy of the Oval Office to exchange a few brief words with the president. It had meant nothing then, but it now was a key that unlocked the door to a new insight that gave her a brief glimpse of the intricacy of the conspiracy. She recalled the president's language the day they had first met, his startling preoccupation with the urgent need for a new national attitude.

Unlike his predecessors who had sought to give their attention to preservation, everything about Robert F. Reardon suggested a preoccupation with the revitalization of the nation he served. She had not been conscious of it before, but this president had always spoken openly about building up the American spirit.

Her mind continued to play with the possibilities behind this man's existence here, but his very attendance among those whose roles she already understood gave evidence of his involvement in Noah's—in their conspiracy.

The mind and imagination of Mariana Locke ran wildly, and her awareness of the current moment, of the here and now, returned only after everyone had seated themselves around the table. She was utterly seized with fascination at where she was, who she was in the company of, and the consequences that their collective presence made possible.

Jonathan looked up at her and spoke a single sentence. "Wouldn't it be more comfortable for us all if you sat down, my love?"

She had not noticed that she was the only one of the group still on her feet.

"I can understand your shock, Mariana," the president said. "Noah told me just a few minutes ago that you were still rather . . . well, rather confused by moving into Phase Two and Phase Three in the same day. I'd like to say that I understand the feeling, but I don't. Even I had seven weeks to get used to the idea that my mind had been visited by Noah for several years without my conscious knowledge of it. The truth is, I *don't* understand—not completely, but you'll just have to get hold of yourself, I suppose."

"I'm—I'm fine, Mr. President," she stammered unconvincingly. "Obviously, I'm not going to wake and find you all gone, am I?"

"Let's hope you don't, Mariana. Were all of this *really* to be a dream, I'm afraid you would awaken in Philadelphia with your first thought being how to find a job and pay your creditors," Noah commented.

His remark brought a short and collective laugh from the three men who sat at the table with her. At the head of the table sat the president. To his left sat Noah, and to his right, Jonathan, with Mariana next to her husband. The remaining two chairs on Noah's side of the table remained empty, as was the single chair next to Mariana. The men who had accompanied those now in the room were gone, and there were but the four of them, sitting in momentary silence while pondering the import of the moment. It was Noah who broke the silence.

"The moment has arrived—at least for the three of you," he began. "The role of the others shall, of course, be secondary to your own. We need to examine the precise status of the current Phase Three participants. First, however, I should say that while each of you will be aware of the facts we must cover, we must go through them just once primarily for the benefit of Mariana. Now, Jonathan, what about Congress?"

"Complete," he announced, "in all details. Brendis moves in to take control of the Appropriations Committee tomorrow. Benstrom, the Senate majority leader . . . well, of course, you moved him into Phase Two this morning," he said, glancing at Noah but then looking at the president as though his remarks were meant more to *inform* him.

Jonathan continued, glancing down at the papers in front of him and looking up from time to time into the eyes of the president. "Justice Horne is now fully aware of Phase Three, giving us a five-to-four majority on the Supreme Court—at least on the key issues. The Senate Finance Committee and the Armed Services Committee are now headed by people in Phase Three."

"Marsh and Butler," the president said.

"Yes sir," Jonathan confirmed. "You need Marsh to limit the spending on non-essential programs, and Butler to upgrade the quality and professionalism of the military."

Mariana's head moved slightly as she shifted her attention from the president to her husband, and briefly toward Noah to study his response to what was being said. The dream was slowly becoming reality now. What she was experiencing *was* real. There would be no awakening to find herself back in Philadelphia. This *was* the president of the United States. This *was* her husband, and the man across the table from her *was* some strange visitor from another place whose mission was to change the moral fiber of America. There *was* a conspiracy and she *was* part of it.

Jonathan opened a file folder in front of him, removed the documents inside, and passed a set of the papers to the president, Noah, and Mariana, keeping one set in front of him.

"Here you will see the names of twenty-two individuals, all of whom are key members of either your cabinet, Mr. President, or within the White House staff. All are now fully in Phase Three and functioning without any knowledge of your involvement."

"Why not?" Reardon asked. "Won't that make things a bit uncomfortable?"

"Noah feels it is wise," Jonathan answered respectfully. "Your policies need to filter down to the various departments, both to and through those in key positions who will enthusiastically support them. Beyond that, there's no real reason to know that their president is a participant."

"Twenty-two," the president said, as though thinking aloud.

"Yes, sir, but with the multiplication factor it will soon become far more."

"I understand," the president replied thoughtfully. Mariana sat silently, her eyes scanning the document that Jonathan had handed to her only a moment before. She found it incomprehensible that so many key positions in government could be staffed by those minds that had been made receptive to and worked in harmony with Noah's philosophy.

The list became more awesome each time she looked at it.

THE WHITE HOUSE STAFF

The President of the United States	Robert F. Reardon
Deputy Chief of Staff	Michael N. Dabny
Press Secretary to the President	James N. Daly
Presidential Assistant for Communications	David D. Hargan
Presidential Assistant for Intergovernmental Affairs	Richard Wilhelm Samuelson

EXECUTIVE AGENCIES

Chairman of the Council of Economic Affairs	Arnold H. Goldstein
Director of the Office of Administration	John J.R. Walters

DEPARTMENT OF STATE

Assistant Secretary of State for Congressional Relations	Robert Weebanks
Assistant Secretary of State for Human Rights and Humanitarian Affairs	Elliot Ahrens
Director of Intelligence and Research	Hugh Mountbatten
Policy Planning Staff	Hal Horowitz
U. S. Representative to the United Nations	Joanne Kilpatrick

TREASURY DEPARTMENT

Assistant Secretary	Thomas Dennison

DEPARTMENT OF DEFENSE

Assistant Secretary of Defense for Program Analysis and Evaluation	David S.C. Chang

DEPARTMENT OF JUSTICE

Associate Attorney General: Civil Rights Division	Dillman Reynolds

DEPARTMENT OF THE INTERIOR

Assistant Secretary for Policy, Budget and Administration	H. Robinette Eastman

DEPARTMENT OF AGRICULTURE

General Counsel	A. James Holmes

DEPARTMENT OF COMMERCE
  Director of Minority Business
  Development Agency   Victor G. Ocala

DEPARTMENT OF LABOR
  Assistant Secretary for Labor—
  Management Relations   Donald Dawson

DEPARTMENT OF HEALTH—
HUMAN SERVICES
  Assistant Secretary for Human
  Development Services   Darrell Brady

DEPARTMENT OF
HUMAN DEVELOPMENT
  Secretary of Human Development   Mariana Locke

DEPARTMENT OF EDUCATION
  Undersecretary   Cecil D. Hall

Noah's voice brought her full attention back to the moment. "Now, Mr. President, you'll be pleased to know that as of less than an hour ago, the other key positions you felt you would need to have influenced are now also in Phase Three. I completed that task during this afternoon, and I will merely remind each of you, primarily for Mariana's information, who and what they are."

Noah spoke from memory. "Saul Vickers of the Federal Reserve Board. That should control your interest rate situation and stimulate your economy."

"Excellent!" Reardon said, a bright smile coming to his face. "So that accounts for his unexpected announcement today that he would let interest rates find their own level!"

"Precisely," Noah confirmed. He looked toward the ceiling now, as if recalling his thoughts. "Now—let me see. The chairman of the Federal Communications Commission, the president of the Motion Picture Producer and Directors Association, the chairman of the American Communications Network, and the president of North American Communications Company are all now complete. With these gentlemen involved, you will begin to see the quality of your films and television programs improving. There will be, I am happy to say, far less violence and immorality being fed into the minds of your young people.

"In addition, the Supreme Court chief justices in seventeen of your states are ready, as you requested, Mr. President. So are the eleven governors and twenty-one commissioners of education who will restore quality in your schools. You will soon see homework being assigned again, and a renewed emphasis upon the value of education. And one other surprise that I'm certain that you did not anticipate."

"Surprise?" The president was obviously overjoyed. His open palms were tapping on the table top in open jubilation. "No surprise could be more exciting than what you've already done, Noah. You've given us a new chance, Noah—a new chance!"

Noah smiled the first shy smile that Mariana had seen, and his head bowed slightly. When he looked upward again, the smile had disappeared.

"Perhaps I *have* given you a new chance, Mr. President, but it is *you*—each of you—and the others who must now work the magic of the multiplication factor. *That* will be the true test of the new chance I've given you. You must now go to battle with the great adversary." He paused. "And the adversary is not happy with my interference here.

"It was my own judgment that told me that I must do something to lessen the power of the adversary. When he presents *his* case to one of your kind, goodness seems so unattractive, which is why in the choice between good and evil, it is evil that becomes the choice of most." He spoke slowly, glancing alternately at each of his small audience.

"Therefore, I have added a member to our little conspiracy—one of the great advocates of pessimism and doom. One of the chief spokesmen of the evil one is now in our camp . . . that is my surprise," Noah said.

Jonathan looked at the president, then at Noah. "Who?"

Noah's smile coupled with his silence told them that his surprise would have to wait for its own moment, for he would not reveal now his meeting earlier in the day with Gloria Simon.

Jonathan took advantage of the lull in the conversation to turn to his wife. "Mari, are you following all of this?"

"Sometimes it is better to remain silent and *appear* to be a fool than to speak and leave no doubt," she answered. Her response brought a laugh from the three men.

"And sometimes, my little one, it is better to let someone learn from observation than to attempt to teach by instruction and explanation," Noah said. "But to rephrase Jonathan's question, are you beginning to grasp the essence of our project?"

"Yes, the infiltration into the government with those of *worthy* purposes can be just as effective as infiltration by those whose purpose is to destroy and overthrow. Jon and I were discussing that very idea tonight on our way here. How frightful it would be if a *foreign* power were to decide to implement such an infallible plan."

"Do we know that it hasn't?"

Jonathan's question brought a strange shrug of the shoulders from the president. "You have no idea how accurate your imagination might be, Mariana," Reardon said quietly.

Noah watched the conversation, neither speaking nor responding. Only an unnoticed sigh signaled his contribution to the subject being discussed.

There were several seconds of silence before Mariana Locke spoke. "The one element of all of this that continues to escape me is the—multiplication factor. I've heard it referred to a dozen times—even here tonight—but . . ."

"Then let us clear it up for you, Miss Mari," Noah offered. "Jonathan?" He extended his arm toward his younger friend as an invitation to answer his wife's question.

Jonathan thought for a moment, then spoke. "Let's look at it this way . . . if you believed in something strongly enough—whether it's a financial opportunity, or a political or philosophical belief—and you studied the thing long enough, you would become rather experienced in the thing, and probably quite enthusiastic about it. Let's assume that you tell *me* about your idea, and I find the thing as intriguing as you. Together we meet often, study it some more, and you continue to teach me everything you know about the idea. I in turn get some rather clever insights of my own which I share with you. These ideas tend to reinforce your own beliefs, thereby making you even stronger. Making sense?"

"Sure."

"Okay—now, let's assume we invite someone else to sit in on one of our sessions. In fact, let's just say that we decide that what we're learning, building and studying has great merit, and we want to share it with lots of others. We then agree that you'll find someone to join us and that *I'll* find someone—one each. Remember though, we want to be careful. We don't want to find someone—well, someone like Gloria who will fight us because of their biases or preconceived notions. We want some people who are open to good ideas and whose attitude is already conducive to the things we believe. Assuming we each find one person, there are now *four* of us. Got the picture so far?"

"Sure," she said with a nod of the head.

"Four of us, who each believe in the things we're sharing—whether it's a product, a philosophy or whatever. We meet together frequently to discuss it, study it, try to improve on it and ponder its applications and possibilities. Through it all, we each grow to believe in our product more each day. You see my love, if you had kept the thing to yourself, you would have derived only so much from the thing; but by sharing it with a few others, we magnify the value that each of us get from it. In fact, I remember that Noah once said that the more you share a good idea, the greater your reward."

"If you plant a cup, you reap a bushel," she said.

"Exactly," Jon agreed. "Now, let's carry the thing out to its logical conclusion. Each of the four of us decides to resume the search for others who might embrace our idea, and we agree that each of us will be or at least have the potential of *becoming* unusually unique. We don't concern ourselves with how long it will take. Remember, we occupy ourselves with the ever-growing strength of the idea."

"Eight."

"What?"

"Eight. Four—each getting one more—is eight."

"That's the concept, little one. Then . . . "

"You simply repeat the procedure. You study the plan—the project— whatever it is, continue to master it, and continue to search for others who will embrace the thing."

"You've got it. The multiplication factor!"

"*That's* the multiplication factor?"

"That's it."

"But it's too simple. What does that have to do with . . . "

"The project? Everything! Look at American Products. They started with three people who had had it with their personal circumstances, with working for someone else for a fraction of what they were *really* worth. They finally decided to start a small sales company. They added a few people and developed a marketing plan that provided incentives for increasing the number of participants in the organization, and look what's happened to them—almost a million people!"

"So—okay, I've got it, except that what you've done is—you've replaced a product with a philosophy—Noah's philosophy. Is that it?

Jonathan smiled. "That's it, my love. So simple that it's missed by most people. Noah merely taught me the same things that he taught you—things that aren't new at all. They were taught by a simple carpenter at a seminar on a hillside two thousand years ago, and by Moses before him. It's the philosophy of Plato, of Socrates, and of Confucius. Gandhi taught much the same thing, and Jefferson, and Emerson. The same theme runs throughout the great teachers of then and now, but we've been too dense to hear it for the most part. The few who do listen hear it mostly with their ears instead of their hearts, and their lives remain virtually untouched and unchanged.

"This time though, we're going to *learn* from the mistakes of the past—while there's still time. Noah was right you know—even God probably has a limit to his patience, and this may well be our last and best chance to make something of this place. We're taking the ideas of how life was intended to be lived, and teaching those principles to people who use and embrace them. Then, by carefully manipulating the political structure, we covertly place those people in extremely powerful positions in government. Once there, they tend to quietly attract others who have gone through the process of being taught by Noah, or by one of his best students—like you, my love. Is that making sense?"

"Completely. But it's going to take a while, Jonathan."

"Probably. Then again, work out the numbers. From Noah to me— that's two. Then it took us a year and a half to go to four. In another eleven months, we were at eight—then it took only seven months to increase the numbers to sixteen. From there it was thirty-two, sixty-four, one twenty-eight, two fifty-six, five twelve, one thousand twenty-four—each incremental jump taking lesser amounts of time. Then of course, we have to move the people from Phase One to Two, and so on. That takes a while."

"Have you thought about how long it will take before you've moved enough of us along to key positions in government so that our influence and philosophies will work their way down through the system?"

Jonathan didn't respond immediately. He pondered her question in a way that suggested he knew the answer, but was reluctant to offer it.

"Jonathan?" He looked at her.

"How long?" she asked again.

"Nearly fifteen years for the effect to be felt—before we can *really* overcome the damage done by so many years of neglect and too many years of government giveaways that rob the people of their dignity."

"That's a long time," she finally said. "Do we have that long before things completely collapse or before we destroy ourselves in the interest of defending ourselves?"

"We'll work under the assumption that we do. One thing is for certain, though—the fifteen years will go by whether we continue with the conspiracy or not. The fifteen years won't care. I don't suppose that Noah will either—or even God, for that matter. That's what free agency is all about. We've been given this planet and its resources, and the intelligence that sets us apart from the other forms of life. What we do with our resources and our intelligence is—as it's always been—up to us."

"Well, there you have the essence of it, Mariana," Noah interjected. "The combining of an idea with intense purpose and patience. And what is rather remarkable is that the simple formula for changing the direction of a nation is the same formula for changing the single life."

"Commitment and purpose, Mariana—commitment and purpose," Reardon added. "And, you must prepare yourself for the curse that will test both the commitment *and* the purpose."

Mariana looked at the president, then to Noah, and her mind flashed a picture from the past—a picture of the document that Noah had handed to her the first evening he visited her. It had mentioned— THE CURSE!

"What do you mean, Mr. President, by—the curse?"

Noah answered part of the question for Reardon, knowing what was in her mind.

"Yes, Mariana," he said. "The same curse I warned you of, and it is just as alive today as on the day that we warned you of it."

"But—but what is it?" she asked again.

Reardon leaned forward now, his arms on the table and his hands folded together.

"Let me try to answer that for you," Reardon offered. "I, perhaps more than most, have witnessed the power and the tenacity of what Noah calls the curse. *You're* going to confront it, and indeed you already have.

"The curse, Mariana, is very simply the voice of doubt and pessimism, from whatever the source," he explained. "It's the natural inclination that most people have toward gossip, ridicule, and the other demeaning tendencies that destroy character and distort truth.

"Believe me, when your decisions, opinions and policies are in the public realm, the press, the television—those given the responsibility for reporting the news—will put you under a microscope that is often vicious. For whatever the reason, the tone of their questions, their language, and their attitude is such that it has as its purpose the assumption of guilt and incompetence. They will, in an incredibly subtle manner, tilt facts toward suspicion, and treat hope with pessimism. Through innuendo and fractional truth, they will appeal to the inherent negative side of people. You must prepare yourself for it, Mari."

Reardon sat back now, and he smiled in spite of the intensity that had been in his voice. "You might say that it comes with the territory, and it's also a major reason why the conspiracy exists. It could well be that if it weren't for a runaway epidemic of the diseases of attitude, there would have been no need for Noah's intervention. He would have let us alone to figure it out for ourselves."

Reardon looked toward Noah as if to give a cue for him to pick up on the thought.

"Your president is precisely accurate, Mariana," Noah said. "He used an excellent phrase—diseases of attitude—for it is quite descriptive of the curse that has gained control of your lives and your words. The curse is at the center of the weeds and bugs of the human existence. You see, we created first the things of beauty and value," he said, and his hand reached out and picked up the apple that had been sitting on the table in front of him.

"The fruit is a thing of beauty and a source of food," he explained. "The *blossom* of the fruit also has its own beauty, locked up in a fragrance and displayed in the emerging petals of the bloom. The tree that gives birth to the blossom and the fruit is a source of strength and life, deriving its existence from the very seed of the fruit it now produces and from the soil that provides nourishment."

He moved the apple from one hand to the other, his eyes following it as he spoke.

"The tree—the blossom—the fruit," he continued, "are meant for man's enjoyment and sustenance. But all things must have their challenge. At the creation, life was given to the bugs and weeds, and because of *their* existence, they have the capacity to destroy the goodness. While the young plant struggles in the soil to become an apple tree, the weeds may well attack it, or the bugs may well devour it, for it is not the plan for goodness to exist without threat. Unfair as it may seem, however, that which threatens—the bugs and weeds—*will* exist without goodness. Bugs may destroy apples, but apples may never destroy bugs. Evil and adversity were given the upper hand, and only the constant efforts by those of goodness will prevent those of evil from finally gaining control."

He looked up from the apple now, and his eyes moved around the table. These were his students, and that which he taught them and made them see, they would teach to others and cause others to see.

He spoke again, still holding the fruit in his hands. "Bugs and weeds are the tools of the adversary, to be used to snuff out the grand design of nature," he said. "But it is the disease of attitude that has reached the level of an epidemic. You are obsessed with gossip—it feeds your minds with a food that will inevitably destroy goodness. Let evil and poor behavior exist! But do not feed it with the power of gossip, for in so doing you give it a strength that has the capacity to destroy.

"You have likewise become obsessed with pessimism. You *anticipate* failure and difficulty, and it is no wonder you now have it in abundance! Your thoughts give life and strength to the very tools which the adversary will use to destroy you, for the adversary has no powers of his own, only those which your thoughts and actions give to him. Command him to be gone and he shall be gone. *Believe in yourselves* and you take away his ability to make you *doubt* yourselves. The adversary, with his bugs, weeds, and diseases does not control *you*; you control the adversary! But you must rid yourselves of the self-doubt, indifference, and worry that have seized your land. You must learn to believe in *yourselves* again, for therein exists the secret to the restoration of goodness and strength, and *that* is the purpose behind our conspiracy."

Noah's last sentence provided the final key to Mariana's understanding of the complex project which they called the conspiracy.

She smiled, looking toward her husband, and Jonathan felt her understanding and knew that all would be well.

The bearded wise man sat back now, his left hand lifting the apple with the thumb and forefinger. Releasing his grip slightly, the apple flipped ninety degrees.

It was Jonathan's words now that interrupted the silence. "It was our pessimism that kept the stock market from ever going well through the one thousand mark. That same attitude of pessimism causes the media to find fault with every attempt an administration makes to bring about lasting change. We've literally thought ourselves into the worst recession since the depression, and now that our poor thinking habits have produced a poor circumstance, the press and television people look for someone to blame—and as is usually the case, the blame goes to the present occupant of the Oval Office." With his words, Jonathan looked toward the president.

Reardon listened, looking intensely at Jonathan, then to Noah. "And we're going to reverse that trend," Reardon said. "We're going to reverse it, and we're going to do it by implementing the multiplication factor and putting into motion the conspiracy that you gentlemen have masterminded. We start, in fact, in less than two hours when I address the nation. Mariana, you must—and you Jonathan—begin to design the seminars and training programs immediately."

"What about the—my confirmation?"

"Don't worry about it," he said, "Get the programs designed. Your confirmation is as certain as tomorrow's sunrise. We've got to have those programs. I want them on videotape so that they can become available in every school in the nation. We'll schedule you around the country, Mariana. A nationwide tour. We'll get you before the chambers of commerce of every major city."

The president began making notes as he spoke. "We'll give the grass roots the benefit of self-help programs while we concurrently start the process of new thinking at the top."

He was becoming consciously obsessed with how the program would develop. Noah and Jonathan had spent over ten years developing the nucleus for the conspiracy, and now this man would guide and direct its implementation. He was the perfect selection. Robert F. Reardon was a man of unquestionable integrity, blessed with the skill of uncommon persuasion and the gift of the single-minded purpose. He would guide the conspiracy through the waters of challenge with both precision and daring. He was surrounded with the best talent the nation had to offer, and their attitudes, intent and skills were equal to his own. He would not have to convince them, fight them, or compromise with them. There would be, for the first time, a unity and purpose that would sweep away any selfish opposition and any narrow interpretation of his programs. What Noah had set in motion, this man and those who surrounded him would now direct.

The four remained together twenty minutes more, discussing final details and making specific arrangements for meetings, events, and the assigning of responsibilities in the days ahead. Finally, the president glanced at his watch and stood up.

Mariana had not noticed Jonathan touch the push-button switch under the edge of the table, and she wondered how the entourage that had accompanied the president had known the exact moment that he was ready to leave.

The final goodbyes were spoken, and the doors leading into the first stage exit cubicle slid silently closed as the president of the United States departed as he had arrived.

Noah walked back to his chair and sat down, breathing in a deep and prolonged breath while closing his eyes and savoring the moment. It was as though he had completed his mission and was now reflecting back upon the entirety of the experience. Only after a full minute did he return to them, a smile coming to his lips even before his eyes were fully opened.

"It is finished," he said. "It is finished, and yet it has only just begun." An expression of total contentment came to his face, and there was a serenity to his being that was the epitome of peace through unique achievement. Jonathan and Mariana remained silent and unmoving, for it was not a time to converse or contribute, but rather to absorb and experience.

Noah spoke *to* them, yet somehow beyond them; he spoke with them and for them, for this hour, this moment represented all things that each of them had in common.

"The project ends, and a new project begins," he said, rephrasing his earlier thought. "You must now continue to grow, to read, and to share. You must teach all of that which you know, and study so that you might one day teach that which you do not know."

The eyes went slowly closed again, and reopened nearly a full minute later. Now, he was here again, and he reached for the red fruit, lifting it gently from the table and staring at it with an interest that nearly suggested that he was conversing with it. His eyes lifted upward now to look upon Jonathan.

"My brother, you have performed well, and because of you our project now has its own life. I thank you . . . I thank you, and . . . and I love you both," he said, looking at Mariana.

"Mariana," he said, looking at the apple resting on the outstretched palm of his left hand, "how do you tell an apple to grow?"

There was no uncertainty or confusion this time, only a courteous delay to be certain that he had finished, and his eyes looking directly into hers confirmed that he had.

"You do not, Noah. You merely nourish the tree and step out of the way so that it might fulfill its destiny," she answered. He smiled proudly, and with only a twinkling of hesitation, Mariana responded with her own question.

"Does the garden of the adversary bear apples?" she asked. Again he smiled.

"I believe it does," he said, "but all of his apples have worms."

"May I be permitted only a question of curiosity?"

"Certainly, my little one."

"That apple of yours is . . . well, it's symbolic of something, isn't it?"

He nodded affirmatively.

"Can you tell us of what?"

He paused for a moment, staring again at the fruit and into it in a strange way. "It is, I suppose, my link to yet another world—a world that someday perhaps you will come to know and understand. It is an apple from an unusual orchard, and it represents many things. It is a symbol of life. It is a symbol of choice . . . and of temptation.

"In truth, its life ended when it was separated from the tree that gave it life; and in much the same way as the life of one of *your* kind ends when separated from the dreams that give them hope. You see, the object continues to appear as an apple, but it has stopped growing. Likewise, many of your people appear to be living and functioning long after *they* have stopped growing."

He paused for a moment before continuing. "And there is another symbol represented by the apple."

Noah did not finish his thought, although it continued to linger in his mind, and he took joy from continuing the thought while withholding his words.

"What *is* it?" Mariana inquired hopefully.

Noah displayed one of his finest smiles, and his eyes glowed with a blend of humor and excitement.

"This strange red fruit also carried a subtle message, one which when understood is perhaps the basic morsel of instruction with the capacity for changing one's life for the better."

He seemed to enjoy the game he was playing, and he looked at them both, seeing their curiosity and sensing their anticipation of the solution to the mystery.

"I will share *that* thought with you both in a short time, and in the way of my final parting phrase. Grant me this one attempt at dramatics. While the rest of the world may not understand, you will know that my mission here is complete when this apple becomes food for my body rather than a symbol of my existence."

Noah spoke with them nearly an hour longer, informing and admonishing. The final plans were covered and the final questions answered. It was critically important that the key upon which the whole conspiracy hinged was clearly understood, for it was *the multiplication factor* that would work its predictable magic, converting in his absence the *theory* of the conspiracy into a fait accompli.

Both Mariana and Jonathan knew that the implementation was *theirs* to perform, that Noah could play no *active* role. Soon, very soon, they would be left alone to invoke a philosophy of life into a world that would be reluctant to accept it.

There was a long silence as both Jonathan and Mariana pondered what they knew to be the imminent hour of Noah's departure. There was a certain finality in the words he spoke, and Mariana felt a twinge of premature loneliness at the thought that this man would one day not exist in their lives as a source of inspiration. She remembered the words that had passed from his mind to hers, and how his wisdom had somehow been indelibly impressed upon her soul. He would leave, and she knew that, but what he stood for would *not* leave for that had been the purpose of his coming. The gift of commitment had been taught. The gift of integrity and sincerity had been restored. The gift of insight had been transplanted from his world to hers. The lives that would be needed to carry on his message and purpose had been found and had been touched, and the world would not again be the same—at least not for a few generations to come. Then, unless mankind could somehow alter its tendencies to destroy itself, the wheel would again turn and moral principles would again give way to immorality, and the destiny that history seems to have outlined for humankind would finally and irrevocably fulfill itself. And then . . . perhaps *this* was to be the *final* intervention.

But for now, in this hour and in this generation, there was a glimmering of hope that a *new* history would evolve with humans *building* upon the existence of others rather than seeking to *destroy* that existence.

She looked at her Jonathan and in his eyes saw the same message that she felt in her own heart. This man who sat before them would not linger long, for this was a time not only of disclosure and implementation but also of departure.

"You're going back . . . back *there*, aren't you? You're going to leave us, aren't you?" Her voice was a near whisper.

"My dear Miss Mari, someday you will discover that both the *here* and the *there* are one." His eyes closed as he spoke and a slightly perceptible smile came to his lips. He pushed his chair back a few inches from the table and stood slowly.

"Jonathan, my good friend, no one could be more prepared than you. And how fortunate that this woman should be at your side. The two of you together to guide the affairs of the project . . . heavens, it just may work at that. It just may work."

Both Jonathan and Mariana Locke remained seated, looking up at the man in white who had stood before each of them in the past—separately, but in much the same way.

"You won't be coming back, will you," Jonathan said.

"No, no I won't," Noah replied. "Even the Creator has his limits of patience," he explained. He held the apple in his right hand and there was a silent exchange among the three of them. It was a moment of unspoken love, mutually given and deeply felt.

"Then we'll not see you again . . . at all . . . ever?" Mariana asked.

"There is no such word as 'never,' little one. You will see me once more, but only briefly. There is but one thing I must observe and then I shall depart. It has been a most enjoyable experience. I would not have missed it for—well, 'for the world,' as you say."

He turned his body slightly now and looked directly at Jonathan. "My friend, I shall leave you now, but we shall not have seen the last of one another."

Jonathan spoke a single word of affirmation and slowly extended his right arm toward Noah who transferred the fruit from his right hand to his left and reached for Jonathan's hand. At the precise moment their fingers touched, the older man was gone as though he had not existed. It was at the same microsecond in time that Mariana Locke felt an indescribable emotion of total confidence, and the knowledge and awareness of all she had been taught by the man who, but a moment before, had shared both the room and her mind with her. She felt neither shock nor bewilderment at the events which had no rational explanation. Her husband moved his suspended arm to her. For a time they sat in silence, letting the loss, the silence, the memories, and the experience touch them for all time and eternity.

CHAPTER TWENTY-FOUR:

The Message

T here were less than ten minutes before Reardon would face the cameras from the Oval Office of the White House. For almost the first time since taking office, he felt comfortable with the speech he was about to deliver to the nation. Although there was no written text to follow, the remarks he would be making were clear in his mind. Perhaps his confidence came from his secret awareness of the unusual significance about this imminent event.

He relaxed now, crossing his legs and letting his body sink deeper into the softness of the black leather chair. The knock on the door would summon him within minutes, but for now they were alone for what would be the final time. He let his head rest against the back of the chair and his eyes closed for a moment, reopening only partially to gaze across the coffee table at this man who had been his closest advisor. Without him, Reardon thought, the pressures of this office, and the nearly uncontrollable immensity and complexity of the system would have caused him to become disillusioned by the obstacles and consumed by the rigid bureaucratic procedures of a government gone wild. But instead of being consumed by the overwhelming responsibility, Robert F. Reardon had been empowered by it. His seven decades of existence on Earth had given him invaluable years to accumulate and assimilate a wealth of experience. Combined with his unique ability to extrapolate wisdom from confusion, and to pursue worthy goals and plans in spite of incessant appeals to abandon his goals, the years had made him an uncommon man in an uncommon age. He would do what he knew to be right where others would have been lured into the trap of doing what they knew to be popular.

The president would not allow himself to become persuaded by opinion polls, for he knew that popular opinion had, when followed in the past, led to unpopular results. He would permit himself to be influenced not by expediency, but by his conscience.

He would condone only those thoughts, that provided rational solutions, and would not permit himself to indulge in thoughts of doubt or fear, even though the world and national conditions gave him cause for concern and apprehension. The course had been set and there would be no deviation from it.

In these, the final moments of their last rendezvous, both Reardon and the bearded man in white who sat across from him had been content with the silence and in the reassurance that each felt because of the presence of the other. But as is always the case, silence must be interrupted, particularly when time leaves only precious few moments before responsibility calls.

"Well, my good friend, we both have our different places to go to and our separate duties to perform," Noah said, sitting slightly forward on his chair.

Reardon did not immediately respond with words, but his smile gave its own answer.

"No plan has been more intricately devised and assembled," Noah continued. "It cannot be altered now, nor stopped. You . . . myself . . . all of us can only step aside now and witness the process of well-conceived plans becoming long-desired realities."

"I won't try to thank you, Noah," Reardon finally said.

"You needn't. The implementation of the conspiracy and the results it will inevitably promote will provide the only form of gratitude which I expect. By the way, the words of your speech that will trigger the implementation . . . just out of interest, where in the message do you intend to speak them?"

"I thought I'd be a bit dramatic and make it my closing line," Reardon answered.

Noah laughed. "You've always been more than a bit dramatic, Mr. President, but I suppose that's one of the reasons you were selected for the position you hold."

Reardon smiled to himself and shook his head.

"So, you've not overlooked anyone—on the trigger phrase, I mean?"

"No one, Mr. President. It will work flawlessly, and tomorrow—while it will appear to be but another workday—will find a new dawning of an age that has no comparison. With the utterance of the final line in your speech tonight, a significant number of people in Phase Two will be instantly progressed into Phase Three, with a full and complete awareness of the existence of the conspiracy and of their specific role in it, and each will be fully aware of all the others involved. They will immediately begin to lay plans for the implementation of Mariana and Jonathan's programs into their areas of influence.

"And there is no chance of detection. A plan of this magnitude is virtually impossible to detect. And, even if someone *could* uncover a few facts suggesting the existence of the conspiracy, the remaining undetected facts are so numerous and unprovable that the few *provable* facts would appear to be merely innocent coincidences."

Both men seemed to become simultaneously aware of the need to end their conversation, and Noah stood slowly, walking around the table and toward Reardon, his arms stretching toward the president in a gesture of departure.

"We will find one another again one day," Noah promised.

"But not here . . . not on Earth?" Reardon asked the question, but in his heart he already knew the answer.

"No—not here."

"We'll continue the project you've started, Noah, and we'll make it work. We *must* make it work this time."

"Yes, Mr. President. This time you must. And you *must* make your people see that, because the consequences of failure are . . . "

The knock on the door did not require words to convey the message. The two men looked briefly into each other's eyes, and with a kind smile and a gentle squeeze of Reardon's hand, the visitor was gone.

The door opened slowly and Fletcher Kennedy glanced into the room to see the extended arm and empty hand of the president.

"It's time, sir," Kennedy advised.

Reardon clenched the hand that had but a moment before held Noah's, and raised his arm slightly above his head in a gesture of eagerness and confidence.

"Let's go for it!" he said, and walked quickly out of the room toward the Oval Office and an unknowing, and for the moment uncaring, audience of Americans.

The limousine carrying Jonathan and Mariana Locke rolled off the exit of Interstate 95 nearly a dozen miles south of the Washington

Beltway and turned left toward the Colonial Motor Inn. There would not be enough time to reach the Marriott Hotel suite that served as their temporary home before the president would begin his message, and it was Mariana's suggestion to watch the address in the lounge of the quaint hotel.

Jonathan had the hostess seat them in the booth at the far end of the dimly lit lounge. The television set looked down on them from eight feet above. The lounge was nearly empty. The two couples sitting together across the room seemed to be discussing business, while the man sitting alone at the bar sipped at a glass of wine and ate pretzels while staring at the television and David Gately who was wrapping up the network news for the World Broadcasting Network.

A waitress had taken their orders for coffee, and they sat quietly for the first few moments, each contemplating what had been done as well as that which was yet to come. They were not aware that twelve miles to the north the president of the United States was entering the Oval Office for the last-minute sound and lighting checks before going before a national audience. They were part of that audience, knowing only that in four minutes the major networks would switch to Washington, focusing their comments on a single man with a message of greater significance than any viewer would ever imagine.

Jonathan Locke, the architect of the conspiracy that would be implemented this night, sat next to his Mariana, whose own role would transform the philosophy into reality. Jonathan tapped his fingers lightly on the tabletop, his eyes staring vacantly across the room. It was his brain that was looking, not his eyes. It was a mental gaze which saw nothing but felt and comprehended all. His mind was running the tapes of the past and future simultaneously. Mariana's hands reached out to silence the drumming fingers bringing him from *his* world of inner thoughts to *their* world of witnessing the transformation of America.

"Nervous?" she asked.

"No—apprehensive, perhaps," he responded.

They said nothing as the waitress set the coffee in front of them, and the silence continued as they watched the final few moments of the news. The voice of David Gately spilled through the lounge in the impersonal and disinterested fashion of one reporting on world and national events as though he were unaffected by those events.

"While administration officials seem to find solace in the latest figures from Wall Street and throughout big business, eleven million people are still without jobs in America. In many states, unemployment funds are nearly depleted, and those on welfare are finding it harder these days to buy the so-called spirit of optimism that the White House feels will make the economy turn the corner away from recession and unemployment."

Jonathan Locke looked away from the television with a slight look of disgust, and tossed the empty sugar wrapper he had rolled into a ball. It fell directly into the center of a trash container a full ten feet away.

His wife smiled, admiring his accuracy and knowing what was on his mind. "You're the only man I know who can test his athletic skills and vent his anger at the same time," she teased.

"You'll notice that he said nothing about three percent inflation levels, interest rates that have been cut in half, an increase in auto and housing sales, or . . ." He caught himself in mid-sentence and looked at Mariana who sat listening and smiling.

"Someone we both know would suggest that you not match pessimism with anger, my love."

"You're right. Gately has been critical of the president's programs ever since he was refused an exclusive interview just after the election, so what can we expect?"

"We'll always have the pessimists with us, Jon. They're like the bugs and the weeds, remember? Perfection and universal harmony only exist in Noah's world. We can only seek improvement and move *toward* perfection; but in moving toward it, we must pass by and encounter the David Gatelys of *our* world."

Jonathan looked at his former student who was now a frequent teacher.

"Pass through them, observe them, ponder their thoughts and words, grant them their opinions and errors . . . "

"But do not permit yourself to be affected and persuaded by them," she said, finishing the sentence her husband was quoting from one of his early books.

Her right hand squeezed his left hand as an underscore to the appropriateness of their common thought and they both looked toward the television.

"This country is going to hell in a handcart." The voice came from the man sitting alone at the bar, and he looked at Jonathan as he spoke.

"It's going to hell in a handcart, it is," he repeated.

"Is it?" Jonathan answered, giving the man the courtesy of a reply.

"You bet. And there ain't nothin' any of us can do about it, 'cept sit around and watch the politicians push us all right into hell."

He sipped at the wine and looked at Mariana for a moment, then back at Jonathan, waiting for and expecting confirmation of his assessment.

"Perhaps we should get out of the handcart and push it in a different direction," Mariana suggested.

Not wishing to continue a conversation with someone who expressed an opposing view, the man turned back to the television.

He seemed to be unable to originate thoughts, Jonathan observed, only to respond. Soon the man was gazing at the television commercial as intensely as he had a moment before, seemingly captivated by a beer commercial.

Then—the words spoken as if by an unknown authority. "We take you now to Washington, D.C., and to the Oval Office. Ladies and gentlemen, the president of the United States."

Jonathan and Mariana fixed their attention on the television screen and the words that their colleague and friend was about to speak.

"Good evening. Tonight I would like to bring a message to America that is of uncommon significance. While I am using the media to reach you, the small minority who bothers even to watch presidential messages in these troubled times, I wish tonight to talk past the media. I want to share some thoughts with you, as one American to another, before the press and the commentators have taken the liberty of dissecting and analyzing my words to give meaning to those words that I did not intend.

"As many of you know, the text of any presidential message to the nation is released in advance to the members of the media as well as to members of Congress. It was my direct request that the advance text not be released this evening, for there is no text, no script, and no written notes. My words are my own. They are spoken by me as I am directed by the spirit to speak them, and they are intended for you who still care enough about your country to take the time to share part of your evening with me. Together, we comprise a body of Americans interested enough in our collective and individual futures to participate in the great American experience.

"I want to assure you tonight that there are a significant number of your elected and appointed leaders in federal and state government who are both capable and committed to the work that lies before us— the work of reestablishing sound moral, philosophical, and political principles in our government so that all of us might have a chance to attain a better life. Those leaders to whom I refer are Democrats and Republicans alike, for their commitment to revitalizing America does not recognize the narrow avenues of political title or persuasion. Like many Americans, I find it totally incomprehensible that any political

party could have all of the right people with all of the right programs. Also, like many of you, I have grown increasingly frustrated at members of any political party who use an appreciable amount of their time condemning the opposing party, for in the bitterness and bigotry of the political system, you are the loser. You pay the price through ill-conceived laws and regulations reached through political compromise by those more interested in the preservation of their image and popularity than in the preservation of freedom and independence of our great land.

"Tonight, I would like to examine two separate subjects. The first is the final arrival at a destination that began two hundred years ago. The second is the beginning of yet another journey—one begun in our own time, using ideas conceived in our own generation, and calling upon the lessons gained from that first great experiment of 1776.

"Now, let me share with you an examination of that dream conceived two centuries ago which fathered our current blessings and our current dilemma. It was a courageous and unimpressive band of relative unknowns who left their homeland in the seventeenth century, bound for a place they knew nothing of. The greatest attraction to this place they called America was that it offered them a new beginning. What they were—and what they were not—would have no meaning in the colonies that were forming. The unpopular aristocracies, the laws that bound them in subservience, and the many limitations that prevented them from developing and using their latent skills and talents had driven them from the homeland of their fathers to this new wilderness. Then, as our history books reveal, these rugged and determined colonialists soon fell victim to the same intrusions of an insensitive government that they had sought to escape earlier, and it quickly became clear that drastic steps would need to be taken. I am reminded tonight of something that President Kennedy once said that appropriately describes their hopeless situation, and I quote it to you now: 'Those who make peaceful revolution impossible, make violent revolution inevitable.'

"Finally, and in pursuit of their dreams and freedoms, those who sought only to escape tyranny now took up arms to prevent the introduction of that same tyranny in their new land. They were, of course, victorious. In establishing a new form of government that would hopefully endure, these brave souls gave birth to what became the American dream. From every corner of the world, people came to our shores in search of their own dream, and the message of

the American miracle created a reputation that made America the
most affluent, the most respected, and the most emulated land and
people since the Roman Empire.

"In the one hundred and fifty years that followed the great revolution that won us our independence, we moved through the delicate
formative years and into the era of the Industrial Revolution.

"Those of great talent and genius who had become Americans—
both by birth as well as those naturalized Americans—gave us
inventions and creations that brought us from relative obscurity to
the forefront of world leadership.

"As the United States emerged into a role of international promi-
nence, so too did hundreds of thousands of our individual citizens
create their own great reputations . . . their own great success stories.
The poets, the industrialists, and the political leaders alike found a
place for the pursuit of their talents—or perhaps it would be better to
say that their talents created a place for them.

"Americans grew to respect and love America, and America and its
capable and respected leadership grew to respect those Americans who
had contributed so much to our collective growth and development.

"In spite of those occasional interruptions by recession, military
hostilities, and the ever-present threat of the cold war and the potential for nuclear disaster, the decades of the fifties and sixties were a
time of prosperity and scientific advancement. It was truly an age of
instant miracles. On Earth and in space, science handed to us more
breakthroughs of uncommon design than in any previous age, and
we came to take for granted the eradication of disease, the miracles
of communication and transportation, and the unique lifestyle that
our talent and genius had created. Those who wanted homes could
buy homes. Those seeking employment had little trouble finding a
job. Those wishing to broaden their knowledge through education
had little trouble finding the proper school that they could afford.
In those times of great prosperity, we—the government, you and
I—loaned money indiscriminately through government-sanctioned
lending programs. We gave guarantees to everyone—guarantees that
no one would go without an income, even though they decided that
they simply didn't want to work; we gave subsidies to farmers if they
would agree not to use their land for producing crops; we gave assurances to foreign governments that we would give whatever support
they needed if they would merely agree to remain loyally allied to our
political philosophies; we gave money to those who did not need it,

promises to those who did not deserve it, assurances to those who did not require it, and a multitude of other commitments to those who did not want it.

"In looking over our conduct of the past twenty years, it seems that to a very large extent we have done those things which we should have left undone, and left undone those things which we should have done. We have given freedoms to those who require discipline. We have become dependent upon those from whom we should seek independence. We have lost the respect of friend and foe alike, and weakened our posture nationally and internationally by trying to be all things to all people.

"The world has lost faith in America. It has lost respect for America, and it has lost the strength that comes from an alliance with a nation whose people have always been industrious, respectful, creative, and fully committed to the preservation and continuance of the American dream.

"Within our borders, our belief in ourselves has slowly crumbled. The errors of the past now are having their effect. The accumulation of a staggering national debt now undermines our financial stability. The price of education, transportation, and of simply maintaining our accustomed standard of living is staggering. We have come to doubt our beliefs and to believe our doubts. The dream of our founding fathers has become obscured by those of our current generation who seek to escape reality by entering a world of dreams of a different kind; this new realm of dreaming is a fantasy world induced by drugs and alcohol, and the use of these chemicals creates a segment of business which makes drug trafficking one of the top ten businesses in our land.

"The dream of Washington, Adams, and Jefferson has become the nightmare of our own generation. Our people want results and they want them now. Americans want jobs, loans, grants, welfare, assistance, and they want it without the responsibility that should come with any form of assistance that government provides.

"On any given day, from the windows of the White House, I witness one group after another walking back and forth, and in large circles, carrying placards that promote themes of resentment, objection, and demand. I listen to and read the themes of doom, ridicule and negativity bombarding us each day in our newspapers and on radio and television stations. Like you, the messages reaching my eyes and ears are demoralizing, and tend to promote fear, doubt and apprehension about our future.

"I must speak objectively and truthfully with you—not to you, but with you, and about us . . . all of us. We must look here and now at where we are. We must look at where we could go if we altered our course . . . if we altered our course of conduct, our course of thinking, and our course of dreaming.

"I believe that our fundamental error is that we have slowly and imperceptibly permitted governments to gain unreasonable control of our lives—of our individual destiny. I believe that we have condoned so much of a massive intrusion by government into our lives that we are now reluctant to take that control back for ourselves. We simultaneously ask government to be responsible to us as well as for us. But, as a good friend once cautioned, we must be extremely careful about who we permit to care for us, for the subtle tendency exists for us to eventually develop deep feelings of hostility towards our caretakers.

"Those who designed our grand republic placed great emphasis upon the value of our freedoms and on the responsibility that each generation inherits to preserve those freedoms. In the last few decades, however, we have relinquished or altered those freedoms in a strange and dangerous way. We demand freedoms, but we are unwilling or reluctant to take upon ourselves the responsibility that inevitably accompanies every freedom. In some cases, individuals and groups of individuals even seek freedom from responsibility, and that is a dangerous trend. To those who seek freedom from want comes the responsibility to work. To those who seek freedom from fear comes the responsibility to be courageous. To those who seek the freedom to rise within business organizations to positions of leadership comes the responsibility to increase our personal value. I say to you that without responsibility there are no freedoms, for each thing of value has its own price and its own responsibility.

"Now, I would like to say to you tonight that all that you have been hearing, reading, and fearing over the past few years is untrue, but I cannot. The facts are that our nation is troubled . . . troubled by an unstable economy, an obsolete national defense system, dependence on raw materials from foreign and often hostile nations, and by an unresponsive government who seems to be insensitive to the basic needs and wishes of its people. I agree with those who say that we are a declining power, and who predict that unless we can reverse our direction through some unlikely miracle, we will lose much of the freedom and independence that we have struggled so long and so hard to obtain. I agree that their assessment is accurate, but I disagree that the miracle so necessary for recovery is unlikely.

"Yes, we are a troubled country; but then, it is true that we live in a troubled world. Inflation affects nearly every country. Shortages of oil and other raw materials know no boundaries. All nations need one another and all nations affect one another. That which challenges one nation generally challenges all. We are, in spite of our political and ideological differences, a world community. Despite our differences, we are all human with the same fears, the same needs, and the same wishes for a world that can live in harmony.

"But if harmony, peace and relative tranquility are to prevail, then some country must lead the way; some leadership must step forward to make bold new efforts to bring together nations who would otherwise destroy one another. The history of the last one hundred years shows that where international leadership and initiative are required, America has answered the call.

"I say to you this night that in spite of what may appear to be a weakened and declining posture in world affairs, the United States will once again carry the banner and sound the trumpet. The miracle necessary for the revitalization and transformation of this great land has already occurred. I suppose I am just naive enough to know and to believe that the voice that spoke to an earlier generation of Americans has chosen to again direct our thoughts and our actions. This most favored nation was, in my opinion, established in a most uncommon . . . a most divine way, and the powers that once were brought to bear in the formation of this great republic will not permit that republic to falter.

"I report to you now that in the wake of years of uncertainty and decline, and amid the rubble of moral decay and political turbulence, this land is in the midst of recovery and on the threshold of a period of growth and prosperity unparalleled in the past half century. Earlier, I said that I would discuss two things with you tonight. To this moment, I've chosen to direct my remarks toward the events that gave our nation its birth and brought us to our current generation. This remarkable two hundred year journey has been a story of incredible achievement, but it has made us complacent, undermined our deter- mination and our unity, and clouded our purpose. Yet we survive with hope, prepared to identify and pursue new objectives.

"But now, I would like to look ahead at the next two hundred years.

"Tonight, at this very hour, we have within our power and among our ranks all of the talent and all of the opportunity necessary for rekindling the sleeping American spirit. In spite of the large numbers of unemployed and the general stagnation of our economy over the past several years, I am convinced that the American dream continues and that the miracle lives on. The ultimate victory or defeat, which we may experience at the hands of any opposition or obstacle, lies within our own minds and with our own attitudes.

"The greatest enemy which threatens is here, within our own borders. That enemy has access to every one of us, and shouts at us daily with a well-intentioned but often misguided voice of negativity and impending doom. While it is not our only enemy, it is nevertheless one of such great power, significance and influence that none can escape it. To attack it, question it, or in any way speak out against it is to feed it even greater power. This enemy that I speak of is the media—not any particular individual or any segment of the media, but the media in general. I am irrevocably convinced that the public is highly responsive and receptive to and greatly influenced by the domineering, ever-present voice of the press, radio and television. On any given day and at any hour there is a steady drumbeat of negative thought emanating from newsrooms across the nation. So massive is the authoritative and collective voice of this industry that the general public places greater respect on and gives greater attention to this source of event gathering and reporting than it does to those designated as the nation's elected and appointed leaders.

"The media has grown to be so influential that a mere summary and review of a president's national address can be totally distorted within minutes by a news commentator who, in sixty seconds, gives to you, the public, his or her assessment of what was said, not said, intended or implied. Those charged with the responsibility of leading our nation must be either perfect or made to look questionable or incompetent. I suppose that the great danger in the current power of the media is that because of the very design of the system, they have the last voice—the last thought. They share with you the final view and the final interpretation. They plant the last mental message and the final seed of thought, as they will tonight. For every one of you watching my entire speech this evening, there will be a thousand or more who will hear only a phrase which will be relayed to them in a single thirty second segment on the eleven o'clock news. Tonight you will be told how unfair I have been, or how I used this time we spend together to attack the media, to place the blame on them for the ineptitude of this administration and its policies and decisions. In my opinion, if the media merely serves as a vehicle for reporting *rather than as a mechanism for interpreting the events taking place in America and around the world, then it functions as a fair and necessary servant of mankind. But when reporters and commentators cloud events with personal opinion, innuendo, and private interpretation, as they often do, then they have taken upon themselves the assumption of undeserved power and authority.*

"Now, here is something of major importance that I must make clear. I take great issue with any individual or with any organizational entity that would grant unto itself the right to assume that it should do your thinking for you. The government, the press, the news commentators—no one must become so presumptuous as to assume that their views and interpretations should prevail over the right of the public to reach their own conclusions. The danger in the current power of the media is that its power to reach you is awesome and nearly without limitation. What goes on within the halls of Congress or within the walls of the White House has become somewhat secondary to what the media assumes is happening.

"I openly condemn the reporting of assumptions. I condemn indiscriminate journalism that distorts true intent. I take issue with remarks taken out of context, and I object to those who blame the media for taking things out of context in order to escape from the responsibility for their comments or actions.

"I believe it is time that someone in this nation addresses the problem of that very explosive combination of biased journalistic reporting combined with the clever methods of advertising firms that use the sensationalism of negative news reporting to sell products.

"I have no doubts or reservations about the very honorable intentions and professional conduct of many of the members of the media. Its value in keeping our people intelligently informed on the many issues before us is what makes America uniquely different from other nations of the world. We give to our people the details of our errors as well as the stories of our achievements, and that is good.

"However, at the risk of alienating many of the members of the media, I must tell you that the media as a general body charged with the delicate responsibility of keeping our people informed has taken upon itself powers beyond those granted by our Constitution and Bill of Rights. There is a power of subtle greed that has consumed that important industry that makes news reporting an immense battle-ground whereupon the battle for ratings is fought with the armaments of sensationalism, distortions and exaggerations of truth. Through

hearsay, gossip, innuendo, and implication, news reporting has become a source of high profits that often places greater emphasis on who gets the story first than it does on who gets the story right. In the process reputations are destroyed, and the full facts are often clouded by partial truths. The driving impetus behind news reporting is to do what is expedient to achieve high ratings, for high ratings bring in large revenues from advertisers of products, and it is the money from those advertisers that keeps the media in business.

"And now, because news reporting is a business more than a service, the quest for great profits has taken priority over the search for truth. It is a known fact that the human inclination toward violence—for murder, terrorism, and other acts of hostility—creates audiences. For some strange reason, we seem to enjoy most those things that destroy character, create fear and reveal the worst in us and among us.

"Within the media there are two factors which cause truth to be distorted and erroneous conclusions to be drawn. First is the limitation of time: there can only be so many stories within thirty minutes of news reporting. The second is the need for profits. Because of the presence of these two important factors, truth and accuracy are often lost. After listening to the network news or reading the newspaper, we are often left with a feeling of hopelessness, an anxiety about our future, and a feeling of fear and anger that a government like ours could allow such terrible things to happen among us and to us.

"I suppose I'm just one of those old-fashioned people who still believes in the biblical admonition that suggests that we become what we think about. I believe that if you lose the vision and the dream of a better tomorrow then a better tomorrow will never occur. We've been warned by the ancient prophets that 'Without a vision, the people perish.' I believe firmly in the concept that thoughts of doubt and fear will inevitably produce the results of that kind of thinking. I believe devoutly that a worthy goal or objective, intensely pursued, will be achieved. I believe that thoughts have the strange capacity to produce circumstance. It is my conviction that we are fully responsible for our own circumstances, and that no government program ever conceived has, or ever will have, the capacity to alter the circumstances of any human being. Until our thoughts are changed, our circumstances will remain unaltered.

"As long as we go on listening to reports on how bad things are, things aren't going to improve. As long as you, out there, sitting and

*listening to my words, go on believing that things are falling apart,
that politicians are all dishonest, or that no government administration will ever change things, then for that long will our nation
continue to walk in darkness, declining in prestige and remain
unable to alter our course from where we are to where we want to be.
I can tell you now that if the bankers and financial leadership of this
nation begin doubting our future and believing that interest rates
will rise again, then the interest rates will rise. Interest rates are an
effect—they do not gather among themselves to vote on whether they
should rise or not. If the business community regains its belief in an
improving business climate, factories will begin producing again and
jobs will be created.*

*"To a far greater degree than most of us will permit ourselves to
believe, our confidence, our courage, and our beliefs determine our
present and our future. If enough of us gathered together and restored
our confidence and attitudes about a better tomorrow, then I can
promise you that all of the economic indicators in the world which
currently suggest that we are a nation in peril would dramatically
reserve themselves . . . and the media would be at a loss to explain
what happened.*

*"If what I am saying to you is true, then why aren't more of us
working together in a spirit of harmony and mutual commitment
to make things better? If there is an answer to that question, it lies
in the strange fact that it seems to be an innate part of the human
existence that causes us to cling to negativity. If someone around us
begins telling a story of a negative nature, a crowd seems to gather, as
though the negative commentary were a magnet, attracting negativity unto itself. Therein, more than any other reason, lies the root of
our present difficulties as a nation. Negativity attracts audiences, and
audiences buy products. We have been subtly swept into a whirlwind
of negative journalistic reporting that captures our attention, and to
use a popular television phrase, 'We'll be back with those stories right
after a word from our sponsors.'*

*"The media is telling us how bad it is, the advertisers are calling
to us about how good it could be, and the average American finds
him or herself hopelessly trapped in the middle ground of frustration—neither winning nor losing, but always walking that fine line
between success and mediocrity where the lonely walk, wondering
and wandering, but making no progress toward their ambitious
dreams of earlier years.*

"An era of American lifestyle is ending and another era of American lifestyle now begins. The dawning of the era that spans over two hundred years has brought us to a position of worldwide influence. But in the acquisition of that influence, the prevailing attitudes of too many of our people have created for us major challenges. We have become too complacent and too wasteful. We have let carelessness and greed affect the quality of our products. We have created too many avenues of dependence on government programs that consume public monies, and the public monies come from a society that is grossly over-taxed. The trends and programs we have created have led us to our current decade of challenge and change. We—you, I, your neighbor next door, your business associates—all must reexamine those things we produce, those things we say, and those thoughts we allow ourselves to think.

"It is time for readjustment and recommitment.

"We must learn to demand as much from ourselves as we have been demanding of our government.

"We must impose greater discipline on ourselves rather than foster dependence upon others.

"We must learn to find as much joy in the encouragement of others as we do in the condemnation of others.

"We must learn to take freedom away from those who would use that freedom to destroy us.

"We must come to understand that every uttered phrase of ridicule is a seemingly insignificant but ultimately deadly blow against our own national confidence.

"We must play down our individual errors and weaknesses, and magnify our strengths.

"It is permissible to condemn our adversaries, but we cannot condemn ourselves.

"We must encourage those who try and applaud those who succeed.

"Within our ranks is an ever-growing and dangerous element that speaks a language designed to mislead our people. They seek programs and sponsor movements that will produce what they call a 'victory for the people.' They seek the redistribution of wealth. They plan for the destruction of centers of power and influence. They seek foolish freedoms for our people and our nation, when what we truly need is greater self-discipline, pride, loyalty, and commitment.

"While I use the phrase I am about to say with caution, I am gravely concerned about a trend toward laws, slogans, movements

and thoughts that are far too reminiscent of a revolutionary era. They have the ring of Marx and Lenin in the beginning of this century.

"The great danger is that those who maneuver and direct our thinking speak in popular tones, promising more to those who have little, and suggesting that those of great wealth and power are the enemy of the people and are to be weakened or eliminated.

"Let it be known, from this moment in time and into the foreseeable future, that America and the American people are not going to condone or permit the slow unraveling of our constitutional freedoms and responsibilities by those few who are among us who smile broadly, promise profusely and speak in the golden tongue of the foreign serpent who would lull us to sleep only to steal away our most prized possessions and treasures.

"There are too many voices among us who promise to take away challenge and difficulty. I believe that the building of human character is not in the absence of challenge, but in how we respond to that challenge. What happens to us is not the issue—the final issue is what we choose to do about what happens.

"We are not going to watch any longer the deterioration of the quality of our children's education permitted by those who would give those young minds more of what they want than what they need.

"We cannot permit the continued emphasis upon the granting of freedom to, or the responsibility for providing comfort for, those who violate our nation's laws.

"We are going to end the complexities of our legal system—one which brings simple disagreements between mature adults into courtrooms where expensive battles are waged over issues of human greed, jealousy and materialistic motives.

"While it is unpopular and deemed wasteful, this nation must continue to develop a strong defense, and explore the mysteries and vastness of space, for in so doing we will continue to enrich our minds and awaken our imaginations while we remain a free, disciplined and prepared nation.

"We shall, through programs currently under study and development, encourage the rebirth and appreciation for those basic human attributes which keep a free nation from becoming hostage to those who would undermine our morality.

"Throughout all levels of our society we are going to once again begin teaching and demanding respect for our nation's laws, and rigidly strike out with sure and certain restitution against those who

would violate those laws. The consequences of breaking our laws must be consistent, predictable, quick and sufficiently firm to match the magnitude of the offense.

"We are going to begin teaching the value of honor, honesty and truth.

"We are going to come again to understand that every violation of legal or moral codes is a violation of the basic freedoms of each citizen of this land, and those violations, if tolerated or allowed to go unpunished, will lead us to lose our respect for the basic codes of honorable human conduct.

"In reading the history books that contain the chronicles of past human conduct, it is totally clear that all nations of the past have served as either an example or as a warning for those nations of future generations. I say tonight, to every ear that hears my words, that this nation will not continue along those paths which are leading us to that cemetery lined with monuments of civilizations which, despite their best intentions, have become warnings for us to study and ponder.

"America will not become another Rome, another Athens, or another crumbled power used by future generations as an example of complacency, greed and internal decay. I say to you that there is no other form of government that provides greater hope for the happiness of mankind than does—America, and I say to you that there are enough loyal servants within our borders to defend our just principles and doctrines to the last drop of our blood and to the last miracle of our collective mental genius.

"What I want to express to you tonight is a challenge—a challenge that calls for the full and active participation of every one of you. Beginning right this moment, I want each one of you listening to me tonight to begin making a conscious effort directed at monitoring your own thoughts and attitudes. I want you, if you possibly can, to act and think as though our circumstances are improving. To make this easier for you, I want to give you some rather good news. Regardless of what the newspeople will say after I'm finished, what I'm about to say is totally accurate. My words are not distorted opinions or interpretations designed as a politically unilateral view to enhance the image of my administration or my own political party. They are facts.

"After four continuous days of objective and impartial fact finding, I can happily report to you tonight that interest rates are now at half the level of just one year ago. Home buying has increased

fifty percent over the level of three months ago. Tool manufacturing companies are receiving orders that are up sixty percent over last month. Help Wanted advertising in twelve of the nation's leading newspapers has increased thirty percent over last month's level. Sales of new automobiles have jumped an average of twenty-six percent in one month.

"I have before me a list of seventy-two economic indicators that we in government rely upon to measure the health and vitality of our business climate, and fifty-four of the seventy-two show that our nation has turned the corner. Of course, that means that eighteen of those important indicators are still in the danger zone. I won't bother to cover that list because I feel certain that there will be many voices coming to you within minutes that will emphasize the importance of the eighteen points, and those same voices will tell you that the fifty-four areas where improvement has occurred were the result of distortions by this administration.

"What I appeal to you for this evening is your confidence. Confidence is our greatest weapon in turning aside the worst recessionary period of the past half-century. Tomorrow, while at lunch or on coffee break, I ask that you change the tone of the normal conversation from one of pessimism to optimism. When a friend or a co-worker begins with the usual stories of how bad it is, do yourself, your country, and your future a favor—change the conversation, or if you find that you can't, then walk away. Your contribution to tomorrow's negative stories will only add one more voice to the chorus that has lulled us into a circumstantial rut that has nearly destroyed our land. Your optimistic views and voice of encouragement will make a difference far beyond what you might expect. We've thought our way into our current circumstances and we're going to work our way out of that dilemma in the same way.

"Now, I can assure you that what I am asking you to do is not going to be easy. There will be a great deal of pressure applied to encourage you to go along with the prophets of doom. Each day, from this office, I am subjected to nearly overwhelming political pressure to go along with the policies that are expedient—policies that treat the symptoms of our national illness rather than the disease.

"I am constantly encouraged to do many things that will only lead to even greater future problems, to delay the day of our commitments for cleaning up the past and solidifying our future. I have been forced to grow and to stand up for what is right, rather than for what may be

expedient. I will ask tonight that you grow so that we might grow, so that together we might continue to exist as the land of the free. In considering the words of my message tonight, I would ask that you study my message. Listen to the interpretations of those who will take issue with my words, but please, let your ultimate decision be a product of your own conclusions. Let no one dictate your thoughts or steal away your inalienable right of free and unbiased opinion. You have been endowed by your creator with life, with liberty and with the pursuit of happiness, and you must let no other person, no other view or appeal, no promise by anyone who seeks to do your thinking for you, steal away your own individual right to think for yourself. It is your greatest gift.

"Several centuries ago, Rene Descartes wrote a Latin phrase worth mentioning here: Cogito, ergo sum. Translated, this phrase carries an appropriate message. The message is simple: I think, therefore I am. And for you and I, this night, the message of Descartes is as true now as it was then. As we think, we become; and as we continue to think, we remain.

"And now, a final thought. Over the past many months, I have carefully selected and placed a number of very unique individuals in key positions within government and had numerous visits with many multi-talented persons within the private sector. Those individuals agree totally that our greatest single need in America is the development of a revitalized and optimistic national attitude, and have committed themselves to a program of sharing some rather unorthodox ideas with all those who seek the improvement of their circumstances. It is for that reason that I have established the Department of Human Development headed by Mariana Locke, whose responsibility it will be to make these principles and fundamentals available to anyone who might wish to be exposed to them. In place at this time is a rather informal organization of business and political leaders who share my interest in our new national direction and our renewed national spirit of optimism. I have been blessed with some of the best counsel available—primarily from a very gifted friend whose insights into human understanding have been invaluable.

"To those who have given to me their support and encouragement, and who have made the preservation of our country a foregone conclusion, I give to you a simple message that has significant and somewhat private meaning:

"Aide-toi, le ciel t'aidera.

"To those of you who have listened, I thank you. Good night."

On this seemingly unimportant and uneventful evening, an American president had delivered a message to two separate and distinct audiences. To one, he had addressed an appeal for their commitment to a new and optimistic attitude for a better America. To the other, and vastly smaller and specialized audience, his words— *Aide-toi, le ciel t'aidera*—had triggered into action the bold conspiracy that would transform the land in the years that lay ahead.

Indeed, his words would be interpreted in many ways by many people, but regardless of the private interpretations, the message had both appealed and transformed.

In the obscurity of a northern Virginia restaurant, Jonathan and Mariana Locke sat alone as the image of Robert F. Reardon faded into the blueness of the presidential seal and an unknown voice spoke the familiar words—"Ladies and gentlemen, you have just heard an address by the president of the United States. And now, to our network studios in New York, and an analysis of the president's remarks. Here is David Gately."

"Well, there you heard it . . . perhaps one of the most bitter attacks yet on the media by any American president in recent memory. We'll be back for some comments on Mr. Reardon's address to the nation right after these messages."

The picture faded from Gately to a commercial, and Mariana Locke looked at her husband who glanced toward her, a slight smile on his face.

"Well, what do you think?" he asked.

"What do I think? Well, it wasn't exactly designed to make friends in the media, was it?"

"That's his way, Mari. He's going to do it his way and tell it like it is, whether the media likes it or not."

"But Jon, the public hears far more directly from the media than it does from the president. I agree with you that he ought to be his own person—everyone should—but . . . well, you're right, of course. Compromise is such a dirty word. I suppose trying to compromise with them wouldn't work, so when in doubt, tell it like it is."

"Exactly, and that's what he's doing. That's precisely what's been needed for far too many years," he said glancing at the television commercial. "By the way, did you notice his closing line?"

"The French phrase? Yes, but what was it?"

"It's the trigger phrase that moved the project members instantly into Phase Three. The wheels are turning, my love, and a lot of minds are spinning this very minute, you can be sure of that."

"But what does it mean?" Mariana asked.

"Loosely translated it means '*God helps those who help themselves.*'"

Mariana thought for a moment. "The newspeople should have fun trying to figure that one out."

There was silence for a half minute before Jonathan spoke again. "It can't be stopped now," he said, looking into his empty coffee cup. "Not for a while, at least. We've turned the corner and now it's as though we are starting all over with a new chance to make something of ourselves—and of our country."

"And if we fail again?"

Jonathan thought for a moment. "He won't be back again, Mari. You can count on that—he won't be back." The last four words were spoken sadly, but with a note of certainty.

"Ever?"

"I don't think so."

"Then he's gone? Somehow I was certain we'd see him again . . . somehow . . ."

"Somehow, I don't think there will be any more direct contact—no formal good-bye—although he mentioned at Fort Lee something about informing us about the . . . what was it . . . something about the symbol of the apple?"

Mariana glanced toward the television set just as the commercials were ending, and both she and Jonathan gave their attention to the words and pictures coming from the box above them.

"All right, let's go back live now to the White House where President Reardon has come downstairs to meet some of those invited guests who watched the president's message from the Green Room. There you can see some of the dignitaries who were on hand . . ."

Mariana grabbed her husband's arm. "Jonathan—look at . . . it's Gloria Simon . . . and look at her!" Mari's eyes widened as she watched the woman who once had spoken out so intensely against the policies of the Reardon administration and who now stood smiling warmly and shaking the president's hand in an obvious display of friendship.

The voice of David Gately added to her surprise. "There's Gloria Simon of the Human Liberties Protective League greeting the president. The two seem to be far friendlier than we've ever seen them. If there's been one chief outspoken critic of the Reardon programs, it's Gloria Simon, but you wouldn't know it by looking at the way they're speaking to one another this evening."

"Jonathan—I don't believe her. Look at her! Look at the president, he's . . . "

"Noah, you're wonderful! Absolutely unbelievable!" Jonathan was laughing, and his words were spoken more to himself than to his bewildered wife.

Mariana glanced at the television and back at her beaming husband. She smiled along with him after a brief second, for she saw the same clear message that he had seen a moment before her.

"Noah got to her, didn't he?" Her question was more of a confirmation of her own thought.

"Of course he did," Jon agreed, laughing still. "It was his version of a going-away present. That was the little secret he mentioned at Fort Lee. I have no idea where he did it or how he did it, but there she is. You're right—look at her. There's an inner spirit that wasn't there before."

"I don't believe it," Mariana said, shaking her head from side to side. "In fact, I'm still not certain I believe any of this. But can you imagine having someone like Gloria Simon supporting the project?"

The television camera panned the after-the-speech reception while the voice of David Gately described the scene.

"Well, there you have it," Gately said. "An unusual speech from a most unusual man. Whether you agree with his program or not, it must be said of this man that there can be no speculation regarding where he stands. You may find issue with his philosophies, but Robert F. Reardon remains steadfastly committed to his own ideas for a better America. The verdict on the popularity of the man and the soundness of his strategies will probably not be known for some time yet—perhaps not until the great American jury, the electorate, re-enters the jury box with their decision in the fall of next year. Perhaps not until then will we know whether America is in need of a new chief executive more than a new attitude.

"We'll return in a moment with a final word."

The inevitable commercial flashed on the screen, cleverly trying to convince the audience to buy a pair of designer blue jeans.

"Gately wasn't nearly as caustic as he usually is," Mariana remarked.

The man at the bar picked up his refilled glass of wine and spoke to the bartender. "What we need is jobs, and Reardon tells us we need a new attitude. The man's out of touch with reality, that's what I think. What can a person do these days to make something of themselves? Sure as heck not get a new attitude. Reardon's crazy, that's what . . . crazy!"

"Hey, maybe the guy's got a point, Maxie," the bartender suggested. "Everywhere you go these days people are puttin' down on everything and everybody—the president's a no-good, the government's no good, the mayor's a bum . . . you oughta hear what I hear in eight hours. Maybe the man's got a point."

Maxie shook his head and waved his right hand in a gesture of rejection.

"The only point Reardon's got is on the top of his head," Maxie countered. "Look at unemployment. There weren't no eleven million people outta work 'til Reardon took over. People sleepin' on the ground and in cars . . . kids goin' hungry. He's another Hoover, that's what this guy is."

Jonathan listened to the conversation. It was but a single and insignificant conversation, but it was undoubtedly being repeated a million times or more across the land. *This* was the disease that was choking the nation, he thought. *This* was the curse that Noah had often spoken of—complaining, condemning and criticizing. It had spread like a plague, and America's confidence in itself was waning because too many individuals were permitting their confidence in *themselves* to wane.

The expressionless face of David Gately was back on the television again, and the conversation and thoughts ended. "In the moment or two remaining to us, let's switch now to Tom Broomall who's standing by in front of the Washington Plaza Hotel in Bethesda, Maryland with some comments from some of those who saw or heard the president's speech tonight. Tom—"

"Yes, David. I know we have just a few moments, but with me are a few of the dozen or so who watched Robert Reardon's address on television inside the lobby here at the Washington Plaza. Sir, you watched the speech. What did you think?" Broomall extended the microphone toward a businessman in his thirties who had a slight resemblance to Dick Cavett.

"Personally, I was impressed. It wasn't the usual political speech about taxes or about why one party is right and the other wrong. Reardon's right—we'd better take a hard look at what we're thinking about ourselves . . . and what we're saying to one another."

Broomall turned completely from his left to his right, holding the microphone down toward a much smaller man who wore the uniform of a company that wasn't immediately recognizable, although he appeared to be a bus driver.

"I want to know what this guy's gonna do for the average working man. Thinkin' different ain't gonna change the fact that me and mosta my friends are broke the day before payday. I didn't hear nothin' about programs that will help guys like me. What's he gonna do for me?"

Broomall pulled the microphone back to ask a question. "Do you think the president was right in suggesting that we play down our errors and weaknesses, and magnify our strengths?"

"Well, since he's responsible for the mess we're in, I can imagine why he'd want those of us who work for a livin' to not talk about it. That's stupid. He's responsible for me havin' to scratch for a livin', and I want somebody in there who's gonna make it easier for the guy on the street to make a decent livin' these days."

Tom Broomall stepped slightly past two people, the camera closing in on him as he moved, blurring out the small crowd that had gathered around him.

Within the warmth of the lounge where Mariana and Jonathan sat watching the event on television, the waitress had just poured them some fresh coffee and Jonathan was adding sugar to his cup when it happened.

"Jonathan—oh my God! Look!"

Jon Locke had started to raise his cup to his mouth, but froze in the act at what he saw. The television camera had faded back for a wider view as Broomall approached another person with his next question.

"Sir—we have time for just one more comment."

And there, as they had come to know him, stood their friend and mentor, dressed in the impeccably neat white suit. It was indeed Noah, smiling that familiar smile and raising his arms to fold them across his chest, revealing the brilliance of the red apple which he held in his right hand. This time it was not part of a dream, and the shock on Jonathan's face told Mariana Locke that what they both saw was not meant to be a part of the plan.

"President Reardon in his speech suggested that America needs a new attitude. In ten seconds, sir, if *you* were giving advice to someone on what they should do to improve their circumstances, what would *you* suggest?"

Noah smiled kindly at Broomall, glanced at the apple in his hand, and then slowly rubbed it once downward and once again upward against his left sleeve while a studious look crossed his brow.

"My good man, I would suggest that they forget everything else and find something that they can sink their teeth into." With that, the bearded man whose philosophies had already changed countless lives, bit once and finally into the apple, making it—as he had predicted— food for his body rather than a symbol of his existence.

Then, the picture faded and they both knew that they would not see him again. In a hundred cities across the land, plans were being made that would change the direction of the nation. The seeds had been planted into the fertile soil, and new sowers of seed were being trained.

Whether the weeds of the adversary would overcome the crops of this new effort would not be known for some time to come, but for now there was indeed a new beginning for mankind.

Jonathan and Mariana Locke said nothing, for there was nothing to be said. They stood together then walked hand in hand from the building and toward the limousine that would carry them to their new responsibilities.

They had a most important gift to share.

Epilogue

"It has been many years, Noah," the older man said.

"Indeed, sir, but as we both knew, a few years of neglect often requires many years of repair."

"Believe me, Noah, I am more conscious than you may know about the magnitude of their deterioration. But since you've been in such close contact with many of them, what are your specific observations?"

Noah pulled the documents from his lap and placed them on the table before him. The older gentleman watched every gesture with steel-blue eyes that seemed not to move; only the twinkle moved.

"Well, sir . . . I will verbally cover only the highlights and leave the detailed information for your review. First, I must say that I became the greatest benefactor of our final intervention. You see, I now understand what it must be like for you to create life and love its existence. I suppose I've come to love those whom I've gotten to know. I think I love them as you must love them."

The old man smiled understandingly. "And now that you've come to love them, and now that you've placed their destiny in their own hands in such a final and irrevocable way, you're afraid they're going to disappoint you or hurt you in some way. Am I correct?"

Noah smiled back at him. "You have such a genius at getting to the heart of the matter, sir."

"Oh well, my loyal friend, when you've created as many worlds as

I, you begin to see all the emotions, involvements and complications there are to see. You will come to understand, Noah, that with the emotion of love comes the responsibility of freedom, for one cannot exist without the other. With love, that most sacred of all emotions, there can be no possessiveness . . . no ownership or obligation; only the unrestricted freedom to be or not to be can accompany that which we call love. That is the center of their difficulty, Noah. When you love something, you must give it its freedom. If the love remains and it returns to you, then it is yours for eternity; and if it does not, then it was the emotion of selfishness disguising itself as love."

There was a silence for a moment as the older man watched the reaction of his friend.

"Finding out is painful, isn't it?" Noah said.

"Indeed, one day when they reside with us here—should that be their just reward—they too will come to see that even love creates its own pain. You cannot escape it."

"Well—" Noah looked downward and paused, then looked up slowly again toward his friend. His moist eyes made the image at the far end of the table difficult to see. "Jonathan . . . Mariana . . . and Mr. Reardon . . . they are such genuine souls, sir."

"Their conduct, Noah, and their commitment to your ideals will determine in the long term the accuracy of your judgment of them. It is easy to cling to worthy principles when the teacher is in your midst, but when he is gone . . . now, what other observations have you?"

The younger man looked at the papers in front of him. He paused momentarily, took a deep breath to discard his earlier thoughts, then spoke in a businesslike voice. "Our assessment of them was correct, sir. They are indeed held in bondage by the shackles of their own design. They are possessed by a contagion of greed and jealousy of one another. They have lost sight of the value of truth and reason. They restrain those of just intent and give foolish freedoms to the unjust. They have created complex institutions with excessive and hopelessly complex laws of their own design, while they have nearly abandoned any obediency to the laws of your design. The temptations of the adversary move among them almost at will."

"I am aware, by the way, that you took upon yourself the authority of direct intervention which went beyond the scope of our original agreement and intent."

"I did, sir, but only because the project had deteriorated far more than my initial reports had indicated."

"While I would have been reluctant to do so once, it is well that you did."

"Thank you, sir," Noah said.

"Will your plan work, do you think?"

"I cannot know, sir. They have so totally deviated from the original plan two hundred years ago that—well, the passage of time and the Law of Diminishing Intent may once again gain control of them."

"Then we must leave them to themselves. How long do you suppose it will be until your plan—your—your . . . "

"Conspiracy, sir."

"Yes. How long before its benefits appear and they return to their era of hope and prosperity?"

"The early signs are already beginning, but I would say . . . perhaps ten to fifteen of their years."

"Then we shall send you back again in fifty."

"Sir?"

"We'll look in on them once more in fifty of their years to observe their response to your plan. We cannot give them forever, Noah. Even forever must have its limits when dealing with those who appear to be intent on making the law of their own kind superior to the laws of eternity."

"And if they have regressed once more?" Noah knew the answer even before he had finished asking the question.

"Then in the interest of those within our realm of creation who have responded, we will no longer tolerate the existence of those who do not," he said emphatically, then rose to his feet.

Noah responded instinctively and stood with him, and the two walked together toward yet another destination with no beginning and no end. It was now Noah who was again the student as the elder one, his arm around his servant, began sharing with him again.

"Noah, life is a remarkable journey . . . an adventure full of pursuit, checkered with both triumph and tragedy, and always demanding an abundance of discipline and patience as a prerequisite to achievement . . ."

The words faded as the two left the room.

And somewhere, on a distant planet, a limousine rolled through the darkness of night, its destination—the mind of mankind.

"For what doth it profit a man if a gift is bestowed upon him,
and he receives not the gift?"

Author's Note

N early a full quarter-century has passed since Noah invoked his plan and returned to his domain. One-half of the fifty years the elder one had given for Noah's plan to bear fruit is now behind us, and what can be said for the restoration of morality and the resurrection of national pride? What evidence do we have that a new wave of optimism and national passion has risen to make our nation a place of greatness?

America is, perhaps, more divided than at any other time in history, and we find ourselves distracted by nations and their power-driven leaders that seem determined to erode our confidence and threaten our security.

Even our government seems to have become infested with those whose appetites for power and influence have take control of them, and their words and their promises have been proven to be mere superficial proclamations in light of their unprincipled actions.

Has the power of the dark side been unleashed by one of its newly appointed proponents in order to offset the plan of Noah? Has an intense, new war between good and evil been unleashed in our own generation, while most of us serve as mere observers rather than as active participants in carrying out Noah's plan?

We are a nation in debt, both collectively and individually; we save or invest little, if anything, of what we earn. We seem to be engrossed in a deeply ingrained habit of self-indulgence. And we give in to our need for instant gratification that finds us—for the most part—surrounding ourselves with the trinkets while we allow the treasures to pass us by. Millions of households have both parents working in order to keep up with an artificial lifestyle, and they are leaving their children in the hands of daycare providers who can provide the care, but not the love that only the parents can give.

We have divided ourselves into thousands of small groups, demanding more of others while requiring less of ourselves. We seek more liberty and more freedom; we demand entitlements but we seem to have forgotten that freedom and liberties require additional responsibilities from each of us and by all of us.

Could all this, however, merely be a sign that the followers of Noah—in making measurable progress against the forces that would diminish us—are engaged in a final battle against evil, and that what seems to be the highest level of discord in our nation's history is really little more than the last gasp of those who have sought to weaken us?

Perhaps the answer lies in what you are doing to honor your principles and adhere to your standards. What side have you chosen, what new disciplines are you imposing upon yourself, and what message are you sharing with others in order to engage them on the side of reason? Are you guiding your family and others around you along a path leading to progress, or have you inadvertently surrendered to a life of ambivalence and indifference? Have you taken steps to take back control of your life and your destiny, or are you allowing others to do that for you? Let us each begin a march to the sound of the same drummer by using the gifts we have been given. If our leaders cannot lead for us, let us lead ourselves by engaging in one of the many opportunities that surround us. Sometimes we must risk going too far in order to discover just how far we can really go. Let us learn to dream again, to set our own course and to be bold enough to follow it. The lives of the generations ahead of us hang in the balance.

Ron Reynolds
Dallas, Texas
January 12, 2007

A Conversation with Ron Reynolds

Q: How you were inspired to write this book?

RR: I had been an aerospace engineer for a dozen years, and I got into direct selling at the age of 32. I made some good money from that endeavor, but more than the money, I took very seriously my involvement in personal development. I didn't look at personal development as temporary positive thinking. I looked at it as a challenge to my way of life and my habits and my lack of discipline. I spent the next ten or eleven years of my life really working hard on . . . me.

Along that ten or eleven year path, because of a lot of years of past neglect, I had gotten deeply into debt, and the financial pressure was so bad that I ended up getting divorced. I found myself at the bottom. At that dark point in my life, I wrote a suicide letter (which today hangs on my office wall). At the end of that letter—just to show you how we have to be broken down before we can be built back up—I got so angry at having to write that letter in the first place that I signed it and wrote, "Never again."

About three months later, I met a lady from France who read my suicide letter, much to my embarrassment. She looked at me and said, "You have a gift. You're a writer, that's what you are; that's what you were meant to be." I had the usual excuses: I'd failed three years of English in high

school, and one of my counselors told me never to take on a job that
required writing because she said I was one of the worst writers she'd
ever seen. And yet, from the time I was a little kid I was writing little
stories about animals.

 That lady who told me I had a gift challenged me. "I'm going to
Columbus, Ohio, for nine days and when I come back, I want to see
something that you have written," she said. "I sense that you have this
gift of expression. If I'm wrong, I'll tell you." When she got back I gave
her this little manuscript that I had written. She read it—I can still see her
face—and she looked at me and said, "I was right! You have a gift."

That manuscript was published as my first book, *The Magic of Goals.* Then
I wrote two more books for a mentor and dear friend of mine, Jim Rohn.
His books did extremely well and eventually, I became president of his
company. Then someone else came into my life. She was a professional
singer with Neil Sedaka and she came to two of my seminars. She asked
me if I could write a Broadway play based upon some of the principles
that I had been teaching. The play never went anywhere, but there was
something speaking to me telling me to write a lengthy story based on
what I put together.

Over the next eleven months, I wrote the book that became *The Gift.* Over
that eleven-month period, I was not much more than a court reporter. I
would get this still, small voice telling me it was time to write, and I'd sit
down and write—sometimes for ten minutes on an airplane, sometimes
for hours—and I knew when I was finished. Then I would sit down and
write again, and at the end of eleven months there was a 365-page book
called *The Gift.*

Q: Why did you decide, after 23 years, to reissue *The Gift?*

RR: When it was written, I told the people who published it we were
going to print it one time. When it sold out, we'd never print it again.
Now, there were a lot of personal reasons for that, and I've stuck to it
for 23 years. When Stuart Johnson at VideoPlus approached me about
re-releasing the book, I told another person that I wouldn't do it. She said
to me, "What's the subtitle of *The Gift?*" I said, "A gift to be used and
shared." And she said, "Then you need to stop being hypocritical! There
are a lot of people out there who want to get *The Gift*, and whatever
reason you have for not wanting to share it . . . you need to take a look in
the mirror."

And that's how we are where we are today

Q. What do you hope new readers will gain from reading *The Gift?*

RR: I hope that they'll read the story and it'll trigger some of the passions that they had when they were maybe 15 or 20 years old—before life got them off on an unintended course. And that they'll look deep inside themselves, as I did at age 32, and see that it's not outside influences that have us where we are, but the choices we've made in the past. Those choices can be altered and we can make new and better choices—that's exactly what I did. So, my wish would be that if you read this book you don't read it for entertainment, or as a fantasy, or as a fictional book, but to trigger a new spark of emotion in you that lets you be passionate again, instead of a robot.

It's all based on one of my pet theories, and that is by age thirty (and this is a line right out of my first book, *The Magic of Goals*), not only have we failed to achieve our dreams of earlier years, we can't even remember what those dreams were.

Q. How do you think your book resonates particularly with people in the direct selling industry?

RR: Most of the characters in the book come together at a meeting for a direct selling company I called "American Products." But some of the darker characters in the book are of the belief that the individuals should surrender to the state, or to what society expects us to do.

I wrote *The Gift* at a time when I had spent almost fifteen years in the direct selling industry. What direct selling did was give me a chance to show what I could do. I think that's a message and a discovery waiting for anybody in direct selling. Why does anybody get into direct selling? Because they look at it as an escape mechanism, perhaps as the chance to show what they can do. They're independent contractors, they're in charge of their own destiny, and if they're willing to make some changes in themselves, they can make changes in their outer circumstances.

I know when I was writing it, what my mind-set was—we were at that time delivering leadership seminars, personal goal-setting seminars, all the little communication seminars to the direct selling industry. So, every fiber of my being was absorbed by the opportunity offered by direct selling companies: a chance to show what you can do.

Every sentence and every page has stimulating ideas for people in direct selling. If you're working for a corporation, you can read that book and get kind of frustrated, because you're kind of owned by the company— they tell you what you're worth. In direct selling, you're worth what you think you're worth. In direct selling, you're next raise becomes effective when you do. Therefore, reading this book and tapping into those ideas I think is going to unleash a lot of people.

When people bought the book at seminars more than twenty years ago, they would often make a return trip and tell me their stories about what the ideas in the book did to advance their self-esteem and self-confidence—that told me that this was a book meant for direct selling distributors.